ATLAS OF

CARBON-13 NMR DATA

VOLUME 1
Compounds 1–999

ATLAS OF

CARBON-13 NMR DATA

E. BREITMAIER
Institut für Organische Chemie
und Biochemie der Universität Bonn

G. HAAS
Institut für Organische Chemie
der Universität Bremen

W. VOELTER
Institut für Organische Chemie
der Universität Tübingen

VOLUME 1
Compounds 1–999

London — Philadelphia — Rheine

Heyden & Son Ltd., Spectrum House, Hillview Gardens, London NW4 2JQ, U.K.
Heyden & Son Inc., 247 South 41st Street, Philadelphia, Pennsylvania 19104, U.S.A.
Heyden & Son GmbH, Münsterstrasse 22, 4440 Rheine, West Germany.

ISBN 0 85501 481 4 (Volume 1)
ISBN 0 85501 480 6 (Complete Set)

Printed in Great Britain by J. W. Arrowsmith Ltd., Winterstoke Road, Bristol BS3 2NT.

CONTENTS

FOREWORD

A few years ago the practice and application of carbon-13 nuclear magnetic resonance spectroscopy was restricted to a handful of laboratories, and a search of the ^{13}C n.m.r. literature was a relatively simple and straightforward matter. Then, with the development of commercial Fourier transform n.m.r. spectrometers, the technique became generally available and ^{13}C n.m.r. applications rapidly became routine, with the result that the ^{13}C literature seems to be following an exponential growth pattern. Consequently a search of the literature has become a formidable task. Although during this period several monographs and reviews of the chemical applications of ^{13}C n.m.r. have appeared and some of these present extensive tabulations of data, these data tend to be illustrative rather than exhaustive. There is a real need for a systematic, regularly appearing collection of data to enable one to locate the results for specific compounds quickly and easily.

This is a continuing series that will serve to fill this need. It should prove extremely valuable as the ^{13}C n.m.r. literature continues its explosive growth, since ^{13}C spectra now rival proton spectra as a primary means for the characterization and identification of a wide variety of compounds. A particularly attractive feature of the Atlas is that all the information is stored on computer files, and these plus search programs are also available from the publishers. The Atlas should be welcomed both by newcomers to the field as well as those currently active in ^{13}C n.m.r.

J. B. STOTHERS

Department of Chemistry
University of Western Ontario
London
Ontario
Canada

PREFACE

It is the aim of the Atlas to present all reasonably verified carbon-13 n.m.r. results, predominantly selected from the published literature. Therefore the literature has been researched from the earliest publication of reasonably accurate results. The data reported in the earlier literature are largely chemical shifts. Only more recently have couplings and spin-lattice relaxation been reported. The first volumes (about 3000 compounds) therefore report shifts and assignments. Shifts are all referred to TMS. When the original reference standard was not TMS the value referred to TMS has been calculated.

It would be in one way logical to present the data in the Atlas in order of publication. However, this would have tended to leave an emphasis on certain chemical classes so the data have been sorted and early volumes contain a representative selection. When concentrations were available in the original literature they are listed in weight per cent. If reported as coupling constants or reduced couplings from proton off-resonance decoupled spectra, carbon–proton multiplicities are given in the Atlas and denoted below the shift values as S, D, T, and Q for singlet, doublet, triplet and quartet, respectively. If only carbon shieldings are available, the same multiplicities are derived from the formula and the assignment and then denoted as 1, 2, 3, and 4, respectively.

Very full indexing is a special feature because of the necessity for ready access to the data, bearing in mind the use of this Atlas in conjunction with other data. Therefore cumulative molecular formula, molecular weight, chemical class, alphabetical and shift indexes are provided and are renewed with each volume. At present the chemical class index (chemical classes according to *Chemischer Informationsdienst*) will offer reasonable access to substructures. Changes in indexing will be considered as the Atlas grows.

The Compilers welcome comment from users and will be pleased to receive suitable carbon-13 data for inclusion in subsequent volumes.

We are especially grateful to Dr. Hanswolf Kilian and his co-workers for their help in producing the computer printout at Hoechst Aktiengesellschaft.

We are indebted to J. Brun, A. R. Hernanto, R. Kimmich, M. Tikhomirov, and H. Wollmann for assistance. Especially the help of Mrs. Erika Ochterbeck, Bonn, is greatly acknowledged.

W. Voelter
E. Breitmaier
G. Haas

GUIDE TO THE PRESENTATION OF THE DATA

This collection of carbon-13 chemical shift data presents the following information for each compound.

1. Name
2. Structural formula
3. Molecular formula
4. Molecular weight
5. Solvent
6. Original standard
7. pH Value (when available)
8. Temperature
9. Carbon-13 chemical shifts
10. Assignments of shifts to carbons
11. Multiplicities of signals
12. Original literature
13. Chemical class code

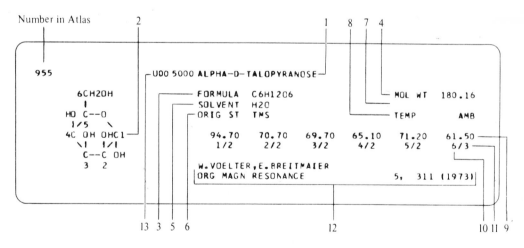

All compounds are numbered and listed in the Atlas in this reference number order. To facilitate fullest possible use of the Atlas five indexes are provided.

1. Alphabetical Index
2. Chemical Class Index
3. Molecular Formula Index
4. Molecular Weight Index
5. Chemical Shift Index

Specially written programs provide computer controlled acquisition, correction and printing of all the parameters and other information listed in the Atlas. The data are stored on magnetic tape which, together with a retrieval program, may be obtained on application to Heyden and Son.

1. Compound Name

Whenever possible and useful, IUPAC names are given. Otherwise the names given in the original literature are cited.

2. Structural Formula

The structural formulae are printed using a special printing chain ("QN" chain) containing the usual characters for single and multiple bonds. The arrangements of the structural formulae largely correspond to normal organic chemistry practice. Coded formulae, such as the Wiswesser line notation, although useful for computer retrieval, are not employed in this Atlas because data are acquired visually and there would be no justification for the reader to learn and code.

Hydrogen atoms attached to ring carbons are not printed. However, those linked to open-chain carbons are given throughout the Atlas.

The numbering of the carbon atoms (for chemical shift assignment) does not always follow IUPAC rules. Frequently, the numbering used in the original publication has been adopted.

3. Molecular Formula

The molecular formula is given as well as the molecular weight to facilitate co-ordination with mass spectral data collections. The symbols and the numbers of atoms in the molecular formulae are printed on the same line.

4. Molecular Weight

The molecular weight, as computed from the molecular formula, is printed to two decimal places.

5. Solvent

The solvent is printed as its molecular formula and, where feasible, additionally by its name. The molecular formulae of some common solvents are:

CHCL3	CHLOROFORM	C4H10O	DIETHYL ETHER
CDCL3	DEUTERIOCHLOROFORM	CH3NO2	NITROMETHANE
CH4O	METHANOL	C4H8O2	DIOXANE
CD4O	TETRADEUTERIOMETHANOL	C2H6OS	DIMETHYLSULFOXIDE
C5H5N	PYRIDINE	C2D6OS	HEXADEUTERIODIMETHYLSULFOXIDE
CCL4	CARBON TETRACHLORIDE	C6H12	CYCLOHEXANE
C6H6	BENZENE	C6D12	DODECADEUTERIOCYCLOHEXANE
C6D6	HEXADEUTERIOBENZENE	CS2	CARBON DISULFIDE
C3H6O	ACETONE	H2O	WATER
C3D6O	HEXADEUTERIOACETONE	D2O	DEUTERIUMOXIDE

Mixtures of solvents are indicated by a sequence of the corresponding molecular formulae. The names of less commonly used solvents are printed in the next line, e.g.

SOLVENT C2H4CL2/C6H12

If neat or almost neat liquid samples are used, the formula of the measured compound is given as the solvent. If known, the mixture ratio is added in parentheses, e.g.

SOLVENT NEAT/CYCLOHEXANE (9/1)

6. Original Standard

The standard to which the carbon-13 shifts were referred in the original literature is given, e.g. TMS,

C4H12SI TETRAMETHYLSILANE : CS2 CARBON DISULFIDE.

7. pH Value

If the carbon-13 shifts reported were obtained at a certain pH value, this value is presented in the Atlas.

8. Temperature

The temperature of measurement is given in degrees Kelvin. If the sample temperature is not mentioned in the publication, the abbreviation " **AMB** " for ambient is printed.

9. Carbon-13 Chemical Shifts

All carbon-13 chemical shifts tabulated in this collection refer to tetramethylsilane (TMS) irrespective of the standard used by the original researchers. They are given to two decimal places with an accuracy of ± 0.1 ppm but not better than ± 0.05 ppm. If reference compounds other than TMS were used originally, the values have been converted to the δ scale relative to TMS using the following shift conversions.

Cyclohexane	26.55	Carbon tetrachloride	96.10
Dimethylsulfoxide	40.60	Benzene	128.50
Methanol	49.90	Acetic acid (carbonyl)	177.05
1,4-Dioxane	66.50	Carbon disulfide	192.50
Chloroform	77.20		

10. Signal Assignments

The assignments of the carbon-13 shifts are given using the numbering of the carbon atoms in the structural formula. These numbers also define the sequence in which the shift values are listed. The identification number of the carbon atom is printed underneath the corresponding shift value and to the left of the decimal point, e.g.

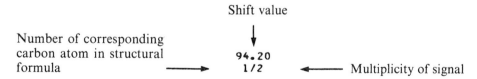

11. Multiplicities of Signals

The multiplicities of signals (1 for a quaternary carbon, 2 for a CH, 3 for a CH2 and 4 for a CH3 carbon, respectively) refer to those obtained or obtainable from proton off-resonance decoupling experiments. If no experimental multiplicity data were given in the original literature, the multiplicities were derived from the structural formula. The multiplicity is printed underneath the corresponding shift and to the right of the decimal point (see the example above). Couplings other than carbon-proton one-bond splittings have not been considered.

12. Original Literature

The full literature source from which the carbon chemical shifts and the assignments were taken is the final item in the box of data for each compound. The abbreviations of the journals are those used in *Chemical Abstracts*.

13. Chemical Class Code

The classification follows the system of *Chemischer Informationsdienst*, Verlag Chemie, Weinheim, 1973. Tables listing the code numbers, the chemical classes and the compounds in this Atlas are given at the beginning of the Cumulative Indexes Volume.

CARBON-13 NMR DATA

Compounds 1–999

1   P 000100 ISOPROPYL CATION

```
    2                FORMULA   C3H7              MOL WT   43.09
  H3C                SOLVENT   CL F602S SB
    \+               ORIG ST   C4H12SI           TEMP      253
    1C-H
    /                 319.60    61.80
  H3C                   1/2      2/4
    3
                     G.A.OLAH,A.M.WHITE
                     J AM CHEM SOC                91, 5801 (1969)
```

2   P 000100 TERT-BUTYL CATION

```
    2                FORMULA   C4H9              MOL WT   57.12
  H3C                SOLVENT   F502S SB
    \+ 3             ORIG ST   C4H12SI           TEMP      253
    1C-CH
    /                 330.00    48.30
  H3C                   1/1      2/4
    4
                     G.A.OLAH,A.M.WHITE
                     J AM CHEM SOC                91, 5801 (1969)
```

3   P 000100 HYDROXYCARBENIUM ION

```
    +                FORMULA   C H3O             MOL WT   31.03
  H2C-OH             SOLVENT   H F605S2SB
    1                ORIG ST   C4H12SI           TEMP      223

                      223.80
                        1/3

                     G.A.OLAH,A.M.WHITE
                     J AM CHEM SOC                91, 5801 (1969)
```

4   P 000100 METHYLHYDROXYCARBENIUM ION

```
    +                FORMULA   C2H5O             MOL WT   45.06
  H3C-CH-OH          SOLVENT   SO2-FSO3H-SBF5
    2 1              ORIG ST   TMS               TEMP      223

                      237.20    35.20
                        1/2      2/4

                     G.A.OLAH,A.M.WHITE
                     J AM CHEM SOC                91, 5801 (1969)
```

5   P 000100 DIMETHYLHYDROXYCARBENIUM ION

```
    2                FORMULA   C3H7O             MOL WT   59.09
  H3C                SOLVENT   SO2-FSO3H-SBF5
    \+               ORIG ST   TMS               TEMP      223
    1C-OH
    /                 250.30    32.60    31.30
  H3C                   1/1      2 3/4    3 2/4
    3
                     G.A.OLAH,A.M.WHITE
                     J AM CHEM SOC                91, 5801 (1969)
```

6   P 000100   DIHYDROXYCARBENIUM ION

```
HO
  \+
   1C—H
  /
HO
```

FORMULA	CH3O2	MOL WT	47.03
SOLVENT	SO2-FSO3H-SBF5		
ORIG ST	TMS	TEMP	243

177.60
1/2

G.A.OLAH,A.M.WHITE
J AM CHEM SOC   91, 5801 (1969)

---

7   P 000100   TRIHYDROXYCARBENIUM ION

```
HO
  \+
   1C—OH
  /
HO
```

FORMULA	CH3O3	MOL WT	63.03
SOLVENT	SO2-FSO3H-SBF5		
ORIG ST	TMS	TEMP	193

166.30
1/1

G.A.OLAH,A.M.WHITE
J AM CHEM SOC   91. 5801 (1969)

---

8   P 000100   METHYLDIHYDROXYCARBENIUM ION

```
HO
  \+
   1C—CH3
  / 2
HO
```

FORMULA	C2H5O2	MOL WT	61.06
SOLVENT	SO2-FSO3H-SBF5		
ORIG ST	TMS	TEMP	243

196.20   21.00
1/1   2/4

G.A.OLAH,A.M.WHITE
J AM CHEM SOC   91, 5801 (1969)

---

9   P 000100   PROTONATED ACROLEIN

```
          H
   3 2  +/
 H2C=CH-C1
          \
           OH
```

FORMULA	C3H5O	MOL WT	57.07
SOLVENT	SO2CLF-FSO3H-SBF5		
ORIG ST	CS2	TEMP	243

211.50   176.50   133.10
1/2   2/2   3/3

G.A.OLAH,Y.HALPERN,Y.K.MO,G.LIANG
J AM CHEM SOC   94, 3554 (1972)

---

10   P 000100   ACETYL CATION

```
     2
    CH3
   1/
 O=C
    +
```

FORMULA	C2H3O	MOL WT	43.05
SOLVENT	SO2-FSO3H-SBF5		
ORIG ST	TMS	TEMP	263

150.30   7.50
1/1   2/4

G.A.OLAH,A.M.WHITE
J AM CHEM SOC   91, 5801 (1969)

11   P 000200   METHANE

CH4
1

FORMULA   CH4   MOL WT   16.04
SOLVENT   C6H12
ORIG ST   C6H6   TEMP   AMB

−2.30
1/5

H.SPIESECKE,W.G.SCHNEIDER
J CHEM PHYS   35,   722 (1961)

---

12   P 000200   ETHANE

CH3—CH3
1

FORMULA   C2H6   MOL WT   30.07
SOLVENT   ———
ORIG ST   C6H6   TEMP   AMB

5.30
1/4

H.SPIESECKE,W.G.SCHNEIDER
J CHEM PHYS   35,   722 (1961)

---

13   P 000200   ETHANE

FORMULA   C2H6   MOL WT   30.07
SOLVENT   C2H6   CYCLOHEXANE

1   2
CH3—CH3

ORIG ST   C4H12SI   TEMP   276

7.26   7.26
1/4   2/4

L.SIMERAL,G.E.MACIEL
J PHYS CHEM   77, 1590 (1973)

---

14   P 000200   PROPANE

CH3—CH2—CH3
1   2

FORMULA   C3H8   MOL WT   44.10
SOLVENT   ———
ORIG ST   C6H6   TEMP   AMB

15.40   15.90
1/4   2/3

D.M.GRANT,E.G.PAUL
J AM CHEM SOC   86, 2984 (1964)

---

15   P 000200   N—BUTANE

CH3—CH2—CH2—CH3
1   2

FORMULA   C4H10   MOL WT   58.12
SOLVENT   ———
ORIG ST   C6H6   TEMP   AMB

13.10   24.90
1/4   2/3

D.M.GRANT,E.G.PAUL
J AM CHEM SOC   86, 2984 (1964)

16   P 000200 N—PENTANE

CH3—CH2—CH2—CH2—CH3   FORMULA C5H12   MOL WT 72.15
1   2   3   SOLVENT C5H12
                        ORIG ST C6H6   TEMP   AMB

          13.60   22.40   34.40
          1/4   2/3   3/3

          D.M.GRANT,E.G.PAUL
          J AM CHEM SOC   86, 2984 (1964)

17   P 000200 N—HEXANE

CH3—CH2—CH2   FORMULA C6H14   MOL WT 86.18
   | SOLVENT C6H14
CH3—CH2—CH2   ORIG ST C6H6   TEMP   AMB
1   2   3
          13.70   22.80   31.90
          1/4   2/3   3/3

          D.M.GRANT,E.G.PAUL
          J AM CHEM SOC   86, 2984 (1964)

18   P 000200 N—HEPTANE

CH3—CH2—CH2   FORMULA C7H16   MOL WT 100.21
      \   SOLVENT C7H16
       4CH2   ORIG ST C6H6   TEMP   AMB
      /
CH3—CH2—CH2   13.80   22.80   32.20   29.30
1   2   3   1/4   2/3   3/3   4/3

          D.M.GRANT,E.G.PAUL
          J AM CHEM SOC   86, 2984 (1964)

19   P 000200 N—OCTANE

CH3—CH2—CH2—CH2   FORMULA C8H18   MOL WT 114.23
   | SOLVENT C8H18
CH3—CH2—CH2—CH2   ORIG ST C6H6   TEMP   AMB
1   2   3   4
          13.90   22.90   32.20   29.50
          1/4   2/3   3/3   4/3

          D.M.GRANT,E.G.PAUL
          J AM CHEM SOC   86, 2984 (1964)

20   P 000200 N—NONANE

CH3—CH2—CH2—CH2   FORMULA C9H20   MOL WT 128.26
      \   SOLVENT C9H20
       5CH2   ORIG ST C6H6   TEMP   AMB
      /
CH3—CH2—CH2—CH2   13.90   22.90   32.20   29.70   30.00
1   2   3   4   1/4   2/3   3/3   4/3   5/3

          D.M.GRANT,E.G.PAUL
          J AM CHEM SOC   86, 2984 (1964)

21   P 000200 N-DECANE

CH3-CH2-CH2-CH2-CH2   FORMULA C10H22   MOL WT   142.29
                    | SOLVENT C10H22
CH3-CH2-CH2-CH2-CH2   ORIG ST C6H6   TEMP   AMB
 1   2   3   4   5

                    14.00   22.80   32.30   29.80   30.10
                    1/4   2/3   3/3   4/3   5/3

                    D.M.GRANT,E.G.PAUL
                    J AM CHEM SOC   86, 2984 (1964)

---

22   P 000200 ISOBUTANE

       CH3   FORMULA C4H10   MOL WT   58.12
        | SOLVENT ----
CH3-CH-CH3   ORIG ST C6H6   TEMP   AMB
 1   2

                    24.30   25.00
                    1/4   2/2

                    D.M.GRANT,E.G.PAUL
                    J AM CHEM SOC   86, 2984 (1964)

---

23   P 000200 2-METHYLBUTANE

       CH3   FORMULA C5H12   MOL WT   72.15
        | SOLVENT C5H12
CH3-CH-CH2-CH3   ORIG ST C6H6   TEMP   AMB
 1   2   3   4

                    21.90   29.70   31.70   11.40
                    1/4   2/2   3/3   4/4

                    D.M.GRANT,E.G.PAUL
                    J AM CHEM SOC   86, 2984 (1964)

---

24   P 000200 NEOPENTANE

       CH3   FORMULA C5H12   MOL WT   72.15
        | SOLVENT C5H12
CH3-C-CH3   ORIG ST C6H6   TEMP   AMB
 1 2|
       CH3   21.40   31.40
                            1/4   2/1

                    H.SPIESECKE,W.G.SCHNEIDER
                    J CHEM PHYS   35, 722 (1961)

---

25   P 000200 2,2-DIMETHYLBUTANE

       CH3   FORMULA C6H14   MOL WT   86.18
        | SOLVENT C6H14
CH3-C-CH2-CH3   ORIG ST C6H6   TEMP   AMB
 1 2| 3   4
     .CH3   28.70   30.20   36.50   8.50
                            1/4   2/1   3/3   4/4

                    D.M.GRANT,E.G.PAUL
                    J AM CHEM SOC   86, 2984 (1964)

26   P 000200   2,3-DIMETHYLBUTANE

```
        CH3
         |
   CH3-CH-CH-CH3
   1   2  |1
          CH3
```

FORMULA   C6H14   MOL WT   86.18
SOLVENT   C6H14
ORIG ST   C6H6   TEMP   AMB

    19.10   33.90
    1/4   2/2

D.M.GRANT,E.G.PAUL
J AM CHEM SOC   86, 2984 (1964)

---

27   P 000200   2-METHYLPENTANE

```
        CH3
         |
   CH3-CH-CH2-CH2-CH3
   1   2   3   4   5
```

FORMULA   C6H14   MOL WT   86.18
SOLVENT   C6H14
ORIG ST   C6H6   TEMP   AMB

    22.40   27.60   41.60   20.50   14.00
    1/4   2/2   3/3   4/3   5/4

D.M.GRANT,E.G.PAUL
J AM CHEM SOC   86, 2984 (1964)

---

28   P 000200   3-METHYLPENTANE

```
        4CH3
          |
   CH3-CH2-CH-CH2-CH3
   1   2    3
```

FORMULA   C6H14   MOL WT   86.18
SOLVENT   C6H14
ORIG ST   C6H6   TEMP   AMB

    11.10   29.10   36.40   18.40
    1/4   2/3   3/2   4/4

D.M.GRANT,E.G.PAUL
J AM CHEM SOC   86, 2984 (1964)

---

29   P 000200   3,3-DIMETHYLPENTANE

```
        CH3
         |
   CH3-CH2-C-CH2-CH3
   1   2  3|
          CH3
          4
```

FORMULA   C7H16   MOL WT   100.21
SOLVENT   C7H16
ORIG ST   C6H6   TEMP   AMB

    6.60   24.90   35.90   4.20
    1/4   2/3   3/1   4/4

H.SPIESECKE,W.G.SCHNEIDER
J CHEM PHYS   35,   722 (1961)

---

30   P 000200   ETHYLENE

```
   H2C=CH2
   1  2
```

FORMULA   C2H4   MOL WT   28.05
SOLVENT   C2H4
ORIG ST   CS2   TEMP   208

    122.10
    1/3

G.B.SAVITSKY,P.ELLIS,K.NAMIKAWA,G.E.MACIEL
J CHEM PHYS   49, 2395 (1968)

---

31   P 000200 **PROPENE**

```
H2C=CH-CH3
 1  2   3
```

FORMULA	C3H6	MOL WT 42.08
SOLVENT	C3H6	
ORIG ST	CS2	TEMP 208

```
114.70   135.00    18.50
 1/3      2/2       3/4
```

G.B.SAVITSKY,P.ELLIS,K.NAMIKAWA,G.E.MACIEL
J CHEM PHYS   49, 2395 (1968)
A.J.JONES,D.M.GRANT
UNPUBLISHED   (1972)

---

32   P 000200 **1—BUTENE**

```
H2C=CH-CH2-CH3
 1  2   3    4
```

FORMULA	C4H8	MOL WT 56.11
SOLVENT	C4H8	
ORIG ST	CS2	TEMP 208

```
112.10   139.00
 1/3      2/2
```

G.B.SAVITSKY,P.ELLIS,K.NAMIKAWA,G.E.MACIEL
J CHEM PHYS   49, 2395 (1968)

---

33   P 000200 **CIS—2—BUTENE**

```
H3C1    4CH3
   \   /
    2C=C3
   /   \
  H     H
```

FORMULA	C4H8	MOL WT 56.11
SOLVENT	C6H12	
ORIG ST	CS2	TEMP AMB

```
10.90   123.40
 1/4     2/2
```

D.E.DORMAN,M.JAUTELAT,J.D.ROBERTS
J ORG CHEM   36, 2757 (1971)

---

34   P 000200 **TRANS—2—BUTENE**

```
 H     4CH3
  \   /
   2C=C3
  /   \
H3C1    H
```

FORMULA	C4H8	MOL WT 56.11
SOLVENT	C6H12	
ORIG ST	CS2	TEMP AMB

```
16.40   124.80
 1/4     2/2
```

D.E.DORMAN,M.JAUTELAT,J.D.ROBERTS
J ORG CHEM   36, 2757 (1971)

---

35   P 000200 **(Z)—2—BUTENE**

```
  H     H
   \2 3/
    C=C
  1/   \4
 CH3   CH3
```

FORMULA	C4H8	MOL WT 56.11
SOLVENT	C4H8	
ORIG ST	C4H12SI	TEMP AMB

```
11.42   124.22   124.22    11.42
 1/4     2/2      3/2       4/4
```

J.W.DE HAAN,L.J.M.VAN DE VEN
ORG MAGN RESONANCE   5, 147 (1973)

36　　　　P 000200 (E)-2-BUTENE

```
              FORMULA  C4H8                    MOL WT   56.11
              SOLVENT  C4H8
   1          ORIG ST  C4H12SI                 TEMP      AMB
 CH3   H
   \2 3/        16.80   125.42   125.42   16.80
    C=C          1/4      2/2      3/2     4/4
   /   \4
  H     CH3    J.W.HAAN,L.J.M.VAN DE VEN
              ORG MAGN RESONANCE              5,  147 (1973)
```

37　　　　P 000200 CIS-2-PENTENE

```
  H     H     FORMULA  C5H10                   MOL WT   70.14
   \   /      SOLVENT  C6H12
   2C=C3       ORIG ST  CS2                     TEMP      AMB
  /    \
 H3C1    CH2—CH3   11.10   122.00   131.50   19.30   12.80
      4    5        1/4      2/2      3/2     4/3     5/4

              D.E.DORMAN,M.JAUTELAT,J.D.ROBERTS
              J ORG CHEM                      36, 2757 (1971)
```

38　　　　P 000200 (Z)-2-PENTENE

```
              FORMULA  C5H10                   MOL WT   70.14
              SOLVENT  C5H10
  H     H     ORIG ST  C4H12SI                 TEMP      AMB
   \2 3/
    C=C          12.01   122.84   132.43   20.33   13.79
  1/   \4  5      1/4      2/2      3/2     4/3     5/4
 CH3    CH2—CH3
              J.W.DE HAAN,L.J.M.VAN DE VEN
              ORG MAGN RESONANCE              5,  147 (1973)
```

39　　　　P 000200 (E)-2-PENTENE

```
   1          FORMULA  C5H10                   MOL WT   70.14
 CH3   H      SOLVENT  C5H10
   \2 3/      ORIG ST  C4H12SI                 TEMP      AMB
    C=C
   /   \4  5    17.34   123.55   133.21   25.81   13.62
  H     CH2—CH3  1/4      2/2      3/2     4/3     5/4

              J.W.DE HAAN,L.J.M.VAN DE VEN
              ORG MAGN RESONANCE              5,  147 (1973)
```

40　　　　P 000200 CIS-2-HEXENE

```
  H     H     FORMULA  C6H12                   MOL WT   84.16
   \   /      SOLVENT  C6H12   CYCLOHEXANE
   2C=C3       ORIG ST  CS2                     TEMP      AMB
  /    \
 H3C1    CH2—CH2—CH3  11.40   122.80   129.70   28.20   21.40   12.50
      4    5    6       1/4      2/2      3/2     4/3     5/3     6/4

              D.E.DORMAN,M.JAUTELAT,J.D.ROBERTS
              J ORG CHEM                      36, 2757 (1971)
```

41   P 000200   TRANS—2—HEXENE

```
    H     CH2—CH2—CH3      FORMULA   C6H12              MOL WT    84.16
     \   /4    5    6       SOLVENT   C6H12  CYCLOHEXANE
      2C=C 3                ORIG ST   CS2                TEMP      AMB
     /      \
   H3C 1      H                16.50  123.90  130.60  34.10   22.00   12.50
                                1/4    2/2     3/2    4/3     5/3     6/4
```

D.E.DORMAN,M.JAUTELAT,J.D.ROBERTS
J ORG CHEM   36, 2757 (1971)

42   P 000200   (Z)—2—HEXENE

```
                           FORMULA   C6H12              MOL WT    84.16
    H      H               SOLVENT   C6H12
     \2  3/                ORIG ST   C4H12SI            TEMP      AMB
      C=C
    1/   \4    5    6         12.29  123.73  130.64  29.26   23.04   13.49
   CH3    CH2—CH2—CH3          1/4    2/2     3/2    4/3     5/3     6/4
```

J.W.DE HAAN,L.J.M.VAN DE VEN
ORG MAGN RESONANCE   5,   147 (1973)

43   P 000200   (E)—2—HEXENE

```
    1                      FORMULA   C6H12              MOL WT    84.16
   CH3    H                SOLVENT   C6H12
     \2  3/                ORIG ST   C4H12SI            TEMP      AMB
      C=C
     /    \4    5    6        17.51  124.74  131.54  35.10   23.07   13.43
    H      CH2—CH2—CH3         1/4    2/2     3/2    4/3     5/3     6/4
```

J.W.DE HAAN,L.J.M.VAN DE VEN
ORG MAGN RESONANCE   5,   147 (1973)

44   P 000200   (Z)—3—HEXENE

```
                           FORMULA   C6H12              MOL WT    84.16
                           SOLVENT   C6H12
    H      H               ORIG ST   C4H12SI            TEMP      AMB
     \3  4/
      C=C                     14.27   20.64  131.02  131.02   20.64   14.27
  1   2 /   \5    6            1/4     2/3     3/2    4/2     5/3     6/4
 CH3—CH2      CH2—CH3
```

J.W.DE HAAN,L.J.M.VAN DE VEN
ORG MAGN RESONANCE   5,   147 (1973)

45   P 000200   (E)—3—HEXENE

```
 1   2                     FORMULA   C6H12              MOL WT    84.16
CH3—CH2    H               SOLVENT   C6H12
     \3  4/                ORIG ST   C4H12SI            TEMP      AMB
      C=C
     /   \5    6              13.90   25.83  131.18  131.18   25.83   13.90
    H     CH2—CH3             1/4     2/3     3/2    4/2     5/3     6/4
```

J.W.DE HAAN,L.J.M.VAN DE VEN
ORG MAGN RESONANCE   5,   147 (1973)

---

46   P 000200 (Z)-2-HEPTENE

```
                              FORMULA   C7H14                MOL WT    98.19
   H      H                   SOLVENT   C7H14
    \2 3/                     ORIG ST   C4H12SI              TEMP      AMB
     C=C
   1/   \4   5   6   7         12.45   123.61  130.97   26.95   32.33   22.75
  CH3    CH2-CH2-CH2-CH3       1/4      2/2     3/2     4/3     5/3     6/3
                               13.89
                               7/4
```

J.W.DE HAAN,L.J.M.VAN DE VEN
ORG MAGN RESONANCE   5, 147 (1973)

---

47   P 000200 (E)-2-HEPTENE

```
                              FORMULA   C7H14                MOL WT    98.19
   1                          SOLVENT   C7H14
  CH3   H                     ORIG ST   C4H12SI              TEMP      AMB
    \2 3/
     C=C                       17.69   124.60  131.82   32.76   32.44   22.65
   /   \4   5   6   7          1/4      2/2     3/2     4/3     5/3     6/3
  H      CH2-CH2-CH2-CH3       13.90
                               7/4
```

J.W.DE HAAN,L.J.M.VAN DE VEN
ORG MAGN RESONANCE   5, 147 (1973)

---

48   P 000200 (Z)-3-HEPTENE

```
                              FORMULA   C7H14                MOL WT    98.19
   H      H                   SOLVENT   C7H14
    \3 4/                     ORIG ST   C4H12SI              TEMP      AMB
     C=C
  1   2 /   \5   6   7         14.29    20.87  131.91  129.16   29.61   23.30
 CH3-CH2     CH2-CH2-CH3       1/4      2/3     3/2     4/2     5/3     6/3
                               13.63
                               7/4
```

J.W.DE HAAN,L.J.M.VAN DE VEN
ORG MAGN RESONANCE   5, 147 (1973)

---

49   P 000200 (E)-3-HEPTENE

```
  1   2                       FORMULA   C7H14                MOL WT    98.19
 CH3-CH2      H               SOLVENT   C7H14
    \3 4/                     ORIG ST   C4H12SI              TEMP      AMB
     C=C
   /   \5   6   7             13.99    25.95  132.42  129.37   35.12   23.15
  H      CH2-CH2-CH3          1/4      2/3     3/2     4/2     5/3     6/3
                               13.50
                               7/4
```

J.W.DE HAAN,L.J.M.VAN DE VEN
ORG MAGN RESONANCE   5, 147 (1973)

---

50   P 000200 1-OCTENE

```
  1 2                         FORMULA   C8H16                MOL WT   112.22
 H2C=CH                       SOLVENT   C6H12
    |                         ORIG ST   CS2                  TEMP      AMB
   CH2-CH2-CH2-CH2-CH2-CH3
    3   4   5   6   7   8     113.20   138.20   33.20   28.40   28.30   31.20
                               1/3      2/2     3/3     4/3     5/3     6/3
                               22.00    13.00
                               7/3      8/4
```

D.E.DORMAN,M.JAUTELAT,J.D.ROBERTS
J ORG CHEM   36, 2757 (1971)

---

51   P 000200   CIS-2-OCTENE

```
  1      4    5    6    7    8    FORMULA  C8H16              MOL WT  112.22
H3C    CH2-CH2-CH2-CH2-CH3 SOLVENT  C6H12
  \    /                         ORIG ST  CS2                  TEMP      AMB
   2C=C3
  /    \                           11.50   122.60  130.00   26.10   28.70   30.90
 H      H                          1/4      2/2     3/2      4/3     5/3     6/3
                                   21.90    13.00
                                   7/3      8/4
```

D.E.DORMAN,M.JAUTELAT,J.D.ROBERTS
J ORG CHEM   36, 2757 (1971)

---

52   P 000200   TRANS-2-OCTENE

```
  1                  FORMULA  C8H16              MOL WT  112.22
H3C      H           SOLVENT  C6H12
  \    /             ORIG ST  CS2                  TEMP      AMB
   2C=C3
  /    \               16.70   123.70  130.90   32.00   28.80   30.90
 H    CH2-CH2-CH2-CH2-CH3  1/4      2/2     3/2      4/3     5/3     6/3
      4    5    6    7    8  21.90    13.00
                             7/3      8/4
```

D.E.DORMAN,M.JAUTELAT,J.D.ROBERTS
J ORG CHEM   36, 2757 (1971)

---

53   P 000200   (Z)-2-OCTENE

```
                      FORMULA  C8H16              MOL WT  112.22
                      SOLVENT  C8H16
 H     H              ORIG ST  C4H12SI              TEMP      AMB
  \2  3/
   C=C                  12.62   123.73  130.69   27.36   32.17   29.90
 1/   \4   5    6    7    8  1/4      2/2     3/2      4/3     5/3     6/3
CH3   CH2-CH2-CH2-CH2-CH3  23.13    14.17
                           7/3      8/4
```

J.W.DE HAAN,L.J.M.VAN DE VEN
ORG MAGN RESONANCE   5,   147 (1973)

---

54   P 000200   (E)-2-OCTENE

```
                      FORMULA  C8H16              MOL WT  112.22
                      SOLVENT  C8H16
 1                    ORIG ST  C4H12SI              TEMP      AMB
CH3   H
  \2 3/                 17.81   124.70  131.98   33.16   32.08   29.97
   C=C                  1/4      2/2     3/2      4/3     5/3     6/3
  /   \4   5    6    7    8  23.09    14.13
 H     CH2-CH2-CH2-CH2-CH3  7/3      8/4
```

J.W.DE HAAN,L.J.M.VAN DE VEN
ORG MAGN RESONANCE   5,   147 (1973)

---

55   P 000200   CIS-3-OCTENE

```
  1 2       5    6    7    8    FORMULA  C8H16              MOL WT  112.22
H3C-CH2    CH2-CH2-CH2-CH3 SOLVENT  C6H12
      \    /                     ORIG ST  CS2                  TEMP      AMB
      3C=C4
      /    \                       13.30   19.70   130.60  128.40   26.10   30.80
     H      H                      1/4      2/3     3/2      4/2     5/3     6/3
                                   21.60    12.90
                                   7/3      8/4
```

D.E.DORMAN,M.JAUTELAT,J.D.ROBERTS
J ORG CHEM   36, 2757 (1971)

56   P 000200   TRANS—3—OCTENE

```
1  2
H3C—CH2    H
    \    /
    3C=C4
    /    \
   H       CH2—CH2—CH2—CH3
           5    6    7    8
```

FORMULA   C8H16   MOL WT   112.22
SOLVENT   C6H12
ORIG ST   CS2   TEMP   AMB

12.90	24.90	131.60	128.60	31.60	31.30
1/4	2/3	3/2	4/2	5/3	6/3
21.50	13.00
7/3	8/4

D.E.DORMAN,M.JAUTELAT,J.D.ROBERTS
J ORG CHEM   36, 2757 (1971)

---

57   P 000200   (Z)—3—OCTENE

```
   H        H
    \3  4/
     C=C
1   2/   \5   6    7    8
CH3—CH2    CH2—CH2—CH2—CH3
```

FORMULA   C8H16   MOL WT   112.22
SOLVENT   C8H16
ORIG ST   C4H12SI   TEMP   AMB

14.46	20.98	131.74	129.45	27.30	32.62
1/4	2/3	3/2	4/2	5/3	6/3
22.83	14.04
7/3	8/4

J.W.DE HAAN,L.J.M.VAN DE VEN
ORG MAGN RESONANCE   5,   147 (1973)

---

58   P 000200   (E)—3—OCTENE

```
1   2
CH3—CH2    H
    \3  4/
     C=C
    /    \5   6    7    8
   H       CH2—CH2—CH2—CH3
```

FORMULA   C8H16   MOL WT   112.22
SOLVENT   C8H16
ORIG ST   C4H12SI   TEMP   AMB

14.15	26.06	132.29	129.67	32.79	32.53
1/4	2/3	3/2	4/2	5/3	6/3
22.68	I4.05
7/3	8/4

J.W.DE HAAN,L.J.M.VAN DE VEN
ORG MAGN RESONANCE   5,   147 (1973)

---

59   P 000200   CIS—4—OCTENE

```
1  2   3      6   7   8
H3C—CH2—CH2    CH2—CH2—CH3
        \    /
        4C=C5
        /    \
       H       H
```

FORMULA   C8H16   MOL WT   112.22
SOLVENT   C6H12
ORIG ST   CS2   TEMP   AMB

| 12.70 | 22.20 | 28.60 | 129.00 |
| 1/4 | 2/3 | 3/3 | 4/2 |

D.E.DORMAN,M.JAUTELAT,J.D.ROBERTS
J ORG CHEM   36, 2757 (1971)

---

60   P 000200   TRANS—4—OCTENE

```
1  2   3
H3C—CH2—CH2    H
        \    /
        4C=C5
        /    \
       H       CH2—CH2—CH3
               6    7    8
```

FORMULA   C8H16   MOL WT   112.22
SOLVENT   C6H12
ORIG ST   CS2   TEMP   AMB

| 12.60 | 22.10 | 32.10 | 129.60 |
| 1/4 | 2/3 | 3/3 | 4/2 |

D.E.DORMAN,M.JAUTELAT,J.D.ROBERTS
J ORG CHEM   36, 2757 (1971)

61   P 000200 (Z)-4-OCTENE

```
            H       H
             \4  5/
              C=C
 1    2    3 /     \6    7    8
CH3-CH2-CH2        CH2-CH2-CH3
```

FORMULA	C8H16			MOL WT	112.22
SOLVENT	C8H16				
ORIG ST	C4H12SI			TEMP	AMB
13.70	23.31	29.77	130.06	130.06	29.77
1/4	2/3	3/3	4/2	5/2	6/3
23.31	13.70				
7/3	8/4				

J.W.DE HAAN,L.J.M.VAN DE VEN
ORG MAGN RESONANCE   5, 147 (1973)

---

62   P 000200 (E)-4-OCTENE

```
 1    2    3
CH3-CH2-CH2       H
             \4  5/
              C=C
             /     \6    7    8
            H       CH2-CH2-CH3
```

FORMULA	C8H16			MOL WT	112.22
SOLVENT	C8H16				
ORIG ST	C4H12SI			TEMP	AMB
13.64	23.26	35.27	130.64	130.64	35.27
1/4	2/3	3/3	4/2	5/2	6/3
23.26	13.64				
7/3	8/4				

J.W.DE HAAN,L.J.M.VAN DE VEN
ORG MAGN RESONANCE   5, 147 (1973)

---

63   P 000200 (Z)-2-NONENE

```
 H       H
  \2  3/
   C=C
  1/     \4    5    6    7    8    9
 CH3     CH2-CH2-CH2-CH2-CH2-CH3
```

FORMULA	C9H18			MOL WT	126.24
SOLVENT	C9H18				
ORIG ST	C4H12SI			TEMP	AMB
12.69	123.70	131.16	27.44	32.50	29.63
1/4	2/2	3/2	4/3	5/3	6/3
30.19	23.22	14.17			
7/3	8/3	9/4			

J.W.DE HAAN,L.J.M.VAN DE VEN
ORG MAGN RESONANCE   5, 147 (1973)

---

64   P 000200 (E)-2-NONENE

```
 1
CH3     H
  \2  3/
   C=C
  /     \4    5    6    7    8    9
 H       CH2-CH2-CH2-CH2-CH2-CH3
```

FORMULA	C9H18			MOL WT	126.24
SOLVENT	C9H18				
ORIG ST	C4H12SI			TEMP	AMB
17.81	124.70	131.99	33.17	32.43	29.48
1/4	2/2	3/2	4/3	5/3	6/3
30.24	23.24	14.16			
7/3	8/3	9/4			

J.W.DE HAAN,L.J.M.VAN DE VEN
ORG MAGN RESONANCE   5, 147 (1973)

---

65   P 000200 (Z)-3-NONENE

```
        H       H
         \3  4/   6    8
          C=C    CH2 CH2
 1    2  /     \5/  \ /  \
CH3-CH2        CH2 CH2 CH3
               7       9
```

FORMULA	C9H18			MOL WT	126.24
SOLVENT	C9H18				
ORIG ST	C4H12SI			TEMP	AMB
14.46	20.96	131.77	129.63	27.66	32.18
1/4	2/3	3/2	4/2	5/3	6/3
30.10	23.13	14.16			
7/3	8/3	9/4			

J.W.DE HAAN,L.J.M.VAN DE VEN
ORG MAGN RESONANCE   5, 147 (1973)

```
66              P 000200   (E)-3-NONENE

1    2                        FORMULA   C9H18              MOL WT   126.24
CH3-CH2      H                SOLVENT   C9H18
     \3 4/   6    8           ORIG ST   C4H12SI            TEMP        AMB
      C=C    CH2  CH2
     /   \5/  \  /  \          14.19    26.C9  132.29  129.74  33.13   32.05
    H       CH2 CH2 CH3        1/4      2/3     3/2     4/2    5/3     6/3
            7   9             30.01    23.09   14.19
                              7/3      8/3     9/4

                             J.W.DE HAAN,L.J.M.VAN DE VEN
                             ORG MAGN RESONANCE             5,  147 (1973)
```

```
67              P 000200   (Z)-4-NONENE

                             FORMULA   C9H18              MOL WT   126.24
       H     H               SOLVENT   C9H18
        \4 5/   7    9        ORIG ST   C4H12SI            TEMP        AMB
         C=C    CH2  CH3
1   2   3 /   \6/  \  /        13.84    23.44   29.90  130.34  129.91  27.47
CH3-CH2-CH2     CH2 CH2        1/4      2/3     3/3     4/2    5/2     6/3
              8              32.66    22.84   14.07
                              7/3      8/3     9/4

                             J.W.DE HAAN,L.J.M.VAN DE VEN
                             ORG MAGN RESONANCE             5,  147 (1973)
```

```
68              P 000200   (E)-4-NONENE

1    2    3                   FORMULA   C9H18              MOL WT   126.24
CH3-CH2-CH2      H            SOLVENT   C9H18
        \4 5/   7    9        ORIG ST   C4H12SI            TEMP        AMB
         C=C    CH2  CH3
        /    \ /  \ /          13.68    23.29   35.34  130.91  130.48  32.88
       H       CH2 CH2         1/4      2/3     3/3     4/2    5/2     6/3
               6   8          32.55    22.68   14.02
                              7/3      8/3     9/4

                             J.W.DE HAAN,L.J.M.VAN DE VEN
                             ORG MAGN RESONANCE             5,  147 (1973)
```

```
69              P 000200   (Z)-2-DECENE

                             FORMULA   C10H20             MOL WT   140.27
                             SOLVENT   C10H20
                             ORIG ST   C4H12SI            TEMP        AMB
H    H
 \2 3/   5    7    9          12.78   123.78  131.22   27.48   32.63   29.97
  C=C    CH2  CH2  CH2        1/4      2/2     3/2     4/3    5/3     6/3
 1/   \4/  \ /  \ /  \ 10     30.30    29.97   23.32   14.30
CH3    CH2 CH2 CH2 CH3        7/3      8/3     9/3    10/4
        6    8

                             J.W.DE HAAN,L.J.M.VAN DE VEN
                             ORG MAGN RESONANCE             5,  147 (1973)
```

```
70              P 000200   (E)-2-DECENE

                             FORMULA   C10H20             MOL WT   140.27
1                            SOLVENT   C10H20
CH3   H                      ORIG ST   C4H12SI            TEMP        AMB
 \2 3/   5    7    9
  C=C    CH2  CH2  CH2        17.98   124.72  132.06   33.26   32.64   29.94
 /   \4/  \ /  \ /  \ 10      1/4      2/2     3/2     4/3    5/3     6/3
H      CH2 CH2 CH2 CH3        30.39    29.94   23.31   14.33
        6    8               7/3      8/3     9/3    10/4

                             J.W.DE HAAN,L.J.M.VAN DE VEN
                             ORG MAGN RESONANCE             5,  147 (1973)
```

71 P 000200 (Z)-3-DECENE

```
       H      H
        \3 4/  6   8   10
         C=C  CH2 CH2 CH3
1   2   /    \5/ \ / \ /
CH3-CH2      CH2 CH2 CH2
              7   9
```

FORMULA	C10H20			MOL WT	140.27
SOLVENT	C10H20				
ORIG ST	C4H12SI			TEMP	AMB

14.60	21.08	131.86	129.65	27.77	32.56
1/4	2/3	3/2	4/2	5/3	6/3
29.71	30.51	23.29	14.32		
7/3	8/3	9/3	10/4		

J.W.DE HAAN,L.J.M.VAN DE VEN
ORG MAGN RESONANCE   5, 147 (1973)

72 P 000200 (E)-3-DECENE

```
1   2
CH3-CH2      H
       \3 4/  6   8   10
        C=C  CH2 CH2 CH3
       /    \5/ \ / \ /
      H      CH2 CH2 CH2
              7   9
```

FORMULA	C10H20			MOL WT	140.27
SOLVENT	C10H20				
ORIG ST	C4H12SI			TEMP	AMB

14.30	26.17	132.36	129.87	33.24	32.52
1/4	2/3	3/2	4/2	5/3	6/3
29.57	30.37	23.27	14.30		
7/3	8/3	9/3	10/4		

J.W.DE HAAN,L.J.M.VAN DE VEN
ORG MAGN RESONANCE   5, 147 (1973)

73 P 000200 (Z)-4-DECENE

```
         H    H
          \4 5/  7   9
           C=C  CH2 CH2
1   2   3 /    \ / \ / \
CH3-CH2-CH2    CH2 CH2 CH3
               6   8   10
```

FORMULA	C10H20			MOL WT	140.27
SOLVENT	C10H20				
ORIG ST	C4H12SI			TEMP	AMB

13.98	23.53	29.95	130.46	129.93	27.84
1/4	2/3	3/3	4/2	5/2	6/3
32.24	30.18	23.23	14.29		
7/3	8/3	9/3	10/4		

J.W.DE HAAN,L.J.M.VAN DE VEN
ORG MAGN RESONANCE   5, 147 (1973)

74 P 000200 (E)-4-DECENE

```
1   2   3
CH3-CH2-CH2      H
          \4 5/  7   9
           C=C  CH2 CH2
          /    \ / \ / \
         H      CH2 CH2 CH3
                6   8   10
```

FORMULA	C10H20			MOL WT	140.27
SOLVENT	C10H20				
ORIG ST	C4H12SITMS			TEMP	AMB

13.81	23.36	35.40	131.02	130.48	33.25
1/4	2/3	3/3	4/2	5/2	6/3
32.13	30.10	23.16	14.27		
7/3	8/3	9/3	10/4		

J.W.DE HAAN,L.J.M.VAN DE VEN
ORG MAGN RESONANCE   5, 147 (1973)

75 P 000200 (Z)-5-DECENE

```
        H     H
1   3   \5 6/  8   10
CH3 CH2  C=C  CH2 CH3
 \ / \   /   \ / \ /
 CH2 CH2     CH2 CH2
 2   4       7   9
```

FORMULA	C10H20			MOL WT	140.27
SOLVENT	C10H20				
ORIG ST	C4H12SI			TEMP	AMB

14.18	22.91	32.68	27.50	130.18	130.18
1/4	2/3	3/3	4/3	5/2	6/2
27.50	32.68	22.91	14.18		
7/3	8/3	9/3	10/4		

J.W.DE HAAN,L.J.M.VAN DE VEN
ORG MAGN RESONANCE   5, 147 (1973)

76 P 000200 (E)-5-DECENE

```
 2    4
CH2  CH2       H
 / \ /     \5 6/  8    10
CH3 CH2     C=C    CH2  CH3
 1   3     /   \ / \ /
          H    CH2 CH2
               7    9
```

FORMULA	C10H20			MOL WT	140.27
SOLVENT	C10H20				
ORIG ST	C4H12SI			TEMP	AMB

14.16	22.78	32.61	32.92	130.77	130.77
1/4	2/3	3/3	4/3	5/2	6/2
32.92	32.61	22.78	14.16		
7/3	8/3	9/3	10/4		

J.W.DE HAAN,L.J.M.VAN DE VEN
ORG MAGN RESONANCE   5, 147 (1973)

77 P 000200 2,3-DIMETHYL-2-BUTENE

```
H3C     4CH3
  \    /
   2C=C 3
  /    \
H3C 1   CH3
```

FORMULA	C6H12		MOL WT	84.16
SOLVENT	C6H12	CYCLOHEXANE		
ORIG ST	CS2		TEMP	AMB

17.70	121.60
1/4	2/1

D.E.DORMAN,M.JAUTELAT,J.D.ROBERTS
J ORG CHEM   36, 2757 (1971)

78 P 000200 (Z)-3-METHYL-2-PENTENE

```
        6
   H    CH3
    \2 3/
     C=C
  1 /   \4  5
 CH3     CH2-CH3
```

FORMULA	C6H12			MOL WT	84.16
SOLVENT	C6H12/CS2				
ORIG ST	C4H12SI			TEMP	AMB

13.99	119.26	138.15	25.63	13.41	23.73
1/4	2/2	3/1	4/3	5/4	6/4

J.W.DE HAAN,L.J.M.VAN DE VEN
ORG MAGNETIC RESONANCE   5, 147 (1973)

79 P 000200 (E)-3-METHYL-2-PENTENE

```
 1        6
 CH3      CH3
   \2 3/
    C=C
   /   \4  5
  H     CH2-CH3
```

FORMULA	C6H12			MOL WT	84.16
SOLVENT	C6H12				
ORIG ST	C4H12SI			TEMP	AMB

12.91	117.16	137.31	32.75	12.63	15.09
1/4	2/2	3/1	4/3	5/4	6/4

J.W.DE HAAN,L.J.M.VAN DE VEN
ORG MAGNETIC RESONANCE   5, 147 (1973)

80 P 000200 (Z)-4-METHYL-2-PENTENE

```
   H    H
    \2 3/
     C=C
  1 /   \4  5
 CH3     CH-CH3
          |
         6CH3
```

FORMULA	C6H12			MOL WT	84.16
SOLVENT	C6H12				
ORIG ST	C4H12SI			TEMP	AMB

12.34	121.28	138.55	26.36	22.89	22.89
1/4	2/2	3/2	4/2	5/4	6/4

J.W.DE HAAN,L.J.M.VAN DE VEN
ORG MAGN RESONANCE   5, 147 (1973)

81 P 000200 (E)-4-METHYL-2-PENTENE

```
  1
CH3       H
  \2 3/
   C=C
  /    \4   5
 H      CH-CH3
         |
        6CH3
```

FORMULA	C6H12			MOL WT	84.16
SOLVENT	C6H12				
ORIG ST	C4H12SI			TEMP	AMB

17.59	121.61	139.04	31.49	22.70	22.70
1/4	2/2	3/2	4/2	5/4	6/4

J.W.DE HAAN,L.J.M.VAN DE VEN
ORG MAGN RESONANCE

5, 147 (1973)

---

82 P 000200 (Z)-3,4-DIMETHYL-2-PENTENE

```
        7
 H        CH3
  \2 3/
   C=C
 1 /    \4   5
CH3      CH-CH3
          |
         6CH3
```

FORMULA	C7H14			MOL WT	98.19
SOLVENT	C7H14				
ORIG ST	C4H12SI			TEMP	AMB

12.43	117.87	140.99	28.54	20.59	20.59
1/4	2/2	3/1	4/2	5/4	6/4
17.82					
7/4					

J.W.DE HAAN,L.J.M.VAN DE VEN
ORG MAGNETIC RESONANCE

5, 147 (1973)

---

83 P 000200 (E)-3,4-DIMETHYL-2-PENTENE

```
  1       7
CH3       CH3
  \2 3/
   C=C
  /    \4   5
 H      CH-CH3
         |
        6CH3
```

FORMULA	C7H14			MOL WT	98.19
SOLVENT	C7H14				
ORIG ST	C4H12SI			TEMP	AMB

12.97	116.16	141.54	37.35	21.63	21.63
1/4	2/2	3/1	4/2	5/4	6/4
13.13					
7/4					

J.W.DE HAAN,L.J.M.VAN DE VEN
ORG MAGNETIC RESONANCE

5, 147 (1973)

---

84 P 000200 (Z)-4,4-DIMETHYL-2-PENTENE

```
 H      H
  \2 3/ 6
   C=C CH3
 1/   \| 5
CH3    4C-CH3
        |
       CH3
        7
```

FORMULA	C7H14			MOL WT	98.19
SOLVENT	C7H14				
ORIG ST	C4H12SI			TEMP	AMB

14.27	122.47	141.02	33.44	31.26	31.26
1/4	2/2	3/2	4/1	5/4	6/4
31.26					
7/4					

J.W.DE HAAN,L.J.M.VAN DE VEN
ORG MAGNETIC RESONANCE

5, 147 (1973)

---

85 P 000200 (E)-4,4-DIMETHYL-2-PENTENE

```
  1
CH3       H
  \2 3/ 6
   C=C CH3
  /   \| 5
 H      4C-CH3
         |
        CH3
         7
```

FORMULA	C7H14			MOL WT	98.19
SOLVENT	C7H14				
ORIG ST	C4H12SI			TEMP	AMB

18.03	119.34	143.04	33.10	30.18	30.18
1/4	2/2	3/2	4/1	5/4	6/4
30.18					
7/4					

J.W.DE HAAN,L.J.M.VAN DE VEN
ORG MAGNETIC RESONANCE

5, 147 (1973)

86　　　　P 000200　(Z)-3-ETHYL-4-METHYL-2-PENTENE

```
        7   8
   H   CH2-CH3
    \2 3/
     C=C
  1  /   \4  5
 CH3     CH-CH3
          |
        6CH3
```

FORMULA	C8H16			MOL WT	112.22
SOLVENT	C8H16				
ORIG ST	C4H12SI			TEMP	AMB

12.67	116.03	146.64	29.17	21.08	21.08
1/4	2/2	3/1	4/2	5/4	6/4
24.18	13.68				
7/3	8/4				

J.W.DE HAAN,L.J.M.VAN DE VEN
ORG MAGNETIC RESONANCE　　　　5,　147 (1973)

87　　　　P 000200　(E)-3-ETHYL-4-METHYL-2-PENTENE

```
  1      7   8
 CH3    CH2-CH3
    \2 3/
     C=C
    /   \4  5
   H     CH-CH3
          |
        6CH3
```

FORMULA	C8H16			MOL WT	112.22
SOLVENT	C8H16				
ORIG ST	C4H12SI			TEMP	AMB

13.77	116.03	148.13	35.23	22.40	22.40
1/4	2/2	3/1	4/2	5/4	6/4
22.40	13.06				
7/3	8/4				

J.W.DE HAAN,L.J.M.VAN DE VEN
ORG MAGNETIC RESONANCE　　　　5,　147 (1973)

88　　　　P 000200　2,4,4-TRIMETHYL-1-PENTENE

```
       7CH3
    3  4|  5
    CH2-C-CH3
   /    |
 H2C=C  8CH3
  1  2\
     CH3
      6
```

FORMULA	C8H16			MOL WT	112.22
SOLVENT	C6H12				
ORIG ST	CS2			TEMP	AMB

113.20	142.50	51.00	30.40	29.20	24.20
1/3	2/1	3/3	4/1	5/4	6/4

D.E.DORMAN,M.JAUTELAT,J.D.ROBERTS
J ORG CHEM　　　　36, 2757 (1971)

89　　　　P 000200　3,4,4-TRIMETHYL-2-PENTENE

```
  1      8
 CH3    CH3
    \2 3/   7
     C=C   CH3
    /  \4/ 5
   H    C-CH3
       /
    6CH3
```

FORMULA	C8H16			MOL WT	112.22
SOLVENT	C8H16				
ORIG ST	C4H12SI			TEMP	AMB

12.48	115.16	143.93	36.37	29.46	29.46
1/4	2/2	3/1	4/1	5/4	6/4
29.46	13.70				
7/4	8/4				

J.W.DE HAAN,L.J.M.VAN DE VEN
ORG MAGNETIC RESONANCE　　　　5,　147 (1973)

90　　　　P 000200　CIS-3-METHYL-2-HEXENE

```
 H3C1    7CH3
    \   /
     2C=C3
    /   \
   H    CH2-CH2-CH3
        4   5   6
```

FORMULA	C7H14			MOL WT	98.19
SOLVENT	C6H12				
ORIG ST	CS2			TEMP	AMB

12.00	118.30	134.80	32.70	20.20	12.80
1/4	2/2	3/1	4/3	5/3	6/4
22.10					
7/4					

D.E.DORMAN,M.JAUTELAT,J.D.ROBERTS
J ORG CHEM　　　　36,　2757 (1971)

91   P 000200 TRANS-3-METHYL-2-HEXENE

```
         4    5    6
H3C 1   CH2-CH2-CH3
   \    /
   2C=C 3
   /    \
  H     7CH3
```

FORMULA	C7H14			MOL WT	98.19
SOLVENT	C6H12				
ORIG ST	CS2			TEMP	AMB

12.00	117.60	134.70	41.20	20.40	12.60
1/4	2/2	3/1	4/3	5/3	6/4
14.20					
7/4					

D.E.DORMAN,M.JAUTELAT,J.D.ROBERTS
J ORG CHEM   36, 2757 (1971)

---

92   P 000200 (Z)-3-METHYL-2-HEXENE

```
     7
 H    CH3
  \2 3/
   C=C
 1 /  \4   5    6
CH3    CH2-CH2-CH3
```

FORMULA	C7H14			MOL WT	98.19
SOLVENT	C7H14/CCL4				
ORIG ST	C4H12SI			TEMP	AMB

13.81	119.81	136.30	34.27	21.60	14.61
1/4	2/2	3/1	4/3	5/3	6/4
23.89					
7/4					

J.W.DE HAAN,L.J.M.VAN DE VEN
ORG MAGNETIC RESONANCE   5, 147 (1973)

---

93   P 000200 (E)-3-METHYL-2-HEXENE

```
 1      7
CH3    CH3
  \2 3/
   C=C
   /  \4   5    6
  H    CH2-CH2-CH3
```

FORMULA	C7H14			MOL WT	98.19
SOLVENT	C7H14/CCL4				
ORIG ST	C4H12SI			TEMP	AMB

13.81	119.03	136.05	42.66	21.79	14.31
1/4	2/2	3/1	4/3	5/3	6/4
16.11					
7/4					

J.W.DE HAAN,L.J.M.VAN DE VEN
ORG MAGNETIC RESONANCE   5, 147 (1973)

---

94   P 000200 (Z)-4-METHYL-2-HEXENE

```
  H    H
   \2 3/
    C=C
 1 /  \4   5    6
CH3    CH-CH2-CH3
        |
       7CH3
```

FORMULA	C7H14			MOL WT	98.19
SOLVENT	C7H14				
ORIG ST	C4H12SI			TEMP	AMB

12.88	122.48	137.31	33.61	30.84	11.93
1/4	2/2	3/2	4/2	5/3	6/4
20.88					
7/4					

J.W.DE HAAN,L.J.M.VAN DE VEN
ORG MAGN RESONANCE   5, 147 (1973)

---

95   P 000200 (E)-4-METHYL-2-HEXENE

```
  1
 CH3    H
   \2 3/
    C=C
   /  \4   5    6
  H    CH-CH2-CH3
        |
       7CH3
```

FORMULA	C7H14			MOL WT	98.19
SOLVENT	C7H14				
ORIG ST	C4H12SI			TEMP	AMB

17.79	123.09	137.80	39.08	30.41	11.70
1/4	2/2	3/2	4/2	5/3	6/4
20.56					
7/4					

J.W.DE HAAN,L.J.M.VAN DE VEN
ORG MAGN RESONANCE   5, 147 (1973)

96   P 000200   (Z)-5-METHYL-2-HEXENE

```
                              FORMULA  C7H14                    MOL WT   98.19
         H      H             SOLVENT  C7H14
          \2 3/              ORIG ST  C4H12SI              TEMP       AMB
           C=C
     1   /    \4   5   6        12.73   124.37   129.64   36.49   29.18   22.42
     CH3        CH2-CH-CH3       1/4      2/2      3/2     4/3     5/2     6/4
                     |          22.42
                     CH3         7/4
                     7
```

J.W.DE HAAN,L.J.M.VAN DE VEN
ORG MAGN RESONANCE   5,   147 (1973)

---

97   P 000200   (E)-5-METHYL-2-HEXENE

```
       1                      FORMULA  C7H14                    MOL WT   98.19
      CH3      H              SOLVENT  C7H14
       \2 3/       6          ORIG ST  C4H12SI              TEMP       AMB
        C=C      CH3
       /    \4   5/             17.77   125.81   130.49   42.56   29.00   22.37
      H       CH2-CH            1/4      2/2      3/2     4/3     5/2     6/4
                   \7          22.37
                    CH3         7/4
```

J.W.DE HAAN,L.J.M.VAN DE VEN
ORG MAGN RESONANCE   5,   147 (1973)

---

98   P 000200   (Z)-2-METHYL-3-HEXENE

```
                              FORMULA  C7H14                    MOL WT   98.19
       H      H               SOLVENT  C7H14
        \3 4/                ORIG ST  C4H12SI              TEMP       AMB
         C=C
   1   2 /    \5   6            23.34   26.89   137.20   129.37   20.96   14.62
   CH3-CH      CH2-CH3          1/4      2/2      3/2     4/2     5/3     6/4
       |                       23.34
       7CH3                     7/4
```

J.W.DE HAAN,L.J.M.VAN DE VEN
ORG MAGN RESONANCE   5,   147 (1973)

---

99   P 000200   (E)-2-METHYL-3-HEXENE

```
       7CH3                   FORMULA  C7H14                    MOL WT   98.19
   1   |2                     SOLVENT  C7H14
   CH3-CH      H              ORIG ST  C4H12SI              TEMP       AMB
       \3 4/
        C=C                     22.87   31.41   136.96   129.16   25.89   14.14
       /    \5   6              1/4      2/2      3/2     4/2     5/3     6/4
      H       CH2-CH3          22.87
                               7/4
```

J.W.DE HAAN,L.J.M.VAN DE VEN
ORG MAGNETIC RESONANCE   5,   147 (1973)

---

100   P 000200   (Z)-3-METHYL-3-HEXENE

```
       7                      FORMULA  C7H14                    MOL WT   98.19
      CH3      H              SOLVENT  C7H14
       \3 4/                 ORIG ST  C4H12SI              TEMP       AMB
        C=C
   1   2 /    \5   6            12.77   25.05   136.25   126.65   21.26   14.62
   CH3-CH2      CH2-CH3         1/4      2/3      3/1     4/2     5/3     6/4
                               22.68
                               7/4
```

J.W.DE HAAN,L.J.M.VAN DE VEN
ORG MAGNETIC RESONANCE   5,   147 (1973)

---

101   P 000200   (E)-3-METHYL-3-HEXENE

```
 1   2
CH3-CH2      H
      \3 4/
       C=C
    7 /   \5   6
   CH3      CH2-CH3
```

FORMULA	C7H14			MOL WT	98.19
SOLVENT	C7H14				
ORIG ST	C4H12SI			TEMP	AMB

12.77	32.78	136.06	125.56	21.46	14.24
1/4	2/3	3/1	4/2	5/3	6/4
15.40					
7/4					

J.W.DE HAAN,L.J.M.VAN DE VEN
ORG MAGNETIC RESONANCE   5, 147 (1973)

---

102   P 000200   (Z)-3,4-DIMETHYL-2-HEXENE

```
          7
   H    CH3
    \2 3/
     C=C
  1 /   \4  5   6
 CH3      CH-CH2-CH3
           |
          CH3
```

FORMULA	C8H16			MOL WT	112.22
SOLVENT	C8H16				
ORIG ST	C4H12SI			TEMP	AMB

12.78	119.40	139.57	35.88	28.21	12.27
1/4	2/2	3/1	4/2	5/3	6/4
17.86					
7/4					

J.W.DE HAAN,L.J.M.VAN DE VEN
ORG MAGNETIC RESONANCE   5, 147 (1973)

---

103   P 000200   (E)-3,4-DIMETHYL-2-HEXENE

```
  1        7
 CH3      CH3
   \2 3/
    C=C
   /   \4  5   6
  H      CH-CH2-CH3
          |
         8CH3
```

FORMULA	C8H16			MOL WT	112.22
SOLVENT	C8H16				
ORIG ST	C4H12SI			TEMP	AMB

13.17	118.13	139.85	45.41	28.52	12.25
1/4	2/2	3/1	4/2	5/3	6/4
12.11	19.73				
7/4,	8/4				

J.W.DE HAAN,L.J.M.VAN DE VEN
ORG MAGNETIC RESONANCE   5, 147 (1973)

---

104   P 000200   (Z)-2,2-DIMETHYL-3-HEXENE

```
     H     H
 8    \3 4/
 CH3    C=C
    \2/   \5   6
     C      CH2-CH3
  1 / \7
 CH3   CH3
```

FORMULA	C8H16			MOL WT	112.22
SOLVENT	C8H16				
ORIG ST	C4H12SI			TEMP	AMB

31.62	33.53	139.48	131.00	22.13	15.02
1/4	2/1	3/2	4/2	5/3	6/4
31.62	31.62				
7/4	8/4				

J.W.DE HAAN,L.J.M.VAN DE VEN
ORG MAGNETIC RESONANCE   5, 147 (1973)

---

105   P 000200   (E)-2,2-DIMETHYL-3-HEXENE

```
 1CH3  7CH3
    \2/
     C     H
 8  / \3 4/
 CH3    C=C
    /   \5   6
   H      CH2-CH3
```

FORMULA	C8H16			MOL WT	112.22
SOLVENT	C8H16				
ORIG ST	C4H12SI			TEMP	AMB

30.34	33.02	140.90	126.77	26.14	14.38
1/4	2/1	3/1	4/2	5/3	6/4
30.34	30.34				
7/4	8/4				

J.W.DE HAAN,L.J.M.VAN DE VEN
ORG MAGNETIC RESONANCE   5, 147 (1973)

106　　　P 000200　(Z)-2,5-DIMETHYL-3-HEXENE

```
        H    H
         \3 4/
          C=C
 1   2 /    \5  6
CH3-CH      CH-CH3
     |        |
    7CH3    8CH3
```

FORMULA	C8H16			MOL WT	112.22
SOLVENT	C8H16				
ORIG ST	C4H12SI			TEMP	AMB

23.76	27.20	135.45	135.45	27.20	23.76
1/4	2/2	3/2	4/2	5/2	6/4
23.76	23.76				
7/4	8/4				

J.W.DE HAAN,L.J.M.VAN DE VEN
ORG MAGNETIC RESONANCE　　　　5,　147 (1973)

107　　　P 000200　(E)-2,5-DIMETHYL-3-HEXENE

```
    7CH3
 1   |2
CH3-CH     H
     \3 4/
      C=C
    /    \5  6
   H     CH-CH3
          |
         8CH3
```

FORMULA	C8H16			MOL WT	112.22
SOLVENT	C8H16				
ORIG ST	C4H12SI			TEMP	AMB

23.24	31.64	134.91	134.91	31.64	23.24
1/4	2/2	3/2	4/2	5/2	6/4
23.24	23.24				
7/4	8/4				

J.W.DE HAAN,L.J.M.VAN DE VEN
ORG MAGNETIC RESONANCE　　　　5,　147 (1973)

108　　　P 000200　1,3-BUTADIENE

```
      4CH2
   2 //
  HC-CH
   // 3
 H2C 1
```

FORMULA	C4H6	MOL WT	54.09
SOLVENT	C6H12		
ORIG ST	CS2	TEMP	AMB

116.30	136.90
1/3	2/2

D.E.DORMAN,M.JAUTELAT,J.D.ROBERTS
J ORG CHEM　　　　36, 2757 (1971)

109　　　P 000200　(Z)-1,3-PENTADIENE

```
    H    H
     \1 2/    5
      C=C    CH3
     /    \3 4/
    H     C=C
          /  \
         H    H
```

FORMULA	C5H8			MOL WT	68.12
SOLVENT	C5H8				
ORIG ST	C4H12SI			TEMP	AMB

116.08	132.21	130.62	126.07	12.87
1/3	2/2	3/2	4/2	5/4

J.W.DE HAAN,L.J.M.VAN DE VEN
ORG MAGNETIC RESONANCE　　　　5,　147 (1973)

110　　　P 000200　(E)-1,3-PENTADIENE

```
    H    H
     \1 2/
      C=C     H
     /    \3 4/
    H     C=C
         /    \5
        H     CH3
```

FORMULA	C5H8			MOL WT	68.12
SOLVENT	C5H8				
ORIG ST	C4H12SI			TEMP	AMB

113.90	137.45	132.93	129.03	17.55
1/3	2/2	3/2	4/2	5/4

J.W.DE HAAN,L.J.M.VAN DE VEN
ORG MAGNETIC RESONANCE　　　　5,　147 (1973)

111   P 000200   (Z,Z)-2,4-HEXADIENE

```
   H      H
    \2 3/      6
     C=C      CH3
  1 /    \4 5/
  CH3     C=C
         /    \
       H       H
```

FORMULA	C6H10			MOL WT	82.15
SOLVENT	C6H10				
ORIG ST	C4H12SI			TEMP	AMB

12.91	124.92	125.32	125.32	124.92	12.91
1/4	2/2	3/2	4/2	5/2	6/4

J.W.DE HAAN,L.J.M.VAN DE VEN
ORG MAGNETIC RESONANCE   5, 147 (1973)

---

112   P 000200   (E,E)-2,4-HEXADIENE

```
    1
   CH3      H
    \2 3/
     C=C      H
    /    \4 5/
   H      C=C
         /    \6
        H      CH3
```

FORMULA	C6H10			MOL WT	82.15
SOLVENT	C6H10				
ORIG ST	C4H12SI			TEMP	AMB

17.60	125.82	132.31	132.31	125.82	17.60
1/4	2/2	3/2	4/2	5/2	6/4

J.W.DE HAAN,L.J.M.VAN DE VEN
ORG MAGNETIC RESONANCE   5, 147 (1973)

---

113   P 000200   (Z,E)-2,4-HEXADIENE

```
   H      H
    \2 3/
     C=C      H
  1 /    \4 5/
  CH3     C=C
         /    \6
        H      CH3
```

FORMULA	C6H10			MOL WT	82.15
SOLVENT	C6H10				
ORIG ST	C4H12SI			TEMP	AMB

13.01	123.12	127.41	130.21	128.31	18.00
1/4	2/2	3/2	4/2	5/2	6/4

J.W.DE HAAN,L.J.M.VAN DE VEN
ORG MAGNETIC RESONANCE   5, 147 (1973)

---

114   P 000200   1,7-OCTADIENE

```
  1 2                7 8
 H2C=CH          HC=CH2
     \          /
     CH2-CH2-CH2-CH2
      3   4   5   6
```

FORMULA	C8H14		MOL WT	110.20
SOLVENT	C6H12			
ORIG ST	CS2		TEMP	AMB

113.50	137.90	33.10	27.80
1/3	2/2	3/3	4/3

D.E.DORMAN,M.JAUTELAT,J.D.ROBERTS
J ORG CHEM   36, 2757 (1971)

---

115   P 000200   2,6-CIS,CIS-OCTADIENE

```
   1      4   5      8
  H3C    CH2-CH2    CH3
   \    /      \    /
   2C=C 3      6C=C 7
   /    \      /    \
  H      H    H      H
```

FORMULA	C8H14		MOL WT	110.20
SOLVENT	C6H12			
ORIG ST	CS2		TEMP	AMB

11.60	123.10	129.50	26.10
1/4	2/2	3/2	4/3

D.E.DORMAN,M.JAUTELAT,J.D.ROBERTS
J ORG CHEM   36, 2757 (1971)

116   P 000200 2,6—CIS,TRANS—OCTADIENE

```
   1      4    5
 H3C    CH2-CH2   H
    \   /     \  /
     2C=C3     6C=C7
    /   \     /  \
   H     H   H    CH3
                   8
```

FORMULA	C8H14			MOL WT	110.20
SOLVENT	C6H12				
ORIG ST	CS2			TEMP	AMB

11.60	123.10	129.50	26.30	31.90	130.40
1/4	2/2	3/2	4/3	5/3	6/2
124.10	16.80				
7/2	8/4				

D.E.DORMAN,M.JAUTELAT,J.D.ROBERTS
J ORG CHEM   36, 2757 (1971)

---

117   P 000200 2,6—TRANS,TRANS—OCTADIENE

```
   1                8
 H3C    H    H    CH3
    \   /     \  /
     2C=C3     6C=C7
    /   \     /  \
   H    CH2-CH2   H
        4    5
```

FORMULA	C8H14			MOL WT	110.20
SOLVENT	C6H12				
ORIG ST	CS2			TEMP	AMB

16.80	124.10	130.40	32.10
1/4	2/2	3/2	4/3

D.E.DORMAN,M.JAUTELAT,J.D.ROBERTS
J ORG CHEM   36, 2757 (1971)

---

118   P 000200 3,5—CIS,CIS—OCTADIENE

```
     H       H
      \4    5/
   H   C---C   H
    \ //     \\ /
     3C        C6
     |         |
  H3C-CH2   H2C-CH3
   1  2      7  8
```

FORMULA	C8H14			MOL WT	110.20
SOLVENT	C6H12				
ORIG ST	CS2			TEMP	AMB

13.20	20.00	132.30	122.50
1/4	2/3	3/2	4/2

D.E.DORMAN,M.JAUTELAT,J.D.ROBERTS
J ORG CHEM   36, 2757 (1971)

---

119   P 000200 (Z)—3—METHYL—1,3—PENTADIENE

```
   H     H
    \1 2/     5
     C=C    CH3
    /    \3 4/
   H      C=C
    6      \
   CH3      H
```

FORMULA	C6H10			MOL WT	82.15
SOLVENT	C6H10				
ORIG ST	C4H12SI			TEMP	AMB

112.63	133.77	133.49	124.60	12.72	19.57
1/3	2/2	3/1	4/2	5/4	6/4

J.W.DE HAAN,L.J.M.VAN DE VEN
ORG MAGNETIC RESONANCE   5, 147 (1973)

---

120   P 000200 (E)—3—METHYL—1,3—PENTADIENE

```
   H     H
    \1 2/
     C=C     H
    /    \3 4/
   H      C=C
    6  /    \5
   CH3      CH3
```

FORMULA	C6H10			MOL WT	82.15
SOLVENT	C6H10				
ORIG ST	C4H12SI			TEMP	AMB

109.70	141.86	135.31	126.61	11.05	13.60
1/3	2/2	3/1	4/2	5/4	6/4

J.W.DE HAAN,L.J.M.VAN DE VEN
ORG MAGNETIC RESONANCE   5, 147 (1973)

---

121   P 000200   1-BUTYNE

| | FORMULA | C4H6 | MOL WT | 54.09 |
| | SOLVENT | C4H6 | | |

1   2
CH≡C—CH2—CH3

ORIG ST   CS2   TEMP   AMB

67.00   84.70
1/2   2/1

R.A.FRIEDEL,H.L.RETCOFSKY
J AM CHEM SOC   85, 1300 (1963)

---

122   P 000200   2-BUTYNE

FORMULA   C4H6   MOL WT   54.09
SOLVENT   C4H6

2   3
CH3—C≡C—CH3

ORIG ST   CS2   TEMP   AMB

73.60   73.60
2/1   3/1

R.A.FRIEDEL,H.L.RETCOFSKY
J AM CHEM SOC   85, 1300 (1963)

---

123   P 000200   1-HEXYNE

1 2 3   4   5   6
H—C≡C—CH2—CH2—CH2—CH3

FORMULA   C6H10   MOL WT   82.15
SOLVENT   C6H10
ORIG ST   CS2   TEMP   AMB

67.40   82.80   17.40   29.90   21.20   12.90
1/2   2/1   3/3   4/3   5/3   6/4

S.RANG,T.PEHK,E.LIPPMA,O.EISEN
EESTI NSV TEAD AKAD TOIM KEEM
GEOL   16,   346 (1967)
                             17,   294 (1968)

---

124   P 000200   1-HEXYNE

FORMULA   C6H10   MOL WT   82.15
SOLVENT   C6H10

1   2
CH≡C—CH2—CH2—CH2—CH3

ORIG ST   C6H6   TEMP   AMB

68.70   84.40
1/2   2/1

D.D.TRAFICANTE,G.E.MACIEL
J PHYS CHEM   69, 1348 (1965)

---

125   P 000200   2-HEXYNE

1 2 3 4   5   6
H3C—C≡C—CH2—CH2—CH3

FORMULA   C6H10   MOL WT   82.15
SOLVENT   C6H10
ORIG ST   CS2   TEMP   AMB

1.70   73.70   76.90   19.60   21.60   12.10
1/4   2/1   3/1   4/3   5/3   6/4

S.RANG,T.PEHK,E.LIPPMA,O.EISEN
EESTI NSV TEAD AKAD TOIM KEEM
GEOL   16,   346 (1967)
                             17,   294 (1968)

---

126   P 000200   **3—HEXYNE**

```
1   2   3 4 5   6
CH3-CH2-C≡C-CH2-CH3
```

FORMULA	C6H10		MOL WT	82.15
SOLVENT	C6H10			
ORIG ST	CS2		TEMP	AMB

| 14.40 | 12.00 | 79.90 |
| 1/4 | 2/3 | 3/1 |

S.RANG,T.PEHK,E.LIPPMA,O.EISEN
EESTI NSV TEAD AKAD TOIM KEEM
GEOL   16,   346 (1967)
          17,   294 (1968)

---

127   P 000200   **3—HEXYNE**

| FORMULA | C6H10 | | MOL WT | 82.15 |
| SOLVENT | C6H10 | | | |

```
        3 4
  CH3-CH2-C≡C-CH2-CH3
```
ORIG ST   CS2   TEMP   AMB

| 80.70 | 80.70 |
| 3/1 | 4/1 |

J.W.EMSLEY,J.FEENY,L.H.SUTCLIFFE
HIGH RESOLUTION NUCLEAR MAGNETIC
RESONANCE SPECTROSCOPY   2, 1001 (1966)

---

128   P 000200   **1—HEPTYNE**

```
  1 2 3   4   5   6   7
H-C≡C-CH2-CH2-CH2-CH2-CH3
```

FORMULA	C7H12		MOL WT	96.17
SOLVENT	C7H12			
ORIG ST	CS2		TEMP	AMB

| 67.40 | 82.90 | 17.70 | 28.10 | 30.70 | 22.40 |
| 1/2 | 2/1 | 3/3 | 4/3 | 5/3 | 6/3 |
| 14.00 |
| 7/4 |

S.RANG,T.PEHK,E.LIPPMA,O.EISEN
EESTI NSV TEAD AKAD TOIM KEEM
GEOL   16,   346 (1967)
          17,   294 (1968)

---

129   P 000200   **2—HEPTYNE**

```
  1 2 3 4   5   6   7
H3C-C≡C-CH2-CH2-CH2-CH3
```

FORMULA	C7H12		MOL WT	96.17
SOLVENT	C7H12			
ORIG ST	CS2		TEMP	AMB

| 2.30 | 74.20 | 77.60 | 17.70 | 31.20 | 21.80 |
| 1/4 | 2/1 | 3/1 | 4/3 | 5/3 | 6/3 |
| 13.50 |
| 7/4 |

S.RANG,T.PEHK,E.LIPPMA,O.EISEN
EESTI NSV TEAD AKAD TOIM KEEM
GEOL   16,   346 (1967)
          17,   294 (1968)

---

130   P 000200   **2—HEPTYNE**

| FORMULA | C7H12 | | MOL WT | 96.17 |
| SOLVENT | C7H12 | | | |

```
       2 3
  CH3-C≡C-CH2-CH2-CH2-CH3
```
ORIG ST   C6H6   TEMP   AMB

| 77.00 | 80.40 |
| 2/1 | 3/1 |

D.D.TRAFICANTE,G.E.MACIEL
J PHYS CHEM   69, 1348 (1965)

---

131   P 000200   **3—HEPTYNE**

```
1    2    3 4 5    6    7
CH3-CH2-C≡C-CH2-CH2-CH3
```

FORMULA	C7H12			MOL WT	96.17
SOLVENT	C7H12				
ORIG ST	CS2			TEMP	AMB

13.70	12.00	78.30	80.20	20.20	22.50
1/4	2/3	3/1	4/1	5/3	6/3
13.10					
7/4					

S.RANG,T.PEHK,E.LIPPMA,O.EISEN
EESTI NSV TEAD AKAD TOIM KEEM
GEOL   16, 346 (1967)
         17, 294 (1968)

---

132   P 000200   **1—OCTYNE**

```
1 2 3   4   5   6   7   8
HC≡C-CH2-CH2-CH2-CH2-CH2-CH3
```

FORMULA	C8H14			MOL WT	110.20
SOLVENT	C8H14				
ORIG ST	CS2			TEMP	AMB

69.00	84.00	18.40	29.20	32.00	23.40
1/2	2/1	3/3	4 5/3	6/3	7/3
14.90					
8/4					

S.RANG,T.PEHK,E.LIPPMA,O.EISEN
EESTI NSV TEAD AKAD TOIM KEEM
GEOL   16, 346 (1967)
         17, 294 (1968)

---

133   P 000200   **2—OCTYNE**

```
 1 2 3 4   5   6   7   8
H3C-C≡C-CH2-CH2-CH2-CH2-CH3
```

FORMULA	C8H14			MOL WT	110.20
SOLVENT	C8H14				
ORIG ST	CS2			TEMP	AMB

2.90	74.80	78.50	18.40	29.50	31.40
1/4	2/1	3/1	4/3	5/3	6/3
22.70	14.50				
7/3	8/4				

S.RANG,T.PEHK,E.LIPPMA,O.EISEN
EESTI NSV TEAD AKAD TOIM KEEM
GEOL   16, 346 (1967)
         17, 294 (1968)

---

134   P 000200   **3—OCTYNE**

```
1    2    3 4 5    6    7    8
CH3-CH2-C≡C-CH2-CH2-CH2-CH3
```

FORMULA	C8H14			MOL WT	110.20
SOLVENT	C8H14				
ORIG ST	CS2			TEMP	AMB

15.10	13.00	79.70	81.00	18.70	31.90
1/4	2/3	3/1	4/1	5/3	6/3
22.80	14.60				
7/3	8/4				

S.RANG,T.PEHK,E.LIPPMA,O.EISEN
EESTI NSV TEAD AKAD TOIM KEEM
GEOL   16, 346 (1967)
         17, 294 (1968)

---

135   P 000200   **4—OCTYNE**

```
1    2    3    4 5 6    7    8
CH3-CH2-CH2-C≡C-CH2-CH2-CH3
```

FORMULA	C8H14			MOL WT	110.20
SOLVENT	C8H14				
ORIG ST	CS2			TEMP	AMB

| 12.70 | 21.40 | 19.20 | 79.00 |
| 1/4 | 2/3 | 3/3 | 4/1 |

S.RANG,T.PEHK,E.LIPPMA,O.EISEN
EESTI NSV TEAD AKAD TOIM KEEM
GEOL   16, 346 (1967)
         17, 294 (1968)

---

136   P 000200   DODECA—5,7—DIYNE

```
                5  6
CH3-CH2-CH2-CH2-C≡C
                8 |
CH3-CH2-CH2-CH2-C≡C7
```

FORMULA	C12H18			MOL WT	162.28
SOLVENT	C12H18				
ORIG ST	C6H6			TEMP	AMB

| 66.70 | 77.40 | 77.40 | 66.70 |
| 5/1 | 6/1 | 7/1 | 8/1 |

D.D.TRAFICANTE,G.E.MACIEL
J PHYS CHEM   69, 1348 (1965)

---

137   P 000300   METHYL FLUORIDE

FORMULA	CH3F		MOL WT	34.03
SOLVENT	CH3F	NEAT		
ORIG ST	C6H6		TEMP	AMB

```
1
CH3-F
```

74.10
1/4

H.SPIESECKE,W.G.SCHNEIDER
J CHEM PHYS   35, 722 (1961)

---

138   P 000300   METHYL CHLORIDE

FORMULA	CH3CL	MOL WT	50.49
SOLVENT	CH3CL		
ORIG ST	C6H6	TEMP	AMB

```
1
CH3-CL
```

23.80
1/4

W.M.LITCHMAN,D.M.GRANT
J AM CHEM SOC   90, 1400 (1968)

---

139   P 000300   METHYL BROMIDE

FORMULA	CH3BR	MOL WT	94.94
SOLVENT	CH3BR		
ORIG ST	C6H6	TEMP	AMB

```
1
CH3-BR
```

8.90
1/4

W.M.LITCHMAN,D.M.GRANT
J AM CHEM SOC   90, 1400 (1968)

---

140   P 000300   METHYL BROMIDE

```
1
CH3-BR
```

FORMULA	CH3BR	MOL WT	94.94
SOLVENT	C CL4		
ORIG ST	TMS	TEMP	298

9.30
1/4

E.BREITMAIER,G.JUNG,W.VOELTER,L.POHL
UNPUBLISHED   (1972)

141   P 000300   TRIDEUTERIOMETHYLBROMIDE

1
CD3—BR

FORMULA   CD3BR   MOL WT   97.96
SOLVENT   C CL4
ORIG ST   TMS   TEMP   298

8.75
1/7

E.BREITMAIER,G.JUNG,W.VOELTER,L.POHL
UNPUBLISHED   (1972)

---

142   P 000300   METHYL IODIDE

FORMULA   CH3I   MOL WT   141.94
SOLVENT   CH3I
1   ORIG ST   C6H6   TEMP   AMB
CH3—J

−21.80
1/4

W.M.LITCHMAN,D.M.GRANT
J AM CHEM SOC   90, 1400 (1968)

---

143   P 000300   METHYL IODIDE

1
CH3—J
FORMULA   CH3I   MOL WT   141.94
SOLVENT   C H3I
ORIG ST   TMS   TEMP   298

−20.25
1/4

E.BREITMAIER,G.JUNG,W.VOELTER,L.POHL
UNPUBLISHED   (1972)

---

144   P 000300   TRIDEUTERIOMETHYLIODIDE

1
CD3—J
FORMULA   CD3I   MOL WT   144.96
SOLVENT   C D3I
ORIG ST   TMS   TEMP   298

−20.50
1/7

E.BREITMAIER,G.JUNG,W.VOELTER,L.POHL
UNPUBLISHED   (1972)

---

145   P 000300   METHYLENE CHLORIDE

FORMULA   C H2CL2   MOL WT   84.93
SOLVENT   C H2CL2
CL   ORIG ST   C6H6   TEMP   AMB
\1
CH2
/
CL   52.85
1/3

W.M.LITCHMAN,D.M.GRANT
J AM CHEM SOC   90, 1400 (1968)

146   P 000300 DICHLOROMETHANE

            1   FORMULA CH2CL2   MOL WT   84.93
            CH2CL2   SOLVENT C H2CL2
                               ORIG ST TMS   TEMP   298

                      53.75
                      1/3

                      E.BREITMAIER,G.JUNG,W.VOELTER,L.POHL
                      UNPUBLISHED   (1972)

147   P 000300 DIDEUTERIODICHLOROMETHANE

            1   FORMULA CD2CL2   MOL WT   86.95
            CD2CL2   SOLVENT C D2CL2
                               ORIG ST TMS   TEMP   298

                      53.10
                      1/5

                      E.BREITMAIER,G.JUNG,W.VOELTER,L.POHL
                      UNPUBLISHED   (1972)

148   P 000300 CHLOROBROMOMETHANE

                               FORMULA CH2CLBR   MOL WT   129.38
            CL   SOLVENT CH2CLBR
             \1   ORIG ST C6H6   TEMP   AMB
              CH2
             /   38.75
            BR   1/3

                      W.M.LITCHMAN,D.M.GRANT
                      J AM CHEM SOC   90, 1400 (1968)

149   P 000300 METHYLENE BROMIDE

                               FORMULA CH2BR2   MOL WT   173.84
            BR   SOLVENT CH2BR2
             \1   ORIG ST C6H6   TEMP   AMB
              CH2
             /   20.30
            BR   1/3

                      W.M.LITCHMAN,D.M.GRANT
                      J AM CHEM SOC   90, 1400 (1968)

150   P 000300 METHYLENE IODIDE

                               FORMULA CH2I2   MOL WT   267.84
            J   SOLVENT CH2I2
             \1   ORIG ST C6H6   TEMP   AMB
              CH2
             /   55.10
            J   1/3

                      W.M.LITCHMAN,D.M.GRANT
                      J AM CHEM SOC   90, 1400 (1968)

151   P 000300   CHLOROFORM

```
CL   H
  \1/
   C
  / \
CL   CL
```

FORMULA   CHCL3
SOLVENT   CHCL3
ORIG ST   C6H6

MOL WT   119.38

TEMP   AMB

76.40
1/2

W.M.LITCHMAN,D.M.GRANT
J AM CHEM SOC

90, 1400 (1968)

---

152   P 000300   CHLOROFORM

```
1
CHCL3
```

FORMULA   CHCL3
SOLVENT   C H CL3
ORIG ST   TMS

MOL WT   119.38

TEMP   298

77.25
1/2

E.BREITMAIER,G.JUNG,W.VOELTER,L.POHL
UNPUBLISHED

(1972)

---

153   P 000300   DEUTERIOCHLOROFORM

```
1
CDCL3
```

FORMULA   CDCL3
SOLVENT   C D CL3
ORIG ST   TMS

MOL WT   120.38

TEMP   298

76.95
1/3

E.BREITMAIER,G.JUNG,W.VOELTER,L.POHL
UNPUBLISHED

(1972)

---

154   P 000300   DICHLOROBROMOMETHANE

```
CL   H
  \1/
   C
  / \
CL   BR
```

FORMULA   CHCL2BR
SOLVENT   CHCL2BR
ORIG ST   C6H6

MOL WT   163.83

TEMP   AMB

56.05
1/2

W.M.LITCHMAN,D.M.GRANT
J AM CHEM SOC

90, 1400 (1968)

---

155   P 000300   CHLORODIBROMOMETHANE

```
BR   H
  \1/
   C
  / \
BR   CL
```

FORMULA   CHCLBR2
SOLVENT   CHCLBR2
ORIG ST   C6H6

MOL WT   208.28

TEMP   AMB

33.25
1/2

W.M.LITCHMAN,D.M.GRANT
J AM CHEM SOC

90, 1400 (1968)

156   P 000300 BROMOFORM

```
    BR  H
      \1/
       C
      / \
    BR  BR
```

FORMULA   CHBR3
SOLVENT   CHBR3
ORIG ST   C6H6

11.05
1/2

MOL WT   252.73

TEMP   AMB

W.M.LITCHMAN,D.M.GRANT
J AM CHEM SOC

90, 1400 (1968)

---

157   P 000300 BROMOFORM

```
 1
CHBR3
```

FORMULA   CHBR3
SOLVENT   C H BR3
ORIG ST   TMS

12.55
1/2

MOL WT   252.73

TEMP   298

E.BREITMAIER,G.JUNG,W.VOELTER,L.POHL
UNPUBLISHED

(1972)

---

158   P 000300 DEUTERIOBROMOFORM

```
 1
CDBR3
```

FORMULA   CDBR3
SOLVENT   C D BR3
ORIG ST   TMS

12.40
1/3

MOL WT   253.74

TEMP   298

E.BREITMAIER,G.JUNG,W.VOELTER,L.POHL
UNPUBLISHED

(1972)

---

159   P 000300 IODOFORM

```
    J   H
      \1/
       C
      / \
    J   J
```

FORMULA   CHI3
SOLVENT   C5H5N
ORIG ST   C6H6

−141.00
1/2

MOL WT   393.73

TEMP   AMB

W.M.LITCHMAN,D.M.GRANT
J AM CHEM SOC

90, 1400 (1968)

---

160   P 000300 CARBON TETRACHLORIDE

```
   CL  CL
     \1/
      C
     / \
   CL  CL
```

FORMULA   CCL4
SOLVENT   CCL4
ORIG ST   C6H6

95.35
1/1

MOL WT   153.82

TEMP   AMB

W.M.LITCHMAN,D.M.GRANT
J AM CHEM SOC

90, 1400 (1968)

161　　　P 000300　**TRICHLOROBROMOMETHANE**

```
CL  CL
 \1/
  C
 / \
CL  BR
```

FORMULA　CCL3BR
SOLVENT　CCL3BR
ORIG ST　C6H6

MOL WT　198.27

TEMP　　AMB

66.50
1/1

W.M.LITCHMAN,D.M.GRANT
J AM CHEM SOC　　90, 1400 (1968)

162　　　P 000300　**DICHLORODIBROMOMETHANE**

```
CL  BR
 \1/
  C
 / \
BR  CL
```

FORMULA　CCL2BR2
SOLVENT　CCL2BR2
ORIG ST　C6H6

MOL WT　242.73

TEMP　　AMB

35.40
1/1

W.M.LITCHMAN,D.M.GRANT
J AM CHEM SOC　　90, 1400 (1968)

163　　　P 000300　**TRIBROMOCHLOROMETHANE**

```
BR  BR
 \1/
  C
 / \
BR  CL
```

FORMULA　CBR3CL
SOLVENT　CBR3CL
ORIG ST　C6H6

MOL WT　287.18

TEMP　　AMB

3.80
1/1

W.M.LITCHMAN,D.M.GRANT
J AM CHEM SOC　　90, 1400 (1968)

164　　　P 000300　**TETRABROMOMETHANE**

```
BR  BR
 \1/
  C
 / \
BR  BR
```

FORMULA　CBR4
SOLVENT　CBR4
ORIG ST　C6H6

MOL WT　331.63

TEMP　　AMB

29.75
1/1

W.M.LITCHMAN,D.M.GRANT
J AM CHEM SOC　　90, 1400 (1968)

165　　　P 000300　**FLUOROETHANE**

```
2   1
CH3—CH2—F
```

FORMULA　C2H5F
SOLVENT　C2H5F
ORIG ST　C6H6

MOL WT　48.06

TEMP　　AMB

78.00　　13.30
1/3　　　2/4

H.SPIESECKE,W.G.SCHNEIDER
J CHEM PHYS　　35,　722 (1961)

166　　　　　P 000300　**CHLOROETHANE**

	FORMULA	C2H5CL	MOL WT	64.52
	SOLVENT	C2H5CL	
2　1	ORIG ST	CS2	TEMP	AMB
CH3—CH2—CL			

38.70　　17.50
　1/3　　　2/4

G.MIYAJIMA,K.TAKAHASHI
J PHYS CHEM　　　　　　　75,　331 (1971)

167　　　　　P 000300　**CHLOROETHANE**

	FORMULA	C2H5CL	MOL WT	64.52
	SOLVENT	C2H5CL/C6H12	
	SOLVENT	NEAT/CYCLOHEXANE(9/1)	
1　2	ORIG ST	C4H12SI	TEMP	276
CL—CH2—CH3			

40.54　　19.16
　1/3　　　2/4

L.SIMERAL,G.E.MACIEL
J PHYS CHEM　　　　　　77, 1590 (1973)

168　　　　　P 000300　**BROMOETHANE**

	FORMULA	C2H5BR	MOL WT	108.97
	SOLVENT	C2H5BR	
2　1	ORIG ST	CS2	TEMP	AMB
CH3—CH2—BR			

26.95　　18.95
　1/3　　　2/4

P.C.LAUTERBUR
ANN NEW YORK ACAD SCI　　70,　841 (1958)

169　　　　　P 000300　**BROMOETHANE**

	FORMULA	C2H5BR	MOL WT	108.97
	SOLVENT	C2H5BR/C6H12	
	SOLVENT	NEAT/CYCLOHEXANE(9/1)	
1　2	ORIG ST	C4H12SI	TEMP	276
BR—CH2—CH3			

27.40　　19.65
　1/3　　　2/4

L.SIMERAL,G.E.MACIEL
J PHYS CHEM　　　　　　77, 1590 (1973)

170　　　　　P 000300　**BROMOETHANE**

2　1	FORMULA	C2H5BR	MOL WT	108.97
CH3—CH2—BR	SOLVENT	C CL4	
	ORIG ST	TMS	TEMP	298

27.40　　19.20
　1/3　　　2/4

E.BREITMAIER,G.JUNG,W.VOELTER,L.POHL
UNPUBLISHED　　　　　　　　　　(1972)

---

171   P 000300   PENTADEUTERIOETHYLBROMIDE

    2   1   FORMULA   C2D5BR   MOL WT   114.00
  CD3-CD2-BR   SOLVENT   CCL4
                    ORIG ST   TMS   TEMP   298

                    27.20   18.65
                     1/5   2/7

                    E.BREITMAIER,G.JUNG,W.VOELTER,L.POHL
                    UNPUBLISHED   (1972)

---

172   P 000300   IODOETHANE

                    FORMULA   C2H5I   MOL WT   155.97
                    SOLVENT   C2H5I
    2   1   ORIG ST   CS2   TEMP   AMB
  CH3-CH2-J
                    -0.25   21.85
                     1/3   2/4

                    P.C.LAUTERBUR
                    ANN NEW YORK ACAD SCI   70, 841 (195P-

---

173   P 000300   IODOETHANE

                    FORMULA   C2H5I   MOL WT   155.97
                    SOLVENT   C2H5I/C6H12
                    SOLVENT   NEAT/CYCLOHEXANE(9/1)
    1   2   ORIG ST   C4H12SI   TEMP   276
  J-CH2-CH3
                    -0.76   21.32
                     1/3   2/4

                    L.SIMERAL,G.E.MACIEL
                    J PHYS CHEM   77, 1590 (1973)

---

174   P 000300   IODOETHANE

                    FORMULA   C2H5I   MOL WT   155.97
                    SOLVENT   C6H12
    1   2   ORIG ST   CS2   TEMP   AMB
  J-CH2-CH3
                    -5.60   19.60
                     1/3   2/4

                    A.MARKER,D.DODDRELL,N.V.RIGGS
                    CHEM COMMUN   724 (1972)

---

175   P 000300   IODOETHANE

                    FORMULA   C2H5I   MOL WT   155.97
                    SOLVENT   C2H5I
    1   2   ORIG ST   CS2   TEMP   AMB
  J-CH2-CH3
                    -1.40   20.50
                     1/3   2/4

                    A.MARKER,D.DODDRELL,N.V.RIGGS
                    CHEM COMMUN   724 (1972)

176   P 000300   IODOETHANE

FORMULA C2H5I	MOL WT 155.97
SOLVENT CH3NO2	
ORIG ST CS2	TEMP AMB

```
    1    2
  J—CH2—CH3
```

```
   -1.20    19.80
    1/3      2/4
```

A.MARKER,D.DODDRELL,N.V.RIGGS
CHEM COMMUN   724 (1972)

---

177   P 000300   IODOETHANE

FORMULA C2H5I	MOL WT 155.97
SOLVENT C3H7ON	
ORIG ST CS2	TEMP AMB

```
    1    2
  J—CH2—CH3
```

```
   -0.40    20.30
    1/3      2/4
```

A.MARKER,D.DODDRELL,N.V.RIGGS
CHEM COMMUN   724 (1972)

---

178   P 000300   1,1-DICHLOROETHANE

FORMULA C2H4CL2	MOL WT 98.96
SOLVENT C2H4CL2	
ORIG ST CS2	TEMP AMB

```
        CL
   2    I1
  CH3—CH
        I
        CL
```

```
   68.00    31.30
    1/2      2/4
```

G.MIYAJIMA,K.TAKAHASHI
J PHYS CHEM   75,   331 (1971)

---

179   P 000300   1,2-DICHLOROETHANE

FORMULA C2H4CL2	MOL WT 98.96
SOLVENT C2H4CL2	
ORIG ST CS2	TEMP AMB

```
     1    2
  CL—CH2—CH2—CL
```

```
   43.90    43.90
    1/3      2/3
```

G.MIYAJIMA,K.TAKAHASHI
J PHYS CHEM   75,   331 (1971)

---

180   P 000300   1,2-DICHLOROETHANE

FORMULA C2H4CL2	MOL WT 98.96
SOLVENT C2H4CL2/C6H12	
SOLVENT NEAT/CYCLOHEXANE(9/1)	
ORIG ST C4H12SI	TEMP 276

```
     1    2
  CL—CH2—CH2—CL
```

```
   44.44    44.44
    1/3      2/3
```

L.SIMERAL,G.E.MACIEL
J PHYS CHEM   77, 1590 (1979)

---

181   P 000300 1,2-DIBROMOETHANE

FORMULA C2H4BR2	MOL WT 187.86
SOLVENT C2H4BR2/C6H12	
SOLVENT NEAT/CYCLOHEXANE(9/1)	
ORIG ST C4H12SI	TEMP 276

```
 1   2
BR-CH2-CH2-BR
```

```
30.74   30.74
 1/3     2/3
```

L.SIMERAL,G.E.MACIEL
J PHYS CHEM   77, 1590 (1973)

---

182   P 000300 1,2-DIBROMOETHANE

```
 1   2
BRCH2-CH2BR
```

FORMULA C2H4BR2	MOL WT 187.86
SOLVENT C2H4BR2	
ORIG ST TMS	TEMP 298

```
31.15
 1/3
```

E.BREITMAIER,G.JUNG,W.VOELTER,L.POHL
UNPUBLISHED   (1972)

---

183   P 000300 1,2-DIBROMOTETRADEUTERICETHANE

```
 1   2
BRCD2-CD2BR
```

FORMULA C2D4BR2	MOL WT 191.89
SOLVENT C2D4BR2	
ORIG ST TMS	TEMP 298

```
30.30
 1/5
```

E.BREITMAIER,G.JUNG,W.VOELTER,L.POHL
UNPUBLISHED   (1972)

---

184   P 000300 1,2-DIIODOETHANE

FORMULA C2H4I2	MOL WT 281.86
SOLVENT C2H4I2/C6H12	
SOLVENT NEAT/CYCLCHEXANE(9/1)	
ORIG ST C4H12SI	TEMP 276

```
 1   2
J-CH2-CH2-J
```

```
 3.57    3.57
 1/3     2/3
```

L.SIMERAL,G.E.MACIEL
J PHYS CHEM   77, 1590 (1973)

---

185   P 000300 1-BROMO-2-CHLOROETHANE

FORMULA C2H4CLBR	MOL WT 143.41
SOLVENT C2H4CLBR/C6H12	
SOLVENT NEAT/CYCLCHEXANE(9/1)	
ORIG ST C4H12SI	TEMP 276

```
 1   2
BR-CH2-CH2-CL
```

```
31.92   43.92
 1/3     2/3
```

L.SIMERAL,G.E.MACIEL
J PHYS CHEM   77, 1590 (1973)

186   P 000300   1,1,1-TRICHLOROETHANE

```
            CL
      2    11
     CH3-C-CL
           |
           CL
```

FORMULA	$C_2H_3CL_3$	MOL WT	133.41
SOLVENT	$C_2H_3CL_3$		
ORIG ST	CS2	TEMP	AMB

95.00   45.10
1/1   2/4

G.MIYAJIMA,K.TAKAHASHI
J PHYS CHEM   75,   331 (1971)

---

187   P 000300   1,1,2-TRICHLOROETHANE

```
     CL
     11 2
     CH-CH2-CL
     |
     CL
```

FORMULA	$C_2H_3CL_3$	MOL WT	133.41
SOLVENT	$C_2H_3CL_3$		
ORIG ST	CS2	TEMP	AMB

71.10   50.40
1/2   2/3

G.MIYAJIMA,K.TAKAHASHI
J PHYS CHEM   75,   331 (1971)

---

188   P 000300   1,1,1,2-TETRACHLOROETHANE

```
            CL
      2    11
   CL-CH2-C-CL
           |
           CL
```

FORMULA	$C_2H_2CL_4$	MOL WT	167.85
SOLVENT	$C_2H_2CL_4$		
ORIG ST	CS2	TEMP	AMB

96.40   59.50
1/1   2/3

G.MIYAJIMA,K.TAKAHASHI
J PHYS CHEM   75,   331 (1971)

---

189   P 000300   1,1,2,2-TETRACHLOROETHANE

```
    CL     CL
     \1   2/
      CH-CH
     /     \
    CL      CL
```

FORMULA	$C_2H_2CL_4$	MOL WT	167.85
SOLVENT	$C_2H_2CL_4$		
ORIG ST	CS2	TEMP	AMB

74.30   74.30
1/2   2/2

G.MIYAJIMA,K.TAKAHASHI
J PHYS CHEM   75,   331 (1971)

---

190   P 000300   1,1,2,2-TETRACHLOROETHANE

```
    CL     CL
     \1   2/
      CH-CH
     /     \
    CL      CL
```

FORMULA	$C_2H_2CL_4$	MOL WT	167.85
SOLVENT	$C_2H_2CL_4$		
ORIG ST	TMS	TEMP	298

74.55
1/2

E.BREITMAIER,G.JUNG,W.VOELTER,L.POHL
UNPUBLISHED   (1972)

191   P 000300   1,1,2,2-TETRACHLORO-1,2-DIDEUTERIOETHANE

```
  1   2
CL2CD-CDCL2
```

FORMULA C2D2CL4	MOL WT 169.86
SOLVENT C2D2CL4	
ORIG ST TMS	TEMP 298

```
74.25
1/3
```

E.BREITMAIER,G.JUNG,W.VOELTER,L.POHL
UNPUBLISHED   (1972)

---

192   P 000300   1,1,1,2,2-PENTACHLOROETHANE

```
  CL  CL
   \1 |2
CL-C-CH
  /  |
  CL  CL
```

FORMULA C2HCL5	MOL WT 202.30
SOLVENT C2HCL5	
ORIG ST CS2	TEMP AMB

```
99.70   80.00
1/1     2/2
```

G.MIYAJIMA,K.TAKAHASHI
J PHYS CHEM   75, 331 (1971)

---

193   P 000300   1,1,1,2,2,2-HEXACHLOROETHANE

```
  CL    CL
   \1  2/
CL-C-C-CL
  /    \
  CL    CL
```

FORMULA C2CL6	MOL WT 236.74
SOLVENT C2CL6	
ORIG ST CS2	TEMP AMB

```
104.90  104.90
1/1     2/1
```

G.MIYAJIMA,K.TAKAHASHI
J PHYS CHEM   75, 331 (1971)

---

194   P 000300   2-CHLOROPROPANE

```
     CL
  1   |2 3
CH3-CH-CH3
```

FORMULA C3H7CL	MOL WT 78.54
SOLVENT C3H7CL	
ORIG ST C S2	TEMP AMB

```
26.85   53.75   26.85
1/4     2/2     3/4
```

P.C.LAUTERBUR
ANN NEW YORK ACAD SCI   70, 841 (1958)

---

195   P 000300   2-BROMOPROPANE

```
     BR
  1   |2 3
CH3-CH-CH3
```

FORMULA C3H7BR	MOL WT 122.99
SOLVENT C3H7BR	
ORIG ST C S2	TEMP AMB

```
28.05   44.05   28.05
1/4     2/2     3/4
```

P.C.LAUTERBUR
ANN NEW YORK ACAD SCI   70, 841 (1958)

196   P 000300 2—IODOPROPANE

```
                          FORMULA   C3H7I                    MOL WT  169.99
                          SOLVENT   C3H7I
        J                 ORIG ST   C S2                     TEMP      AMB
    1   12 3
    CH3-CH-CH3            31.85    20.95    31.85
                          1/4      2/2      3/4

                          P.C.LAUTERBUR
                          ANN NEW YORK ACAD SCI              70,  841 (1958)
```

197   P 000300 2—IODOPROPANE

```
                          FORMULA   C3H7I                    MOL WT  169.99
                          SOLVENT   C6H12
    1   2   3             ORIG ST   CS2                      TEMP      AMB
    CH3-CH-CH3
        I                 30.60    16.90    30.60
        J                 1/4      2/2      3/4

                          A.MARKER,D.DODDRELL,N.V.RIGGS
                          CHEM COMMUN                        724 (1972)
```

198   P 000300 2—IODOPROPANE

```
                          FORMULA   C3H7I                    MOL WT  169.99
                          SOLVENT   C3H7I
    1   2   3             ORIG ST   CS2                      TEMP      AMB
    CH3-CH-CH3
        I                 31.40    20.20    31.40
        J                 1/4      2/2      3/4

                          A.MARKER,D.DODDRELL,N.V.RIGGS
                          CHEM COMMUN                        724 (1972)
```

199   P 000300 2—IODOPROPANE

```
                          FORMULA   C3H7I                    MOL WT  169.99
                          SOLVENT   CH3O2N
    1   2   3             ORIG ST   CS2                      TEMP      AMB
    CH3-CH-CH3
        I                 30.50    22.40    30.50
        J                 1/4      2/2      3/4

                          A.MARKER,D.DODDRELL,N.V.RIGGS
                          CHEM COMMUN                        724 (1972)
```

200   P 000300 2—IODOPROPANE

```
                          FORMULA   C3H7I                    MOL WT  169.99
                          SOLVENT   C3H7CN
    1   2   3             ORIG ST   CS2                      TEMP      AMB
    CH3-CH-CH3
        I                 30.90    22.80    30.90
        J                 1/4      2/2      3/4

                          A.MARKER,D.DODDRELL,N.V.RIGGS
                          CHEM COMMUN                        724 (1972)
```

201   P 000300   2—CHLORO—2—METHYLPROPANE

```
      4
      CH3
  1   |2 3
 CH3-C-CH3
      |
      CL
```

FORMULA	C4H9CL			MOL WT	92.57
SOLVENT	C4H9CL				
ORIG ST	C S2			TEMP	AMB

33.45	165.15	33.45	33.45
1/4	2/1	3/4	4/4

P.C.LAUTERBUR
ANN NEW YORK ACAD SCI   70, 841 (1958)

---

202   P 000300   2—BROMO—2—METHYLPROPANE

```
      4
      CH3
  1   |2 3
 CH3-C-CH3
      |
      BR
```

FORMULA	C4H9BR			MOL WT	137.02
SOLVENT	C4H9BR				
ORIG ST	C S2			TEMP	AMB

36.35	60.55	36.35	36.35
1/4	2/1	3/4	4/4

P.C.LAUTERBUR
ANN NEW YORK ACAD SCI   70, 841 (1958)

---

203   P 000300   2—IODO—2—METHYLPROPANE

```
      4
      CH3
  1   |2 3
 CH3-C-CH3
      |
      J
```

FORMULA	C4H9I			MOL WT	184.02
SOLVENT	C4H9I				
ORIG ST	C S2			TEMP	AMB

40.45	41.85	40.45	40.45
1/4	2/1	3/4	4/4

P.C.LAUTERBUR
ANN NEW YORK ACAD SCI   70, 841 (1958)

---

204   P 000300   2—IODO—2—METHYLPROPANE

```
      J
  1   |2 3
 CH3-C-CH3
      |
      4CH3
```

FORMULA	C4H9I			MOL WT	184.02
SOLVENT	C6H12				
ORIG ST	C S2			TEMP	AMB

39.90	38.30	39.90	39.90
1/4	2/1	3/4	4/4

A.MARKER,D.DODDRELL,N.V.RIGGS
CHEM COMMUN   724 (1972)

---

205   P 000300   2—IODO—2—METHYLPROPANE

```
      J
  1   |2 3
 CH3-C-CH3
      |
      4CH3
```

FORMULA	C4H9I			MOL WT	184.02
SOLVENT	C4H9I				
ORIG ST	C S2			TEMP	AMB

40.80	41.70	40.80	40.80
1/4	2/1	3/4	4/4

A.MARKER,D.DODDRELL,N.V.RIGGS
CHEM COMMUN   724 (1972)

206   P 000300   2—IODO—2—METHYLPROPANE

```
                J
    1      12 3
    CH3—C—CH3
           I
        4CH3
```

FORMULA	C4H9I	MOL WT	184.02
SOLVENT	CH3NO2		
ORIG ST	CS2	TEMP	AMB

39.90	45.40	39.90	39.90
1/4	2/1	3/4	4/4

R.A.FRIEDEL,H.L.RETCOFSKY
J AM CHEM SOC   85, 1300 (1963)

---

207   P 000300   1—IODOPENTANE

```
    1   2   3   4   5
    J—CH2—CH2—CH2—CH2—CH3
```

FORMULA	C5H11I	MOL WT	198.05
SOLVENT	C6H12		
ORIG ST	CS2	TEMP	AMB

3.10	33.10	32.40	21.20	12.80
1/3	2/3	3/3	4/3	5/4

A.MARKER,D.DODDRELL,N.V.RIGGS
CHEM COMMUN   724 (1972)

---

208   P 000300   1—IODOPENTANE

```
    1   2   3   4   5
    J—CH2—CH2—CH2—CH2—CH3
```

FORMULA	C5H11I	MOL WT	198.05
SOLVENT	C5H11I		
ORIG ST	CS2	TEMP	AMB

5.90	33.20	32.50	21.40	13.60
1/3	2/3	3/3	4/3	5/4

A.MARKER,D.DODDRELL,N.V.RIGGS
CHEM COMMUN   724 (1972)

---

209   P 000300   1—IODOPENTANE

```
    1   2   3   4   5
    J—CH2—CH2—CH2—CH2—CH3
```

FORMULA	C5H11I	MOL WT	198.05
SOLVENT	CH3O2N		
ORIG ST	CS2	TEMP	AMB

7.00	33.20	32.50	21.30	12.90
1/3	2/3	3/3	4/3	5/4

A.MARKER,D.DODDRELL,N.V.RIGGS
CHEM COMMUN   724 (1972)

---

210   P 000300   1—IODOPENTANE

```
    1   2   3   4   5
    J—CH2—CH2—CH2—CH2—CH3
```

FORMULA	C5H11I	MOL WT	198.05
SOLVENT	C3H7ON		
ORIG ST	CS2	TEMP	AMB

7.50	33.30	32.50	21.30	13.30
1/3	2/3	3/3	4/3	5/4

A.MARKER,D.DODDRELL,N.V.RIGGS
CHEM COMMUN   724 (1972)

211   P 000300   1—IODOHEPTANE

FORMULA   C7H15I   MOL WT   226.10
SOLVENT   C6H12
ORIG ST   CS2   TEMP   AMB

```
 1    2    3    4    5    6    7
J-CH2-CH2-CH2-CH2-CH2-CH2-CH3    3.30   33.50   30.30   28.00   31.50   22.20
                                 1/3     2/3     3/3     4/3     5/3     6/3
                                13.10
                                 7/4
```

A.MARKER,D.DODDRELL,N.V.RIGGS
CHEM COMMUN   724 (1972)

---

212   P 000300   1—IODOHEPTANE

FORMULA   C7H15I   MOL WT   226.10
SOLVENT   C7H15I
ORIG ST   CS2   TEMP   AMB

```
 1    2    3    4    5    6    7
J-CH2-CH2-CH2-CH2-CH2-CH2-CH3    5.80   33.50   30.30   28.00   31.50   22.30
                                 1/3     2/3     3/3     4/3     5/3     6/3
                                13.70
                                 7/4
```

A.MARKER,D.DODDRELL,N.V.RIGGS
CHEM COMMUN   724 (1972)

---

213   P 000300   1—IODOHEPTANE

FORMULA   C7H15I   MOL WT   226.10
SOLVENT   CH3O2N
ORIG ST   CS2   TEMP   AMB

```
 1    2    3    4    5    6    7
J-CH2-CH2-CH2-CH2-CH2-CH2-CH3    7.10   33.60   30.30   28.00   31.50   22.30
                                 1/3     2/3     3/3     4/3     5/3     6/3
                                13.20
                                 7/4
```

A.MARKER,D.DODDRELL,N.V.RIGGS
CHEM COMMUN   724 (1972)

---

214   P 000300   1—IODOHEPTANE

FORMULA   C7H15I   MOL WT   226.10
SOLVENT   C3H7ON
ORIG ST   CS2   TEMP   AMB

```
 1    2    3    4    5    6    7
J-CH2-CH2-CH2-CH2-CH2-CH2-CH3    7.70   33.70   28.00   31.60   22.30   13.50
                                 1/3     2/3     4/3     5/3     6/3     7/4
```

A.MARKER,D.DODDRELL,N.V.RIGGS
CHEM COMMUN   724 (1972)

---

215   P 000300   MESO—2,3—DICHLOROBUTANE

FORMULA   C4H8CL2   MOL WT   127.01
SOLVENT   C4H8CL2
ORIG ST   CS2   TEMP   AMB

```
        CL CL
 1      |  |   4
CH3-CH-CH-CH3                     21.80   61.30   61.30   21.80
    2     3                        1/4     2/2     3/2     4/4
```

C.J.CARMAN,A.R.TARPLEY,J.H.GOLDSTEIN
J AM CHEM SOC   93, 2864 (1971)

---

216   P 000300   RACEM-2,3-DICHLOROBUTANE

FORMULA   C4H8CL2   MOL WT   127.01
SOLVENT   C4H8CL2
ORIG ST   CS2   TEMP   AMB

```
        CL
1   1   3   4
CH3-CH-CH-CH3
    2   1
        CL
```

19.70	60.20	60.20	19.70
1/4	2/2	3/2	4/4

C.J.CARMAN,A.R.TARPLEY,J.H.GOLDSTEIN
J AM CHEM SOC   93, 2864 (1971)

---

217   P 000300   MESO-2,4-DICHLOROPENTANE

FORMULA   C5H10CL2   MOL WT   141.04
SOLVENT   C5H10CL2
ORIG ST   CS2   TEMP   AMB

```
1   2   3   4   5
CH3-CH-CH2-CH-CH3
    1       1
    CL      CL
```

24.40	54.20	50.20	54.20	24.40
1/4	2/2	3/3	4/2	5/4

C.J.CARMAN,A.R.TARPLEY,J.H.GOLDSTEIN
J AM CHEM SOC   93, 2864 (1971)

---

218   P 000300   RACEM-2,4-DICHLOROPENTANE

FORMULA   C5H10CL2   MOL WT   141.04
SOLVENT   C5H10CL2
ORIG ST   CS2   TEMP   AMB

```
        CL
1   1 2 3   4   5
CH3-CH-CH2-CH-CH3
            1
            CL
```

25.20	55.30	50.40	55.30	25.20
1/4	2/2	3/3	4/2	5/4

C.J.CARMAN,A.R.TARPLEY,J.H.GOLDSTEIN
J AM CHEM SOC   93, 2864 (1971)

---

219   P 000300   1-CHLORO-2-HYDROXYETHANE

FORMULA   C2H5OCL   MOL WT   80.51
SOLVENT   C2H5OCL/C6H12(9/1)
SOLVENT   NEAT/CYCLOHEXANE
ORIG ST   C4H12SI   TEMP   276

```
1   2
CL-CH2-CH2-OH
```

46.67	63.38
1/3	2/3

L.SIMERAL,G.E.MACIEL
J PHYS CHEM   77, 1590 (1973)

---

220   P 000300   1-BROMO-2-HYDROXYETHANE

FORMULA   C2H5OBR   MOL WT   124.97
SOLVENT   C2H5OBR/C6H12
SOLVENT   NEAT/CYCLOHEXANE(9/1)
ORIG ST   C4H12SI   TEMP   276

```
1   2
BR-CH2-CH2-OH
```

35.20	63.24
1/3	2/3

L.SIMERAL,G.E.MACIEL
J PHYS CHEM   77, 1590 (1973)

221   P 000300   1-IODO-2-HYDROXYETHANE

          FORMULA   C2H5CI   MOL WT   171.97
          SOLVENT   C2H5CI/C6H12
          SOLVENT   NEAT/CYCLOHEXANE(9/1)
1   2   ORIG ST   C4H12SI   TEMP   276
J-CH2-CH2-OH

          14.01   67.53
          1/3   2/3

          L.SIMERAL,G.E.MACIEL
          J PHYS CHEM   77, 1590 (1973)

---

222   P 000300   CHLOROETHYLENE

          FORMULA   C2H3CL   MOL WT   62.50
     CL   SOLVENT   C2H3CL
2   !1   ORIG ST   CS2   TEMP   AMB
CH2=CH

          124.90   116.00
          1/2   2/3

          G.MIYAJIMA,K.TAKAHASHI
          J PHYS CHEM   75, 331 (1971)

---

223   P 000300   BROMOETHYLENE

          FORMULA   C2H3BR   MOL WT   106.95
     BR   SOLVENT   C6H12
2   !1   ORIG ST   C6H6   TEMP   AMB
CH2=CH

          114.30   120.80
          1/2   2/3

          G.E.MACIEL
          J PHYS CHEM   69, 1947 (1965)

---

224   P 000300   IODOETHYLENE

          FORMULA   C2H3I   MOL WT   153.95
     J   SOLVENT   C2H3I
2   !1   ORIG ST   C6H6   TEMP   AMB
CH2=CH

          84.10   129.20
          1/2   2/3

          G.E.MACIEL
          J PHYS CHEM   69, 1947 (1965)

---

225   P 000300   1,1-DICHLOROETHYLENE

          FORMULA   C2H2CL2   MOL WT   96.94
     CL   SOLVENT   C2H2CL2   NEAT
1   2/   ORIG ST   CS2   TEMP   AMB
CH2=C
     \
      CL 112.10   125.90
          1/3   2/1

          G.MIYAJIMA,K.TAKAHASHI
          J PHYS CHEM   75, 331 (1971)

226   P 000300 CIS—1,2—DICHLOROETHYLENE

FORMULA	C2H2CL2	MOL WT 96.94
SOLVENT	C2H2CL2	
ORIG ST	CS2	TEMP AMB

```
CL      CL
 \1   2/
  CH=CH
```

118.10   118.10
  1/2   2/2

G.MIYAJIMA,K.TAKAHASHI
J PHYS CHEM   75, 331 (1971)

---

227   P 000300 TRANS—1,2—DICHLOROETHYLENE

FORMULA	C2H2CL2	MOL WT 96.94
SOLVENT	C2H2CL2	
ORIG ST	CS2	TEMP AMB

```
CL
 \1   2
  CH=CH
       \
        CL
```

119.90   119.90
  1/2   2/2

G.MIYAJIMA,K.TAKAHASHI
J PHYS CHEM   75, 331 (1971)

---

228   P 000300 CIS—1,2—DIBROMOETHYLENE

FORMULA	C2H2BR2	MOL WT 185.85
SOLVENT	C2H2BR2	
ORIG ST	C6H6	TEMP AMB

```
BR      BR
 \1   2/
  CH=CH
```

115.10   115.10
  1/2   2/2

G.B.SAVITSKY,K.NAMIKAWA
J PHYS CHEM   67, 2754 (1963)

---

229   P 000300 TRANS—1,2—DIBROMOETHYLENE

FORMULA	C2H2BR2	MOL WT 185.85
SOLVENT	C2H2BR2	
ORIG ST	C6H6	TEMP AMB

```
BR
 \1   2
  CH=CH
       \
        BR
```

108.10   108.10
  1/2   2/2

G.B.SAVITSKY,K.NAMIKAWA
J PHYS CHEM   67, 2754 (1963)

---

230   P 000300 CIS—1,2—DIIODOETHYLENE

FORMULA	C2H2I2	MOL WT 279.85
SOLVENT	C2H2I2	
ORIG ST	C6H6	TEMP AMB

```
J       J
 \1   2/
  CH=CH
```

95.20   95.20
  1/2   2/2

G.B.SAVITSKY,K.NAMIKAWA
J PHYS CHEM   67, 2754 (1963)

231   P 000300   TRANS—1,2—DIIODOETHYLENE

                        FORMULA   C2H2I2   MOL WT   279.85
                        SOLVENT   C2H2I2
        J   ORIG ST   C6H6   TEMP   AMB
       \1 2
        CH=CH   78.10   78.10
            \   1/2   2/2
             J
                        G.B.SAVITSKY,K.NAMIKAWA
                        J PHYS CHEM   67, 2754 (1963)

232   P 000300   1,1,2—TRICHLOROETHYLENE

                        FORMULA   C2HCL3   MOL WT   131.39
                        SOLVENT   C2HCL3
            CL   ORIG ST   CS2   TEMP   AMB
       2 1/
    CL—CH=C   123.90   116.40
            \   1/1   2/2
            CL
                        G.MIYAJIMA,K.TAKAHASHI
                        J PHYS CHEM   75,   331 (1971)

233   P 000300   1,1,2,2—TETRACHLOROETHYLENE

                        FORMULA   C2CL4   MOL WT   165.83
                        SOLVENT   C2CL4
    CL   CL   ORIG ST   CS2   TEMP   AMB
     \1 2/
      C=C   120.10   120.10
     /   \   1/1   2/1
    CL   CL
                        G.MIYAJIMA,K.TAKAHASHI
                        J PHYS CHEM   75,   331 (1971)

234   P 000300   CIS—1—CHLOROPROPENE

                        FORMULA   C3H5CL   MOL WT   76.53
                        SOLVENT   C3H5CL
    CH3   CL   ORIG ST   CS2   TEMP   AMB
     \2 1/
      CH=CH   118.80   125.40
                               1/2   2/2
                        G.B.SAVITSKY,P.D.ELLIS,K.NAMIKAWA,G.B.MACIEL
                        J CHEM PHYS   49, 2395 (1968)

235   P 000300   TRANS—1—CHLOROPROPENE

                        FORMULA   C3H5CL   MOL WT   76.53
                        SOLVENT   C3H5CL
    CH3   ORIG ST   CS2   TEMP   AMB
     \2 1
      CH=CH   116.40   128.10
          \   1/2   2/2
           CL
                        G.B.SAVITSKY,P.D.ELLIS,K.NAMIKAWA,G.B.MACIEL
                        J CHEM PHYS   49, 2395 (1968)

236 P 000300 CIS-1-BROMOPROPENE

FORMULA C3H5BR   MOL WT 120.98
SOLVENT C3H5BR
ORIG ST CS2   TEMP   AMB

```
CH3   BR
 \2  1/
  CH=CH
```

110.10 129.60
1/2   2/2

G.B.SAVITSKY,P.D.ELLIS,K.NAMIKAWA,G.B.MACIEL
J CHEM PHYS   49, 2395 (1968)

---

237 P 000300 TRANS-1-BROMOPROPENE

FORMULA C3H5BR   MOL WT 120.98
SOLVENT C3H5BR
ORIG ST CS2   TEMP   AMB

```
CH3
 \2  1
  CH=CH
       \
        BR
```

104.40 133.40
1/2   2/2

G.B.SAVITSKY,P.D.ELLIS,K.NAMIKAWA,G.B.MACIEL
J CHEM PHYS   49, 2395 (1968)

---

238 P 000400 NITROMETHANE

```
   1
H3C-NO2
```

FORMULA CH3NO2   MOL WT 61.04
SOLVENT C H3N O2
ORIG ST TMS   TEMP   298

61.15
1/4

E.BREITMAIER,G.JUNG,W.VOELTER,L.POHL
UNPUBLISHED   (1972)

---

239 P 000400 TRIDEUTERIONITROMETHANE

```
D3C-NO2
   1
```

FORMULA CD3NO2   MOL WT 64.06
SOLVENT C D3N O2
ORIG ST TMS   TEMP   298

60.55
1/7

E.BREITMAIER,G.JUNG,W.VOELTER,L.POHL
UNPUBLISHED   (1972)

---

240 P 000400 NITROETHANE

FORMULA C2H5NO2   MOL WT 75.07
SOLVENT C2H5NO2/C6H12(9/1)
SOLVENT NEAT/CYCLOHEXANE
ORIG ST C4H12SI   TEMP   276

```
 1   2
CH3-CH2-NO2
```

12.18 71.16
1/4   2/3

L.SIMERAL,G.E.MACIEL
J PHYS CHEM   77, 1590 (1973)

241   P 000600 METHYLAMINE

```
                    FORMULA   CH5N                  MOL WT    31.06
                    SOLVENT   CH5N
        1           ORIG ST   C6H6                  TEMP      AMB
     CH3-NH2
                         26.90
                         1/4

                    W.J.HORSLEY,H.STERNLICHT
                    J AM CHEM SOC                   90, 3738 (1968)
```

242   P 000600 ETHYLAMINE

```
                    FORMULA   C2H7N                 MOL WT    45.08
                    SOLVENT   C2H7N
     2   1          ORIG ST   C6H6                  TEMP      AMB
   CH3-CH2-NH2
                         35.90     17.70
                         1/3       2/4

                    W.J.HORSLEY,H.STERNLICHT
                    J AM CHEM SOC                   90, 3738 (1968)
```

243   P 000600 N—NITROSODIMETHYLAMINE

```
     -       1      FORMULA   C2H6ON2               MOL WT    74.08
   O      CH3       SOLVENT   C2H6ON2
    \   +/          ORIG ST   C4H12SI               TEMP      AMB
     N=N
        \                32.60     40.50
         CH3            1/4       2/4
         2
                    P.S.PREGOSIN,E.RANDALL
                    CHEM COMMUN                     1971,  399 (1971)
```

244   P 000600 N—NITROSODIETHYLAMINE

```
                    FORMULA   C4H10ON2              MOL WT    102.14
     -      1   2   SOLVENT   C4H10ON2
   O      CH2-CH3   ORIG ST   C4H12SI   TMS         TEMP      AMB
    \   +/
     N=N
        \                38.40     11.50     47.00     14.50
         CH2-CH3        1/3       2/4       3/3       4/4
         3    4
                    P.S.PREGOSIN,E.RANDALL
                    CHEM COMMUN                     1971,  399 (1971)
```

245   P 000600 N—NITROSODIPROPYLAMINE

```
     -      1   2   3
   O      CH2-CH2-CH3   FORMULA  C6H14ON2               MOL WT   130.19
    \   +/              SOLVENT  C6H14ON2
     N=N                ORIG ST  C4H12SI   TMS              TEMP      AMB
        \                   45.20     20.30     11.30     54.20     22.50     11.80
         CH2-CH2-CH3        1/3       2/3       3/4       4/3       5/3       6/4
         4    5   6
                       P.S.PREGOSIN,E.RANDALL
                       CHEM COMMUN                     1971,  399 (1971)
```

---

246   P 000600   N-NITROSODIISOPROPYLAMINE

```
            CH3
   —      1/
  O       CH
   \   +/  \2
    N=N    CH3
     |
    3CH
     / \4
  H3C    CH3
```

FORMULA	C6H14ON2			MOL WT	130.19
SOLVENT	C6H14ON2				
ORIG ST	C4H12SI			TEMP	AMB

45.40	19.10	51.10	23.70
1/2	2/4	3/2	4/4

P.S.PREGOSIN,E.RANDALL
CHEM COMMUN   1971, 399 (1971)

---

247   P 000600   N-NITROSODIBUTYLAMINE

```
   —    1   2   3
  O     CH2—CH2—CH2—CH3
   \  +/
    N=N
      \4   5   6
       CH2—CH2—CH2—CH3
```

FORMULA	C8H18ON2			MOL WT	158.25
SOLVENT	C8H18ON2				
ORIG ST	C4H12SI			TEMP	AMB

41.80	28.90	20.30	51.90	31.10	20.90
1/3	2/3	3/3	4/3	5/3	6/3

P.S.PREGOSIN,E.RANDALL
CHEM COMMUN   1971, 399 (1971)

---

248   P 000600   N-NITROSODIISOBUTYLAMINE

```
             CH3
   —    1   2/
  O     CH2—CH
   \  +/      \3
    N=N       CH3
      \4   5
       CH2—CH
         / \ 6
       H3C   CH3
```

FORMULA	C8H18ON2			MOL WT	158.25
SOLVENT	C8H18ON2				
ORIG ST	C4H12SI			TEMP	AMB

50.40	26.50	20.10	59.90	27.50	20.50
1/3	2/2	3/4	4/3	5/2	6/4

P.S.PREGOSIN,E.RANDALL
CHEM COMMUN   1971, 399 (1971)

---

249   P 001100   METHANOL

```
  1
 CH3—OH
```

FORMULA	CH4O			MOL WT	32.04
SOLVENT	C H4O				
ORIG ST	C S2			TEMP	AMB

49.00
1/4

J.D.ROBERTS,F.J.WEIGERT,J.I.KROSCHWITZ,H.J.REICH
J AM CHEM SOC   92, 1338 (1970)

---

250   P 001100   METHANOL

```
  1
 CH3—OH
```

FORMULA	CH4O			MOL WT	32.04
SOLVENT	C H4O				
ORIG ST	TMS			TEMP	298

48.00
1/4

E.BREITMAIER,G.JUNG,W.VOELTER,L.POHL
UNPUBLISHED   (1972)

251   P 001100   TETRADEUTERIOMETHANOL

       1
       CD3–OD

FORMULA	CD4O	MOL WT	36.07
SOLVENT	C D4O		
ORIG ST	TMS	TEMP	298

      47.05
       1/7

E.BREITMAIER,G.JUNG,W.VOELTER,L.POHL
UNPUBLISHED   (1972)

---

252   P 001100   ETHANOL

    2   1
    CH3–CH2–OH

FORMULA	C2H6O	MOL WT	46.07
SOLVENT	C2H6O		
ORIG ST	CS2	TEMP	AMB

      57.00   17.60
       1/3   2/4

J.D.ROBERTS,F.J.WEIGERT,J.I.KROSCHWITZ,H.J.REICH
J AM CHEM SOC   92, 1338 (1970)

---

253   P 001100   ETHANOL

FORMULA	C2H6O	MOL WT	46.07
SOLVENT	C2H6O/C6H12(9/1)		
SOLVENT	NEAT/CYCLOHEXANE		
ORIG ST	C4H12SI	TEMP	276

    2   1
    CH3–CH2–OH

      57.66   18.21
       1/3   2/4

L.SIMERAL,G.E.MACIEL
J PHYS CHEM   77, 1590 (1973)

---

254   P 001100   ETHANOL

    2   1
    CH3–CH2–OH

FORMULA	C2H6O	MOL WT	46.07
SOLVENT	C2H6O		
ORIG ST	TMS	TEMP	298

      56.30   16.95
       1/3   2/4

E.BREITMAIER,G.JUNG,W.VOELTER,L.POHL
UNPUBLISHED   (1972)

---

255   P 001100   HEXADEUTERIOETHANOL

    2   1
    CD3–CD2–OD

FORMULA	C2D6O	MOL WT	52.11
SOLVENT	C2D6O		
ORIG ST	TMS	TEMP	298

      55.35   15.75
       1/5   2/7

E.BREITMAIER,G.JUNG,W.VOELTER,L.POHL
UNPUBLISHED   (1972)

256   P 001100   1—PROPANOL

CH3—CH2—CH2—OH   FORMULA   C3H8O   MOL WT   60.10
3   2   1   SOLVENT   C3H8O
                   ORIG ST   CS2   TEMP   AMB

                   63.60   25.80   10.00
                   1/3   2/3   3/4

                   J.D.ROBERTS,F.J.WEIGERT,J.I.KROSCHWITZ,H.J.REICH
                   J AM CHEM SOC   92, 1338 (1970)

257   P 001100   1—BUTANOL

CH3—CH2—CH2—CH2—OH   FORMULA   C4H10O   MOL WT   74.12
4   3   2   1   SOLVENT   C4H10O
                     ORIG ST   CS2   TEMP   AMB

                   61.40   35.00   19.10   13.60
                   1/3   2/3   3/3   4/4

                   J.D.ROBERTS,F.J.WEIGERT,J.I.KROSCHWITZ,H.J.REICH
                   J AM CHEM SOC   92, 1338 (1970)

258   P 001100   1—PENTANOL

CH3—CH2—CH2—CH2—CH2—OH   FORMULA   C5H12O   MOL WT   88.15
5   4   3   2   1   SOLVENT   C5H12O
                           ORIG ST   CS2   TEMP   AMB

                   61.80,   32.50   28.20   22.60   13.80
                   1/3   2/3   3/3   4/3   5/4

                   J.D.ROBERTS,F.J.WEIGERT,J.I.KROSCHWITZ,H.J.REICH
                   J AM CHEM SOC   92, 1338 (1970)

259   P 001100   1—HEXANOL

5CH2—CH2—CH2—CH2—CH2—OH   FORMULA   C6H14O   MOL WT   102.18
 | 4   3   2   1   SOLVENT   C6H14O
CH3   ORIG ST   CS2   TEMP   AMB
6
                   61.90   32.80   25.80   32.00   22.80   14.20
                   1/3   2/3   3/3   4/3   5/3   6/4

                   J.D.ROBERTS,F.J.WEIGERT,J.I.KROSCHWITZ,H.J.REICH
                   J AM CHEM SOC   92, 1338 (1970)

260   P 001100   1—HEPTANOL

5CH2—CH2—CH2—CH2—CH2—OH   FORMULA   C7H16O   MOL WT   116.20
 | 4   3   2   1   SOLVENT   NEAT
6CH2   ORIG ST   CS2   TEMP   AMB
 |
7CH3   61.90   32.90   26.10   29.40   32.10   22.80
                   1/3   2/3   3/3   4/3   5/3   6/3
                   13.90
                   7/4

                   J.D.ROBERTS,F.J.WEIGERT,J.I.KROSCHWITZ,H.J.REICH
                   J AM CHEM SOC   92, 1338 (1970)

261   P 001100   1-OCTANOL

```
5CH2-CH2-CH2-CH2-CH2-OH
 |   4   3   2   1
6CH2
 |
7CH2-CH3
      8
```

FORMULA	C8H18O			MOL WT	130.23
SOLVENT	C8H18O				
ORIG ST	CS2			TEMP	AMB

61.90	32.90	26.10	29.70	29.60	32.10
1/3	2/3	3/3	4/3	5/3	6/3
22.80	13.90				
7/3	8/4				

J.D.ROBERTS,F.J.WEIGERT,J.I.KROSCHWITZ,H.J.REICH
J AM CHEM SOC   92, 1338 (1970)

262   P 001100   1-NONANOL

```
5CH2-CH2-CH2-CH2-CH2-OH
 |   4   3   2   1
6CH2
 |
7CH2-CH2-CH3
      8   9
```

FORMULA	C9H20O			MOL WT	144.26
SOLVENT	C8H18O				
ORIG ST	CS2			TEMP	AMB

62.00	32.90	26.20	29.80	29.90	29.60
1/3	2/3	3/3	4/3	5/3	6/3
32.20	22.90	14.00			
7/3	8/3	9/4			

J.D.ROBERTS,F.J.WEIGERT,J.I.KROSCHWITZ,H.J.REICH
J AM CHEM SOC   92, 1338 (1970)

263   P 001100   1-DECANOL

```
 5    4   3   2   1
CH2-CH2-CH2-CH2-CH2-OH
 |
CH2-CH2-CH2-CH2-CH3
 6   7   8   9   10
```

FORMULA	C10H22O			MOL WT	158.29
SOLVENT	C10H22O				
ORIG ST	CS2			TEMP	AMB

61.90	32.90	26.10	29.80	29.80	29.90
1/3	2/3	3/3	4/3	5/3	6/3
29.60	32.20	22.80	14.00		
7/3	8/3	9/3	10/4		

J.D.ROBERTS,F.J.WEIGERT,J.I.KROSCHWITZ,H.J.REICH
J AM CHEM SOC   92, 1338 (1970)

264   P 001100   2-PROPANOL

```
  1    2
 CH3-CH-OH
       |
      CH3
```

FORMULA	C3H8O	MOL WT	60.10
SOLVENT	C3H8O		
ORIG ST	CS2	TEMP	AMB

25.10	63.40
1/4	2/2

J.D.ROBERTS,F.J.WEIGERT,J.I.KROSCHWITZ,H.J.REICH
J AM CHEM SOC   92, 1338 (1970)

265   P 001100   2-PROPANOL

```
  1   2   3
 CH3-CH-CH3
      |
      OH
```

FORMULA	C3H8O	MOL WT	60.10
SOLVENT	C3H8O		
ORIG ST	TMS	TEMP	298

24.40	62.70
1/4	2/2

E.BREITMAIER,G.JUNG,W.VOELTER,L.POHL
UNPUBLISHED   (1972)

266　　　　　　　P 001100　OCTADEUTERIO-2-PROPANOL

```
  1   2   3
 CD3-CD-CD3
      |
      OD
```

FORMULA　C3D8O　　　　　　　MOL WT　68.15
SOLVENT　C3D8O
ORIG ST　TMS　　　　　　　　TEMP　　298

　　23.20　　62.15
　　1/7　　　2/3

E.BREITMAIER,G.JUNG,W.VOELTER,L.POHL
UNPUBLISHED　　　　　　　　　　　　　(1972)

267　　　　　　　P 001100　2-BUTANOL

```
  1   2
 CH3-CH-OH
      |
 CH3-CH2
  4   3
```

FORMULA　C4H10O　　　　　　　MOL WT　74.12
SOLVENT　C4H10O
ORIG ST　CS2　　　　　　　　TEMP　　AMB

　　22.60　　68.70　　32.00　　9.90
　　1/4　　　2/2　　　3/3　　　4/4

J.D.ROBERTS,F.J.WEIGERT,J.I.KROSCHWITZ,H.J.REICH
J AM CHEM SOC　　　　　　　　　92, 1338 (1970)

268　　　　　　　P 001100　2-PENTANOL

```
  1   2
 CH3-CH-OH
      |
 CH3-CH2-CH2
  5   4   3
```

FORMULA　C5H12O　　　　　　　MOL WT　88.15
SOLVENT　C5H12O
ORIG ST　CS2　　　　　　　　TEMP　　AMB

　　23.30　　67.00　　41.60　　19.10　　14.00
　　1/4　　　2/2　　　3/3　　　4/3　　　5/4

J.D.ROBERTS,F.J.WEIGERT,J.I.KROSCHWITZ,H.J.REICH
J AM CHEM SOC　　　　　　　　　92, 1338 (1970)

269　　　　　　　P 001100　2-HEXANOL

```
   1   2
  CH3-CH-OH
       |
 CH3-CH2-CH2-CH2
  6   5   4   3
```

FORMULA　C6H14O　　　　　　　MOL WT　102.18
SOLVENT　C6H14O
ORIG ST　CS2　　　　　　　　TEMP　　AMB

　　23.30　　67.20　　39.20　　28.30　　22.90　　13.90
　　1/4　　　2/2　　　3/3　　　4/3　　　5/3　　　6/3

J.D.ROBERTS,F.J.WEIGERT,J.I.KROSCHWITZ,H.J.REICH
J AM CHEM SOC　　　　　　　　　92, 1338 (1970)

270　　　　　　　P 001100　2-HEPTANOL

```
   1   2
  CH3-CH-OH
       |
 CH3-CH2-CH2-CH2-CH2
  7   6   5   4   3
```

FORMULA　C7H16O　　　　　　　MOL WT　116.20
SOLVENT　C7H16O
ORIG ST　CS2　　　　　　　　TEMP　　AMB

　　23.30　　67.20　　39.50　　25.80　　32.30　　22.90
　　1/4　　　2/2　　　3/3　　　4/3　　　5/3　　　6/3
　　13.90
　　7/4

J.D.ROBERTS,F.J.WEIGERT,J.I.KROSCHWITZ,H.J.REICH
J AM CHEM SOC　　　　　　　　　92, 1338 (1970)

271   P 001100   **2—OCTANOL**

```
        1    2
       CH3—CH—OH
                 |
CH3—CH2—CH2—CH2—CH2—CH2
 8   7   6   5   4   3
```

FORMULA	C8H18O
SOLVENT	C8H18O
ORIG ST	CS2

MOL WT 130.23

TEMP   AMB

23.40	67.20	39.60	26.10	29.70	32.20
1/4	2/2	3/3	4/3	5/3	6/3
22.80	14.00				
7/3	8/4				

J.D.ROBERTS,F.J.WEIGERT,J.I.KROSCHWITZ,H.J.REICH
J AM CHEM SOC   92, 1338 (1970)

---

272   P 001100   **2—DECANOL**

```
        1    2
       CH3—CH—OH
                 |
 8   7           |
CH2—CH2—CH2—CH2—CH2—CH2
 |       6   5   4   3
CH2—CH3
 9   10
```

FORMULA	C10H22O
SOLVENT	C10H22O
ORIG ST	CS2

MOL WT 158.29

TEMP   AMB

23.40	67.20	39.60	26.20	30.10	30.00
1/4	2/2	3/3	4/3	5/3	6/3
29.60	32.20	22.90	14.00		
7/3	8/3	9/3	10/4		

J.D.ROBERTS,F.J.WEIGERT,J.I.KROSCHWITZ,H.J.REICH
J AM CHEM SOC   92, 1338 (1970)

---

273   P 001100   **3—PENTANOL**

```
  1    2    3
 CH3—CH2—CH—OH
            |
          CH2—CH3
```

FORMULA	C5H12O
SOLVENT	C5H12O
ORIG ST	CS2

MOL WT 88.15

TEMP   AMB

| 9.80 | 29.70 | 73.80 |
| 1/4 | 2/3 | 3/2 |

J.D.ROBERTS,F.J.WEIGERT,J.I.KROSCHWITZ,H.J.REICH
J AM CHEM SOC   92, 1338 (1970)

---

274   P 001100   **3—HEXANOL**

```
  1    2    3
 CH3—CH2—CH—OH
            |
 CH3—CH2—CH2
  6   5    4
```

FORMULA	C6H14O
SOLVENT	C6H14O
ORIG ST	CS2

MOL WT 102.18

TEMP   AMB

| 9.90 | 10.30 | 72.30 | 39.40 | 19.40 | 14.00 |
| 1/4 | 2/3 | 3/2 | 4/3 | 5/3 | 6/4 |

J.D.ROBERTS,F.J.WEIGERT,J.I.KROSCHWITZ,H.J.REICH
J AM CHEM SOC   92, 1338 (1970)

---

275   P 001100   **3—HEPTANOL**

```
  1    2    3
 CH3—CH2—CH—OH
            |
 CH3—CH2—CH2—CH2
  7   6    5   4
```

FORMULA	C7H16O
SOLVENT	C7H16O
ORIG ST	CS2

MOL WT 116.20

TEMP   AMB

10.00	29.70	72.60	36.90	28.20	23.00
1/4	2/3	3/2	4/3	5/3	6/3
14.00					
7/4					

J.D.ROBERTS,F.J.WEIGERT,J.I.KROSCHWITZ,H.J.REICH
J AM CHEM SOC   92, 1338 (1970)

276 P 001100 **3-OCTANOL**

```
    1    2    3
   CH3-CH2-CH-OH
            |
CH3-CH2-CH2-CH2-CH2
 8    7    6    5    4
```

FORMULA	C8H18O			MOL WT	130.23
SOLVENT	C8H18O				
ORIG ST	CS2			TEMP	AMB

10.00	30.30	72.60	37.20	25.70	32.30
1/4	2/3	3/2	4/3	5/3	6/3
22.90	13.90				
7/3	8/4				

J.D.ROBERTS,F.J.WEIGERT,J.I.KROSCHWITZ,H.J.REICH
J AM CHEM SOC   92, 1338 (1970)

---

277 P 001100 **4-HEPTANOL**

```
    1    2    3    4
   CH3-CH2-CH2-CH-OH
                |
         CH3-CH2-CH2
          7    6    5
```

FORMULA	C7H16O			MOL WT	116.20
SOLVENT	C7H16O				
ORIG ST	CS2			TEMP	AMB

| 14.10 | 19.10 | 40.00 | 70.60 |
| 1/4 | 2/3 | 3/3 | 4/2 |

J.D.ROBERTS,F.J.WEIGERT,J.I.KROSCHWITZ,H.J.REICH
J AM CHEM SOC   92, 1338 (1970)

---

278 P 001100 **4-OCTANOL**

```
    1    2    3    4
   CH3-CH2-CH2-CH-OH
                |
      CH3-CH2-CH2-CH2
       8    7    6    5
```

FORMULA	C8H18O			MOL WT	130.23
SOLVENT	C8H18O				
ORIG ST	CS2			TEMP	AMB

14.00	19.10	40.00	70.90	37.50	28.20
1/4	2/3	3/3	4/2	5/3	6/3
23.00,	14.00				
7/3	8/4				

J.D.ROBERTS,F.J.WEIGERT,J.I.KROSCHWITZ,H.J.REICH
J AM CHEM SOC   92, 1338 (1970)

---

279 P 001100 **5-NONANOL**

```
  1    2    3    4    5
 CH3-CH2-CH2-CH2-CH-OH
                  |
       CH3-CH2-CH2-CH2
        9    8    7    6
```

FORMULA	C9H20O			MOL WT	144.26
SOLVENT	C9H20O				
ORIG ST	CS2			TEMP	AMB

| 14.00 | 23.00 | 28.30 | 37.50 | 71.10 |
| 1/4 | 2/3 | 3/2 | 4/3 | 5/2 |

J.D.ROBERTS,F.J.WEIGERT,J.I.KROSCHWITZ,H.J.REICH
J AM CHEM SOC   92, 1338 (1970)

---

280 P 001100 **2-METHYL-1-PROPANOL**

```
  3   2   1
 CH3-CH-CH2-OH
      |
      CH3
```

FORMULA	C4H10O			MOL WT	74.12
SOLVENT	C4H10O				
ORIG ST	CS2			TEMP	AMB

| 68.90 | 30.80 | 18.90 |
| 1/3 | 2/2 | 3/4 |

J.D.ROBERTS,F.J.WEIGERT,J.I.KROSCHWITZ,H.J.REICH
J AM CHEM SOC   92, 1338 (1970)

---

281   P 001100   2—METHYL—2—PROPANOL

```
        CH3
        I 2
     CH3-C-OH
     1   I
        CH3
```

FORMULA	C4H10O		MOL WT	74.12
SOLVENT	C4H10O			
ORIG ST	CS2		TEMP	AMB

| 31.30 | 68.40 |
| 1/4 | 2/1 |

J.D.ROBERTS,F.J.WEIGERT,J.I.KROSCHWITZ,H.J.REICH
J AM CHEM SOC   92, 1338 (1970)

---

282   P 001100   2—METHYL—1—BUTANOL

```
  4   3   2   1
 CH3-CH2-CH-CH2-OH
            I
           5CH3
```

FORMULA	C5H12O		MOL WT	88.15
SOLVENT	C5H12O			
ORIG ST	CS2		TEMP	AMB

| 66.90 | 37.50 | 25.90 | 11.10 | 16.00 |
| 1/3 | 2/2 | 3/3 | 4/4 | 5/4 |

J.D.ROBERTS,F.J.WEIGERT,J.I.KROSCHWITZ,H.J.REICH
J AM CHEM SOC   92, 1338 (1970)

---

283   P 001100   3—METHYL—1—BUTANOL

```
  4   3    2   1
 CH3-CH-CH2-CH2-OH
      I
     CH3
```

FORMULA	C5H12O		MOL WT	88.15
SOLVENT	C5H12O			
ORIG ST	CS2		TEMP	AMB

| 60.20 | 41.80 | 24.80 | 22.50 |
| 1/3 | 2/3 | 3/2 | 4/4 |

J.D.ROBERTS,F.J.WEIGERT,J.I.KROSCHWITZ,H.J.REICH
J AM CHEM SOC   92, 1338 (1970)

---

284   P 001100   3—METHYL—2—BUTANOL

```
  4   3   2
 CH3-CH-CH-OH
     I  I
    H3C 1CH3
```

FORMULA	C5H12O		MOL WT	88.15
SOLVENT	C5H12O			
ORIG ST	CS2		TEMP	AMB

| 19.70 | 72.00 | 35.10 | 18.10 |
| 1/4 | 2/2 | 3/2 | 4/4 |

J.D.ROBERTS,F.J.WEIGERT,J.I.KROSCHWITZ,H.J.REICH
J AM CHEM SOC   92, 1338 (1970)

---

285   P 001100   4—METHYL—2—PENTANOL

```
  5   4   3   2
 CH3-CH-CH2-CH-OH
     I       I
    H3C      1CH3
```

FORMULA	C6H14O		MOL WT	102.18
SOLVENT	C6H14O			
ORIG ST	CS2		TEMP	AMB

| 24.00 | 65.20 | 48.90 | 24.80 | 22.80 |
| 1/4 | 2/2 | 3/3 | 4/2 | 5/4 |

J.D.ROBERTS,F.J.WEIGERT,J.I.KROSCHWITZ,H.J.REICH
J AM CHEM SOC   92, 1338 (1970)

286   P 001100   2,2-DIMETHYL-1-PROPANOL

```
        CH3
  3    |2 1
  CH3-C-CH2-OH
        |
        CH3
```

FORMULA   C5H12O   MOL WT   88.15
SOLVENT   C5H12O
ORIG ST   CS2   TEMP   AMB

72.60   32.60   26.30
 1/3   2/1   3/4

J.D.ROBERTS,F.J.WEIGERT,J.I.KROSCHWITZ,H.J.REICH
J AM CHEM SOC   92, 1338 (1970)

287   P 001100   3,3-DIMETHYL-1-BUTANOL

```
        CH3
  4    |3 2  1
  CH3-C-CH2-CH2-OH
        |
        CH3
```

FORMULA   C6H14O   MOL WT   102.18
SOLVENT   C6H14O
ORIG ST   CS2   TEMP   AMB

58.90   46.40   29.70   29.80
 1/3   2/3   3/1   4/4

J.D.ROBERTS,F.J.WEIGERT,J.I.KROSCHWITZ,H.J.REICH
J AM CHEM SOC   92, 1338 (1970)

288   P 001100   2,3-DIMETHYL-2-BUTANOL

```
          CH3
  4    3 |2
  CH3-CH-C-OH
       |  |
       H3C  CH3
            1
```

FORMULA   C6H14O   MOL WT   102.18
SOLVENT   C6H14O
ORIG ST   CS2   TEMP   AMB

26.30   72.20   38.80   17.50
 1/4   2/1   3/2   4/4

J.D.ROBERTS,F.J.WEIGERT,J.I.KROSCHWITZ,H.J.REICH
J AM CHEM SOC   92, 1338 (1970)

289   P 001100   3,3-DIMETHYL-2-BUTANOL

```
        CH3
  4    |3 2
  CH3-C-CH-OH
       |  |
       H3C CH3
            1
```

FORMULA   C6H14O   MOL WT   102.18
SOLVENT   C6H14O
ORIG ST   CS2   TEMP   AMB

17.90   74.80   35.00   25.50
 1/4   2/2   3/1   4/4

J.D.ROBERTS,F.J.WEIGERT,J.I.KROSCHWITZ,H.J.REICH
J AM CHEM SOC   92, 1338 (1970)

290   P 001100   2,3,3-TRIMETHYL-2-BUTANOL

```
     H3C CH3
  4    |3|2
  CH3-C-C-OH
       |  |
       H3C CH3
            1
```

FORMULA   C7H16O   MOL WT   116.20
SOLVENT   C7H16O
ORIG ST   CS2   TEMP   AMB

25.40   74.10   37.50   25.60
 1/4   2/1   3/1   4/4

J.D.ROBERTS,F.J.WEIGERT,J.I.KROSCHWITZ,H.J.REICH
J AM CHEM SOC   92, 1338 (1970)

291 P 001100 2,2,4,4-TETRAMETHYL-3-PENTANOL

```
    1CH3
    2|
CH3-C-CH3
    |
    3CH-OH
    |
CH3-C-CH3
    |
    CH3
```

FORMULA	C9H20O		MOL WT	144.26
SOLVENT	C9H20O			
ORIG ST	CS2		TEMP	AMB

| 28.50 | 36.90 | 84.70 |
| 1/4 | 2/1 | 3/2 |

L.M.JACKMAN,D.P.KELLY
J CHEM SOC   B, 102 (1970)

292 P 001100 GLYCOL

```
1CH2-OH
   |
 CH2-OH
```

FORMULA	C2H6O2	MOL WT	62.07
SOLVENT	H2O		
ORIG ST	CS2	TEMP	AMB

67.30
1/3

W.VOELTER,E.BREITMAIER,G.JUNG,T.KELLER,D.HISS
ANGEW CHEM   82, 812 (1970)
ANGEW CHEM INTERN ED   9, 803 (1970)

293 P 001100 GLYCOL

```
   1     2
HO-CH2-CH2-OH
```

FORMULA	C2H6O2	MOL WT	62.07
SOLVENT	C2H6O2/C6H12		
SOLVENT	NEAT/CYCLOHEXANE(9/1)		
ORIG ST	C4H12SI	TEMP	276

| 63.98 | 63.98 |
| 1/3 | 2/3 |

L.SIMERAL,G.E.MACIEL
J PHYS CHEM   77, 1590 (1973)

294 P 001100 GLYCOL

```
  1     2
HOCH2-CH2OH
```

FORMULA	C2H6O2	MOL WT	62.07
SOLVENT	C2H6O2		
ORIG ST	TMS	TEMP,	298

63.00
1/3

E.BREITMAIER,G.JUNG,W.VOELTER,L.POHL
UNPUBLISHED   (1972)

295 P 001100 HEXADEUTERIOETHANEDIOL

```
   1     2
DOCD2-CD2OD
```

FORMULA	C2D6O2	MOL WT	68.11
SOLVENT	C2D6O2		
ORIG ST	TMS	TEMP	298

61.95
1/5

E.BREITMAIER,G.JUNG,W.VOELTER,L.POHL
UNPUBLISHED   (1972)

296   P 001100 1,2—PROPANEDIOL

1CH2—OH

2CH—OH

3CH3

FORMULA   C3H8O2   MOL WT   76.10
SOLVENT   H2O
ORIG ST   CS2   TEMP   AMB

71.60   72.70   22.95
1/3   2/2   3/4

W.VOELTER,E.BREITMAIER,G.JUNG,T.KELLER,D.HISS
ANGEW CHEM   82, 812 (1970)
ANGEW CHEM INTERN ED   9,   803 (1970)

---

297   P 001100 1,3—BUTANEDIOL

1CH2—OH

2CH2

3CH—OH

4CH3

FORMULA   C4H10O2   MOL WT   90.12
SOLVENT   H2O
ORIG ST   CS2   TEMP   AMB

63.20   44.80   69.30   26.90
1/3   2/3   3/2   4/4

W.VOELTER,E.BREITMAIER,G.JUNG,T.KELLER,D.HISS
ANGEW CHEM   82, 812 (1970)
ANGEW CHEM INTERN ED   9,   803 (1970)

---

298   P 001100 1,4—BUTANEDIOL

1CH2—OH

2CH2

3CH2

4CH2—OH

FORMULA   C4H10O2   MOL WT   90.12
SOLVENT   H2O
ORIG ST   CS2   TEMP   AMB

65.50   31.70
1/3   2/3

W.VOELTER,E.BREITMAIER,G.JUNG,T.KELLER,D.HISS
ANGEW CHEM   82, 812 (1970)
ANGEW CHEM INTERN ED   9,   803 (1970)

---

299   P 001100 GLYCEROL

1CH2—OH

2CH—OH

3CH2—OH

FORMULA   C3H8O3   MOL WT   92.10
SOLVENT   H2O
ORIG ST   CS2   TEMP   AMB

66.90   76.40
1/3   2/2

W.VOELTER,E.BREITMAIER,G.JUNG,T.KELLER,D.HISS
ANGEW CHEM   82, 812 (1970)
ANGEW CHEM INTERN ED   9,   803 (1970)

---

300   P 001500 DIMETHYL ETHER

2   1
CH3—O—CH3

FORMULA   C2H6O   MOL WT   46.07
SOLVENT   C4H8O2
ORIG ST   CS2   TEMP   AMB

59.70
1/4

M.CHRISTL,H.J.REICH,J.D.ROBERTS
J AM CHEM SOC   93, 3463 (1971)

301   P 001500   ETHYL METHYL ETHER

```
3     1    2
CH3-O-CH2-CH3
```

FORMULA	C3H8O	MOL WT 60.10
SOLVENT	C4H8O2	
ORIG ST	CS2	TEMP AMB

```
67.70    14.70    57.60
 1/3      2/4      3/4
```

M.CHRISTL,H.J.REICH,J.D.ROBERTS
J AM CHEM SOC   93, 3463 (1971)

---

302   P 001500   DIETHYLETHER

```
   1    2
  CH2-CH3
  /
 O
  \
  CH2-CH3
```

FORMULA	C4H10O	MOL WT 74.12
SOLVENT	C4H10O	
ORIG ST	TMS	TEMP 298

```
64.75    14.05
 1/3      2/4
```

E.BREITMAIER,G.JUNG,W.VOELTER,L.POHL
UNPUBLISHED   (1972)

---

303   P 001500   DECADEUTERIODIETHYLETHER

```
   1    2
  CD2-CD3
  /
 O
  \
  CD2-CD3
```

FORMULA	C4D10O	MOL WT 84.18
SOLVENT	C4D10O	
ORIG ST	TMS	TEMP 298

```
64.15    13.55
 1/5      2/7
```

E.BREITMAIER,G.JUNG,W.VOELTER,L.POHL
UNPUBLISHED   (1972)

---

304   P 001500   2-PROPYL METHYL ETHER

```
3     1  2
CH3-O-CH-CH3
      |
      CH3
```

FORMULA	C4H10O	MOL WT 74.12
SOLVENT	C4H8O2	
ORIG ST	CS2	TEMP AMB

```
72.60    21.40    54.90
 1/2      2/4      3/4
```

M.CHRISTL,H.J.REICH,J.D.ROBERTS
J AM CHEM SOC   93, 3463 (1971)

---

305   P 001500   2-METHYL-2-PROPYL METHYL ETHER

```
        CH3
3     1 |  2
CH3-O-C-CH3
      |
      CH3
```

FORMULA	C5H12O	MOL WT 88.15
SOLVENT	C4H8O2	
ORIG ST	CS2	TEMP AMB

```
72.10    26.70    48.60
 1/1      2/4      3/4
```

M.CHRISTL,H.J.REICH,J.D.ROBERTS
J AM CHEM SOC   93, 3463 (1971)

306   P 002000   PROPANONE (ACETONE)

```
  1 2
H3C-C-CH3
    ‖
    O
```

FORMULA	C3H6O	MOL WT 58.08
SOLVENT	C3H6O	
ORIG ST	TMS	TEMP 298

```
 28.90  204.15
 1/4     2/1
```

E.BREITMAIER,G.JUNG,W.VOELTER,L.POHL
UNPUBLISHED   (1970)

---

307   P 002000   HEXADEUTERIOPROPANONE (HEXADEUTERIOACETONE)

```
  1 2 3
D3C-C-CD3
    ‖
    O
```

FORMULA	C3D6O	MOL WT 64.12
SOLVENT	C3D6O	
ORIG ST	TMS	TEMP 298

```
 28.05  204.35
 1/7     2/1
```

E.BREITMAIER,G.JUNG,W.VOELTER,L.POHL
UNPUBLISHED   (1972)

---

308   P 002000   HEXAFLUOROPROPANONE SESQUIDEUTERATE

```
  1 2 3
F3C-C-CF3
   ╱ ╲
  DO   OD
```

FORMULA	C3D2F6O2	MOL WT 186.05
SOLVENT	C3D2F6O2	
ORIG ST	TMS	TEMP 298

```
 120.25   90.30
 1/4      2/4
```

E.BREITMAIER,G.JUNG,W.VOELTER,L.POHL
UNPUBLISHED   (1972)

---

309   P 002000   BUTANONE (METHYLETHYLKETONE)

```
  1 2 3   4
H3C-C-CH2-CH3
    ‖
    O
```

FORMULA	C4H8O	MOL WT 72.11
SOLVENT	CS2	
ORIG ST	CS2	TEMP AMB

```
 27.50  206.25  35.20  7.00
 1/4     2/1     3/3   4/4
```

L.M.JACKMAN,D.P.KELLY
J CHEM SOC B   1970, 102 (1970)

---

310   P 002000   2-PENTANONE

```
  1 2 3   4   5
H3C-C-CH2-CH2-CH3
    ‖
    O
```

FORMULA	C5H10O	MOL WT 86.13
SOLVENT	C6D12	
ORIG ST	TMS	TEMP 298

```
 29.25  206.55  45.10  17.60  13.35
 1/4     2/1     3/3    4/3    5/4
```

E.BREITMAIER,W.VOELTER
UNPUBLISHED   (1972)

311   P 002000   3—PENTANONE

```
1    2   3 4   5
CH3-CH2-C-CH2-CH3
        ||
        O
```

FORMULA	C5H10O	MOL WT 86.13
SOLVENT	CS2	
ORIG ST	CS2	TEMP AMB

7.00	35.00	208.70
1/4	2/3	3/1

L.M.JACKMAN,D.P.KELLY
J CHEM SOC B   1970, 102 (1970)

312   P 002000   2—HEXANONE

```
  1 2 3   4   5   6
H3C-C-CH2-CH2-CH2-CH3
    ||
    O
```

FORMULA	C6H12O	MOL WT 100.16
SOLVENT	C6D12	
ORIG ST	TMS	TEMP 298

29.40	207.20	43.40	31.75	23.75	13.95
1/4	2/1	3/3	4/3	5/3	6/4

E.BREITMAIER,W.VOELTER
UNPUBLISHED   (1972)

313   P 002000   3—METHYLBUTANONE

```
          CH3
 1 2 3/4
H3C-C-CH
    ||  \5
    O    CH3
```

FORMULA	C5H10O	MOL WT 86.13
SOLVENT	CS2	
ORIG ST	CS2	TEMP AMB

	209.30	40.50	17.60
1/4	2/1	3/2	4/4

L.M.JACKMAN,D.P.KELLY
J CHEM SOC B   1970, 102 (1970)

314   P 002000   3,3—DIMETHYLBUTANONE

```
       5
      CH3
 1 2 3/4
H3C-C-C-CH3
    ||  \
    O    CH3
         6
```

FORMULA	C6H12O	MOL WT 100.16
SOLVENT	CS2	
ORIG ST	CS2	TEMP AMB

	210.40	43.40	26.30
1/4	2/1	3/1	4/4

L.M.JACKMAN,D.P.KELLY
J CHEM SOC B   1970, 102 (1970)

315   P 002000   2,4—DIMETHYL—3—PENTANONE

```
 H3C1     5CH3
   \2  3 4/
   HC-C-CH
  /   ||  \
H3C6  O   7CH3
```

FORMULA	C7H14O	MOL WT 114.19
SOLVENT	CS2	
ORIG ST	CS2	TEMP AMB

17.80	38.00	215.10
1/4	2/2	3/1

L.M.JACKMAN,D.P.KELLY
J CHEM SOC B   1970, 102 (1970)

316   P 002000   2,2,4-TRIMETHYLPENTANONE

```
     6        5
   H3C      CH3
     1\2 3 4/
   H3C-C-C-CH
     /  ||  \
   H3C  O    C
     7        8
```

FORMULA	C8H16O		MOL WT	128.22
SOLVENT	CS2			
ORIG ST	CS2		TEMP	AMB

24.80	43.20	217.05
1/4	2/1	3/1

L.M.JACKMAN,D.P.KELLY
J CHEM SOC B   1970, 102 (1970)

317   P 002000   2,2,4,4-TETRAMETHYLPENTANONE

```
     6        8
   H3C      CH3
     1\2 3 4/5
   H3C-C-C-C-CH3
     /  ||  \
   H3C  O   CH3
     7        9
```

FORMULA	C9H18O		MOL WT	142.24
SOLVENT	CS2			
ORIG ST	CS2		TEMP	AMB

27.80	44.50	215.15
1/4	2/1	3/1

L.M.JACKMAN,D.P.KELLY
J CHEM SOC B   1970, 102 (1970)

318   P 002000   BUTENONE

```
   1    2  3  4
   CH3-C-CH=CH2
        ||
        O
```

FORMULA	C4H7O		MOL WT	71.10
SOLVENT	C4H7O			
ORIG ST	CS2		TEMP	AMB

196.90	136.30	127.40
2/1	3/3	4/3

D.H.MARR,J.B.STOTHERS
CAN J CHEM   43, 596 (1965)

319   P 002300   KETENE

```
    2 1
   H2C=C=O
```

FORMULA	C2H2O		MOL WT	42.04
SOLVENT	CDCL3			
ORIG ST	TMS		TEMP	213

194.00	2.50
1/1	2/3

J.FIRL,W.RUNGE
ANGEW CHEM   85, 671 (1973)

320   P 002500   FORMIC ACID

```
     1
   H-COOH
```

FORMULA	CH2O2		MOL WT	46.03
SOLVENT	H2O/N(CH3)4CL			
ORIG ST	CS2		TEMP	AMB

166.00
1/1

R.HAGEN,J.D.ROBERTS
J AM CHEM SOC   91, 4504 (1969)

321   P 002500   FORMIC ACID

       1   FORMULA CH_2O_2 MOL WT   46.03
   H—COOH   SOLVENT $C H_2O_2$
                ORIG ST   TMS   TEMP   298

              165.70
               1/2

           E.BREITMAIER,G.JUNG,W.VOELTER,L.POHL
           UNPUBLISHED   (1972)

---

322   P 002500   DIDEUTERIOFORMIC ACID

       1   FORMULA CD_2O_2 MOL WT   48.04
   D—COOD   SOLVENT CD_2O_2
                ORIG ST   TMS   TEMP   298

              165.30
               1/3

           E.BREITMAIER,G.JUNG,W.VOELTER,L.POHL
           UNPUBLISHED   (1972)

---

323   P 002500   ACETIC ACID

     2   1   FORMULA $C_2H_4O_2$ MOL WT   60.05
   CH3—COOH   SOLVENT $H_2O/N(CH_3)_4CL$
                ORIG ST   CS2   TEMP   AMB

              176.90   20.80
               1/1   2/4

           R.HAGEN,J.D.ROBERTS
           J AM CHEM SOC   91, 4504 (1969)

---

324   P 002500   ACETIC ACID

     2   1   FORMULA $C_2H_4O_2$ MOL WT   60.05
   CH3—COOH   SOLVENT $C_2H_4O_2$
                ORIG ST   TMS   TEMP   298

              177.05   19.10
               1/1   2/4

           E.BREITMAIER,G.JUNG,W.VOELTER,L.POHL
           UNPUBLISHED   (1972)

---

325   P 002500   TETRADEUTERIOACETIC ACID

     2   1   FORMULA $C_2D_4O_2$ MOL WT   64.08
   CD3—COOD   SOLVENT $C_2D_4O_2$
                ORIG ST   TMS   TEMP   298

              176.60   18.25
               1/1   2/7

           E.BREITMAIER,G.JUNG,W.VOELTER,L.POHL
           UNPUBLISHED   (1972)

---

326   P 002500   **PROPIONIC ACID**

```
 3   2   1
CH3-CH2-COOH
```

FORMULA   C3H6O2   MOL WT   74.08
SOLVENT   H2O/N(CH3)4CL
ORIG ST   CS2   TEMP   AMB

```
180.10    27.50     8.70
 1/1       2/3       3/4
```

R.HAGEN,J.D.ROBERTS
J AM CHEM SOC   91, 4504 (1969)

---

327   P 002500   **BUTYRIC ACID**

```
 4   3   2   1
CH3-CH2-CH2-COOH
```

FORMULA   C4H8O2   MOL WT   88.11
SOLVENT   H2O/N(CH3)4CL
ORIG ST   CS2   TEMP   AMB

```
179.30    36.00    18.20    13.10
 1/1       2/3      3/3      4/4
```

R.HAGEN J.D.ROBERTS
J AM CHEM SOC   91, 4504 (1969)

---

328   P 002500   **VALERIC ACID**

```
 5   4   3   2   1
CH3-CH2-CH2-CH2-COOH
```

FORMULA   C5H10O2   MOL WT   102.13
SOLVENT   H2O/N(CH3)4CL
ORIG ST   CS2   TEMP   AMB

```
179.40    33.80    26.70    21.70    13.20
 1/1       2/3      3/3      4/3      5/4
```

R.HAGEN,J.D.ROBERTS
J AM CHEM SOC   91, 4504 (1969)

---

329   P 002500   **TETRAMETHYLAMMONIUM FORMATE**

```
  1   -+
H-COO N(CH3)4
```

FORMULA   C5H13NO2   MOL WT   119.16
SOLVENT   H2O
ORIG ST   CS2   TEMP   AMB

```
171.10
 1/1
```

R.HAGEN,J.D.ROBERTS
J AM CHEM SOC   91, 4504 (1969)

---

330   P 002500   **TETRAMETHYLAMMONIUM ACETATE**

```
  2   1   -+
CH3-COO N(CH3)4
```

FORMULA   C6H15NO2   MOL WT   133.19
SOLVENT   H2O
ORIG ST   CS2   TEMP   AMB

```
181.40    23.70
 1/1       2/4
```

R.HAGEN,J.D.ROBERTS
J AM CHEM SOC   91, 4504 (1969)

331   P 002500 **TETRAMETHYLAMMONIUM PROPIONATE**

```
3   2   1   -+
CH3-CH2-COO N(CH3)4
```

FORMULA	C7H17NO2		MOL WT	147.22
SOLVENT	H2O			
ORIG ST	CS2		TEMP	AMB

| 184.80 | 31.00 | 10.50 |
| 1/1 | 2/3 | 3/4 |

R.HAGEN,J.D.ROBERTS
J AM CHEM SOC   91, 4504 (1969)

---

332   P 002500 **TETRAMETHYLAMMONIUM BUTYRATE**

```
4   3   2   1   -+
CH3-CH2-CH2-COO N(CH3)4
```

FORMULA	C8H19NO2		MOL WT	161.25
SOLVENT	H2O			
ORIG ST	CS2		TEMP	AMB

| 184.00 | 39.90 | 19.60 | 13.60 |
| 1/1 | 2/3 | 3/3 | 4/4 |

R.HAGEN,J.D.ROBERTS
J AM CHEM SOC   91, 4504 (1969)

---

333   P 002500 **TETRAMETHYLAMMONIUM VALERATE**

```
4   3   2   1   -+
CH2-CH2-CH2-COO N(CH3)4
|
5CH3
```

FORMULA	C9H21NO2		MOL WT	175.27
SOLVENT	H2O			
ORIG ST	CS2		TEMP	AMB

| 184.10 | 37.70 | 28.40 | 22.30 | 13.40 |
| 1/1 | 2/3 | 3/3 | 4/3 | 5/4 |

R.HAGEN,J.D.ROBERTS
J AM CHEM SOC   91, 4504 (1969)

---

334   P 002500 **ACRYLIC ACID**

```
3   2   1
CH2=CH-COOH
```

FORMULA	C3H4O2		MOL WT	72.06
SOLVENT	NEAT			
ORIG ST	CS2		TEMP	323

| 170.40 | 127.20 | 131.90 |
| 1/1 | 2/2 | 3/3 |

E.LIPPMAA,T.PEHK,K.ANDERSSON,C.RAPPE
ORG MAGN RESONANCE   2, 109 (1970)

---

335   P 002500 **METHACRYLIC ACID**

```
3   2 1
CH2=C-COOH
     |
     CH3
     4
```

FORMULA	C4H6O2		MOL WT	86.09
SOLVENT	NEAT			
ORIG ST	CS2		TEMP	323

| 171.90 | 135.20 | 126.30 | 16.50 |
| 1/1 | 2/1 | 3/3 | 4/4 |

E.LIPPMAA,T.PEHK,K.ANDERSSON,C.RAPPE
ORG MAGN RESONANCE   2, 109 (1970)

336   P 002500 3,3—DIMETHYLACRYLIC ACID

```
    4      1        FORMULA  C5H8O2                    MOL WT  100.12
    CH3    COOH      SOLVENT  NEAT
     \3 2/           ORIG ST  CS2                      TEMP      323
      C=C
     /    \          169.00   115.60   156.90   19.10   26.10
    CH3    H          1/1      2/2      3/1      4/4     5/4
    5
```

E.LIPPMAA,T.PEHK,K.ANDERSSON,C.RAPPE
ORG MAGN RESONANCE   2,   109 (1970)

337   P 002500 TIGLIC ACID

```
           1        FORMULA  C5H8O2                    MOL WT  100.12
    H      COOH      SOLVENT  NEAT
     \3 2/           ORIG ST  CS2                      TEMP      323
      C=C
     /    \          168.90   128.40   136.30   13.50   11.50
    CH3    CH3        1/1      2/1      3/2      4/4     5/4
    4      5
```

E.LIPPMAA,T.PEHK,K.ANDERSSON,C.RAPPE
ORG MAGN RESONANCE   2,   109 (1970)

338   P 002500 Z—2—PENTENOIC ACID

```
   5    4     1      FORMULA  C5H8O2                    MOL WT  100.12
   CH3—CH2   COOH     SOLVENT  NEAT
      \3 2/           ORIG ST  CS2                      TEMP      323
       C=C
      /    \          171.50   118.50   154.00   22.30   12.70
     H      H          1/1      2/2      3/2      4/3     5/4
```

E.LIPPMAA,T.PEHK,K.ANDERSSO ,C.RAPPE
ORG MAGN RESONANCE   2,   109 (1970)

339   P 002500 E—2—PENTENOIC ACID

```
           1        FORMULA  C5H8O2                    MOL WT  100.12
    H      COOH      SOLVENT  NEAT
     \3 2/           ORIG ST  CS2                      TEMP      323
      C=C
   5  4/   \          171.90   119.20   152.50   24.60   11.10
   CH3—CH2   H         1/1      2/2      3/2      4/3     5/4
```

E.LIPPMAA,T.PEHK,K.ANDERSSON,C.RAPPE
ORG MAGN RESONANCE   2,   109 (1970)

340   P 002500 Z—2—HEXENOIC ACID

```
   6    5    4     1   FORMULA  C6H10O2                  MOL WT  114.15
   CH3—CH2—CH2   COOH   SOLVENT  NEAT
        \3 2/           ORIG ST  CS2                     TEMP      323
         C=C
        /    \          171.50   118.70   152.00   30.40   21.50   12.60
       H      H          1/1      2/2      3/2      4/3     5/3     6/4
```

E.LIPPMAA,T.PEHK,K.ANDERSSON,C.RAPPE
ORG MAGN RESONANCE   2,   109 (1970)

341   P 002500   E—2—HEXENOIC ACID

```
              1        FORMULA   C6H10O2              MOL WT   114.15
       H       COOH    SOLVENT   NEAT
        \3  2/         ORIG ST   CS2                  TEMP        323
          C=C
      6  5   4/   \    171.80   120.50   151.30   33.90   20.80   13.00
     CH3-CH2-CH2   H    1/1      2/2      3/2      4/3     5/3     6/4
```

E.LIPPMAA,T.PEHK,K.ANDERSSON,C.RAPPE
ORG MAGN RESONANCE   2, 109 (1970)

342   P 002500   Z—4—METHYL—2—PENTENOIC ACID

```
    5    4       1    FORMULA   C6H10O2              MOL WT   114.15
  (CH3)2CH    COOH    SOLVENT   NEAT
         \3  2/       ORIG ST   CS2                  TEMP        323
           C=C
          /   \       171.40   116.40   158.30   27.00   21.20
         H     H       1/1      2/2      3/2      4/2     5/4
```

E.LIPPMAA,T.PEHK,K.ANDERSSON,C.RAPPE
ORG MAGN RESONANCE   2, 109 (1970)

343   P 002500   E—4—METHYL—2—PENTENOIC ACID

```
              1        FORMULA   C6H10O2              MOL WT   114.15
       H       COOH    SOLVENT   NEAT
        \3  2/         ORIG ST   CS2                  TEMP        323
          C=C
      5   4/    \      171.60   117.70   157.00   30.40   20.20
  (CH3)2CH      H       1/1      2/2      3/2      4/2     5/4
```

E.LIPPMAA,T.PEHK,K.ANDERSSON,C.RAPPE
ORG MAGN RESONANCE   2, 109 (1970)

344   P 002500   Z—2—HEPTENOIC ACID

```
 7   6   5   4       1    FORMULA   C7H12O2          MOL WT   128.17
CH3-CH2-CH2-CH2    COOH    SOLVENT   NEAT
            \3  2/         ORIG ST   CS2              TEMP        323
              C=C
             /   \        171.50   118.80   152.30   28.30   30.70   21.80
            H     H        1/1      2/2      3/2      4/3     5/3     6/3
                          13.00
                           7/4
```

E.LIPPMAA,T.PEHK,K.ANDERSSON,C.RAPPE
ORG MAGN RESONANCE   2, 109 (1970)

345   P 002500   E—4,4—DIMETHYL—2—PENTENOIC ACID

```
              1        FORMULA   C7H12O2              MOL WT   128.17
       H       COOH    SOLVENT   NEAT
        \3  2/         ORIG ST   CS2                  TEMP        323
          C=C
      5   4/    \      168.10   117.50   158.20   33.30   28.50
  (CH3)3C       H       1/1      2/2      3/2      4/1     5/4
```

E.LIPPMAA,T.PEHK,K.ANDERSSON,C.RAPPE
ORG MAGN RESONANCE   2, 109 (1970)

346 — P 002500 Z—2—OCTENOIC ACID

```
7   6   5   4       1
CH2-CH2-CH2-CH2   COOH
|               \3 2/
CH3              C=C
8              /     \
             H       H
```

FORMULA	C8H14O2			MOL WT	142.20
SOLVENT	NEAT				
ORIG ST	CS2			TEMP	323

173.10	120.10	153.60	29.70	29.70	32.30
1/1	2/2	3/2	4/3	5/3	6/3
23.30	14.50				
7/3	8/4				

E.LIPPMAA,T.PEHK,K.ANDERSSON,C.RAPPE
ORG MAGN RESONANCE   2, 109 (1970)

347 — P 002500 E—2—NONENOIC ACID

```
              1
     H      COOH
      \3 2/
       C=C
7   6   5   4/     \
CH2-CH2-CH2-CH2     H
|
CH2-CH3
8   9
```

FORMULA	C9H16O2			MOL WT	156.23
SOLVENT	NEAT				
ORIG ST	CS2			TEMP	323

171.50	120.70	151.10	31.90	27.80	28.50
1/1	2/2	3/2	4/3	5/3	6/3
31.50	22.10	13.40			
7/3	8/3	9/4			

E.LIPPMAA,T.PEHK,K.ANDERSSON,C.RAPPE
ORG MAGN RESONANCE   2, 109 (1970)

348 — P 002530 **MALEIC ACID**

```
              1
HOOC        COOH
    \  2/
     C=C
    /     \
   H       H
```

FORMULA	C4H4O4	MOL WT	116.07
SOLVENT	C2H6O S		
ORIG ST	CS2	TEMP	323

167.10	130.50
1/1	2/2

E.LIPPMAA,T.PEHK,K.ANDERSSON,C.RAPPE
ORG MAGN RESONANCE   2, 109 (1970)

349 — P 002530 FUMARIC ACID

```
              1
    H       COOH
     \  2/
      C=C
     /    \
  HOOC     H
```

FORMULA	C4H4O4	MOL WT	116.07
SOLVENT	C2H6O S		
ORIG ST	CS2	TEMP	323

166.60	134.20
1/1	2/2

E.LIPPMAA,T.PEHK,K.ANDERSSON,C.RAPPE
ORG MAGN RESONANCE   2, 109 (1970)

350 — P 002530 BROMOCITRACONIC ACID

```
     4       1
  HOOC     COOH
      \3 2/
       C=C
      /    \
    BR     CH3
           5
```

FORMULA	C5H5O4BR			MOL WT	209.00
SOLVENT	C2H6O S				
ORIG ST	CS2			TEMP	323

166.40	138.20	121.50	164.60	20.10
1/1	2/1	3/1	4/1	5/4

E.LIPPMAA,T.PEHK,K.ANDERSSON,C.RAPPE
ORG MAGN RESONANCE   2, 109 (1970)

351　　　　　P 002530　BROMOCITRACONIC ANHYDRIDE

```
      4
  BR   CO
   \ / \
    C3   \
    ||    O
    C2   /
   / \ /
 H3C   CO
  5    1
```

FORMULA	C5H3O3BR		MOL WT	190.98
SOLVENT	C2H6O S			
ORIG ST	CS2		TEMP	323

163.70	145.70	125.90	160.80	11.10
1/1	2/1	3/1	4/1	5/4

E.LIPPMAA,T.PEHK,K.ANDERSSON,C.RAPPE
ORG MAGN RESONANCE　　　　　2, 109 (1970)

352　　　　　P 002530　MESACONIC ACID

```
  5       1
 H3C     COOH
   \3 2/
    C=C
   /    \
 HOOC    H
  4
```

FORMULA	C5H6O4		MOL WT	130.10
SOLVENT	C2H6O S			
ORIG ST	CS2		TEMP	323

168.20	126.80	142.80	167.00	13.70
1/1	2/2	3/1	4/1	5/4

E.LIPPMAA,T.PEHK,K.ANDERSSON,C.RAPPE
ORG MAGN RESONANCE　　　　　2, 109 (1970)

353　　　　　P 002530　BROMOMESACONIC ACID

```
  5       1
 H3C     COOH
   \3 2/
    C=C
   /    \
 HOOC    BR
  4
```

FORMULA	C5H5O4BR		MOL WT	209.00
SOLVENT	C2H6O S			
ORIG ST	CS2		TEMP	323

169.00	141.30	109.90	164.50	18.30
1/1	2/1	3/1	4/1	5/4

E.LIPPMAA,T.PEHK,K.ANDERSSON,C.RAPPE
ORG MAGN RESONANCE　　　　　2, 109 (1970)

354　　　　　P 002600　Z—MUCOCHLORIC ACID

```
          1
  CL     COOH
   \3 2/
    C=C
  4/    \
 O=C    CL
   |
   H
```

FORMULA	C4H2O3CL2		MOL WT	168.96
SOLVENT	C2H6O S			
ORIG ST	CS2		TEMP	AMB

161.30	122.20	149.70	97.10
1/1	2/1	3/1	4/2

E.LIPPMAA,T.PEHK,K.ANDERSSON,C.RAPPE
ORG MAGN RESONANCE　　　　　2, 109 (1970)

355　　　　　P 002600　Z—MUCOBROMIC ACID

```
          1
  BR     COOH
   \3 2/
    C=C
  4/    \
 O=C    BR
   |
   H
```

FORMULA	C4H2O3BR2		MOL WT	257.87
SOLVENT	C2H6O S			
ORIG ST	CS2		TEMP	AMB

164.60	117.00	147.00	99.70
1/1	2/1	3/1	4/2

E.LIPPMAA,T.PEHK,K.ANDERSSON,C.RAPPE
ORG MAGN RESONANCE　　　　　2, 109 (1970)

356   P 002600   TRIFLUOROACETIC ACID

    2   1   FORMULA   C2HF3O2   MOL WT   114.02
    CF3—COOH   SOLVENT   C2H F3O2
            ORIG ST   TMS   TEMP   298

          161.35   113.60
           1/4   2/4

         E.BREITMAIER,G.JUNG,W.VOELTER,L.POHL
         UNPUBLISHED   (1972)

---

357   P 002600   DEUTERIOTRIFLUOROACETIC ACID

    2   1   FORMULA   C2DF3O2   MOL WT   115.03
    CF3—COOD   SOLVENT   C2D F3O2
            ORIG ST   TMS   TEMP   298

          161.10   113.50
           1/4   2/4

         E.BREITMAIER,G.JUNG,W.VOELTER,L.POHL
         UNPUBLISHED   (1972)

---

358   P 002600   Z—3—CHLOROACRYLIC ACID

        1   FORMULA   C3H3O2CL   MOL WT   106.51
  CL   COOH   SOLVENT   (CH3)2S O
    \3 2/   ORIG ST   CS2   TEMP   323
     C=C
    /   \   164.70   122.20   131.60
   H   H   1/1   2/2   3/2

         E.LIPPMAA,T.PEHK,K.ANDERSSON,C.RAPPE
         ORG MAGN RESONANCE   2,   109 (1970)

---

359   P 002600   E—3—CHLOROACRYLIC ACID

        1   FORMULA   C3H3O2CL   MOL WT   106.51
  H   COOH   SOLVENT   (CH3)2S O
    \3 2/   ORIG ST   CS2   TEMP   323
     C=C
    /   \   164.70   125.00   136.30
  CL   H   1/1   2/2   3/2

         E.LIPPMAA,T.PEHK,K.ANDERSSON,C.RAPPE
         ORG MAGN RESONANCE   2,   109 (1970)

---

360   P 002600   Z—3—BROMOACRYLIC ACID

        1   FORMULA   C3H3O2BR   MOL WT   150.96
  BR   COOH   SOLVENT   (CH3)2S O
    \3 2/   ORIG ST   CS2   TEMP   323
     C=C
    /   \   165.10   120.60   124.90
   H   H   1/1   2/2   3/2

         E.LIPPMAA,T.PEHK,K.ANDERSSON,C.RAPPE
         ORG MAGN RESONANCE   2,   109 (1970)

---

361   P 002600 E-3-BROMOACRYLIC ACID

```
         1            FORMULA  C3H3O2BR            MOL WT  150.96
  H      COOH         SOLVENT  (CH3)2S O
   \3 2/              ORIG ST  CS2                 TEMP       323
    C=C
   /    \             165.10   130.00   126.40
  BR     H             1/1      2/2      3/2
```

E.LIPPMAA,T.PEHK,K.ANDERSSON,C.RAPPE
ORG MAGN RESONANCE   2, 109 (1970)

---

362   P 002600 Z-3-IODOACRYLIC ACID

```
         1            FORMULA  C3H3O2I             MOL WT  197.96
  J      COOH         SOLVENT  (CH3)2S O
   \3 2/              ORIG ST  CS2                 TEMP       323
    C=C
   /    \             165.70   130.20    95.90
  H      H             1/1      2/2      3/1
```

E.LIPPMAA,T.PEHK,K.ANDERSSON,C.RAPPE
ORG MAGN RESONANCE   2, 109 (1970)

---

363   P 002600 E-3-IODOACRYLIC ACID

```
         1            FORMULA  C3H3O2I             MOL WT  197.96
  H      COOH         SOLVENT  C2H6O S
   \3 2/              ORIG ST  CS2                 TEMP       323
    C=C
   /    \             165.10   137.20   100.90
  J      H             1/1      2/2      3/2
```

E.LIPPMAA,T.PEHK,K.ANDERSSON,C.RAPPE
ORG MAGN RESONANCE   2, 109 (1970)

---

364   P 002600 Z-2,3-DICHLOROACRYLIC ACID

```
         1            FORMULA  C3H2O2CL2           MOL WT  140.95
  H      COOH         SOLVENT  C2H6O S
   \3 2/              ORIG ST  CS2                 TEMP       323
    C=C
   /    \             161.50   128.10   131.40
  CL     CL            1/1      2/1      3/2
```

E.LIPPMAA,T.PEHK,K.ANDERSSON,C.RAPPE
ORG MAGN RESONANCE   2, 109 (1970)

---

365   P 002600 Z-2,3-DIBROMOACRYLIC ACID

```
         1            FORMULA  C3H2O2BR2           MOL WT  229.86
  H      COOH         SOLVENT  C2H6O S
   \3 2/              ORIG ST  CS2                 TEMP       323
    C=C
   /    \             161.80   124.20   126.90
  BR     BR            1/1      2/1      3/2
```

E.LIPPMAA,T.PEHK,K.ANDERSSON,C.RAPPE
ORG MAGN RESONANCE   2, 109 (1970)

366   P 002600 E-2,3-DIBROMOACRYLIC ACID

```
        1          FORMULA   C3H2O2BR2              MOL WT   229.86
  BR       COOH     SOLVENT   C2H6O S
   \3  2/           ORIG ST   CS2                   TEMP        323
     C=C
   /      \         162.70    113.10   110.70
  H        BR        1/1        2/1      3/2
```

E.LIPPMAA,T.PEHK,K.ANDERSSON,C.RAPPE
ORG MAGN RESONANCE   2, 109 (1970)

---

367   P 002600 E-2,3-DIIODOACRYLIC ACID

```
        1          FORMULA   C3H2O2I2               MOL WT   323.86
  J        COOH     SOLVENT   C2H6O S
   \3  2/           ORIG ST   CS2                   TEMP        323
     C=C
   /      \         165.90    89.10    86.50
  H        J         1/1        2/1      3/2
```

E.LIPPMAA,T.PEHK,K.ANDERSSON,C.RAPPE
ORG MAGN RESONANCE   2, 109 (1970)

---

368   P 002600 E-2-IODO-3-CHLOROACRYLIC ACID

```
        1          FORMULA   C3H2O2CLI              MOL WT   232.41
  CL       COOH     SOLVENT   C2H6O S
   \3  2/           ORIG ST   CS2                   TEMP        323
     C=C
   /      \         164.50    87.40    126.20
  H        J         1/1        2/1      3/2
```

E.LIPPMAA,T.PEHK,K.ANDERSSON,C.RAPPE
ORG MAGN RESONANCE   2, 109 (1970)

---

369   P 002600 Z-3-IODO-3-BROMOACRYLIC ACID

```
        1          FORMULA   C3H2O2BRI              MOL WT   276.86
  J        COOH     SOLVENT   C2H6O S
   \3  2/           ORIG ST   CS2                   TEMP        323
     C=C
   /      \         164.60    134.70   70.20
  BR       H         1/1        2/2      3/1
```

E.LIPPMAA,T.PEHK,K.ANDERSSON,C.RAPPE
ORG MAGN RESONANCE   2, 109 (1970)

---

370   P 002600 3,3-DICHLOROACRYLIC ACID

```
        1          FORMULA   C3H2O2CL2              MOL WT   140.95
  CL       COOH     SOLVENT   C2H6O S
   \3  2/           ORIG ST   CS2                   TEMP        323
     C=C
   /      \         163.00    121.30   135.00
  CL       H         1/1        2/2      3/1
```

E.LIPPMAA,T.PEHK,K.ANDERSSON,C.RAPPE
ORG MAGN RESONANCE   2, 109 (1970)

---

371   P 002600   **3,3—DIBROMOACRYLIC ACID**

```
        1
BR      COOH
 \3 2/
  C=C
 /    \
BR     H
```

FORMULA	C3H2O2BR2		MOL WT	229.86
SOLVENT	C2H6O S			
ORIG ST	CS2		TEMP	323

164.00	129.70	103.80
1/1	2/2	3/1

E.LIPPMAA,T.PEHK,K.ANDERSSON,C.RAPPE
ORG MAGN RESONANCE   2, 109 (1970)

---

372   P 002600   **3,3—DIBROMOMETHACRYLIC ACID**

```
        1
BR      COOH
 \3 2/
  C=C
 /    \
BR     CH3
        4
```

FORMULA	C4H4O2BR2		MOL WT	243.88
SOLVENT	C2H6O S			
ORIG ST	CS2		TEMP	323

167.50	137.70	92.40	21.60
1/1	2/1	3/1	4/4

E.LIPPMAA,T.PEHK,K.ANDERSSON,C.RAPPE
ORG MAGN RESONANCE   2, 109 (1970)

---

373   P 002600   **3,3—DIBROMO—2—BROMOMETHYLACRYLIC ACID**

```
        1
BR      COOH
 \3 2/
  C=C
 /    \
BR     CH2BR
        4
```

FORMULA	C4H3O2BR3		MOL WT	322.78
SOLVENT	C2H6O S			
ORIG ST	CS2		TEMP	323

165.30	137.40	103.00	32.50
1/1	2/1	3/1	4/3

E.LIPPMAA,T.PEHK,K.ANDERSSON,C.RAPPE
ORG MAGN RESONANCE   2, 109 (1970)

---

374   P 002600   **3,3—DIBROMO—2—HYDROXYMETHYLACRYLIC ACID**

```
        1
BR      COOH
 \3 2/
  C=C
 /    \
BR     CH2—OH
        4
```

FORMULA	C4H4O3BR2		MOL WT	259.88
SOLVENT	C2H6O S			
ORIG ST	CS2		TEMP	323

166.60	142.80	92.20	63.40
1/1	2/1	3/1	4/3

E.LIPPMAA,T.PEHK,K.ANDERSSON,C.RAPPE
ORG MAGN RESONANCE   2, 109 (1970)

---

375   P 002600   **3,3—DIIODOACRYLIC ACID**

```
        1
J       COOH
 \3 2/
  C=C
 /    \
J       H
```

FORMULA	C3H2O2I2		MOL WT	323.86
SOLVENT	C2H6O S			
ORIG ST	CS2		TEMP	323

165.60	141.50	32.30
1/1	2/2	3/1

E.LIPPMAA,T.PEHK,K.ANDERSSON,C.RAPPE
ORG MAGN RESONANCE   2, 109 (1970)

---

376   P 002600   2,3,3—TRICHLOROACRYLIC ACID

```
            1
  CL      COOH
    \3  2/
     C=C
    /     \
  CL       CL
```

FORMULA	C3HO2CL3		MOL WT	175.40
SOLVENT	C2H6O S			
ORIG ST	C S2		TEMP	323

161.00   123.10   124.80
1/1   2/1   3/1

E.LIPPMAA,T.PEHK,K.ANDERSSON,C.RAPPE
ORG MAGN RESONANCE   2,   109 (1970)

---

377   P 002600   3,3—DIIODOACRYLIC ACID

```
            1
  J       COOH
    \3  2/
     C=C
    /     \
  J        H
```

FORMULA	C3H2O2I2		MOL WT	323.86
SOLVENT	C2H6O S			
ORIG ST	C S2		TEMP	323

165.60   141.50   32.30
1/1   2/2   3/1

E.LIPPMAA,T.PEHK,K.ANDERSSON,C.RAPPE
ORG MAGN RESONANCE   2,   109 (1970)

---

378   P 002600   2,3,3—TRIIODOACRYLIC ACID

```
            1
  J       COOH
    \3  2/
     C=C
    /     \
  J        J
```

FORMULA	C3HO2I3		MOL WT	449.75
SOLVENT	C2H6O S			
ORIG ST	C S2		TEMP	323

168.60   105.60   28.60
1/1   2/1   3/1

E.LIPPMAA,T.PEHK,K.ANDERSSON,C.RAPPE
ORG MAGN RESONANCE   2,   109 (1970)

---

379   P 002600   E—3—CHLOROMETHACRYLIC ACID

```
            1
  H       COOH
    \3  2/
     C=C
    /     \
  CL       CH3
            4
```

FORMULA	C4H5O2CL		MOL WT	120.54
SOLVENT	C2H6O S			
ORIG ST	C S2		TEMP	323

167.10   131.30   131.30   12.20
1/1   2/1   3/2   4/4

E.LIPPMAA,T.PEHK,K.ANDERSSON,C.RAPPE
ORG MAGN RESONANCE   2,   109 (1970)

---

380   P 002600   Z—3—BROMOMETHACRYLIC ACID

```
            1
  BR      COOH
    \3  2/
     C=C
    /     \
  H        CH3
            4
```

FORMULA	C4H5O2BR		MOL WT	164.99
SOLVENT	C2H6O S			
ORIG ST	C S2		TEMP	323

166.50   133.60   107.50   19.20
1/1   2/1   3/2   4/4

E.LIPPMAA,T.PEHK,K.ANDERSSON,C.RAPPE
ORG MAGN RESONANCE   2,   109 (1970)

---

381   P 002600   E—3—BROMOMETHACRYLIC ACID

```
            1
   H       COOH
    \3  2/
     C=C
    /     \
  BR       CH3
```

FORMULA   C4H5O2BR   MOL WT   164.99
SOLVENT   C2H6O S
ORIG ST   CS2   TEMP   323

165.60   133.70   121.80   14.60
 1/1   2/1   3/2   3/4

E.LIPPMAA,T.PEHK,K.ANDERSSON,C.RAPPE
ORG MAGN RESONANCE   2, 109 (1970)

---

382   P 002600   E—2—BROMOCROTONIC ACID

```
            1
 H3C       COOH
   4\3  2/
      C=C
     /     \
   H         BR
```

FORMULA   C4H5O2BR   MOL WT   164.99
SOLVENT   C2H6O S
ORIG ST   CS2   TEMP   323

162.10   114.60   140.60   16.40
 1/1   2/1   3/1   4/4

E.LIPPMAA,T.PEHK,K.ANDERSSON,C.RAPPE
ORG MAGN RESONANCE   2, 109 (1970)

---

383   P 002600   2—BROMO—3—METHYLCROTONIC ACID

```
            1
 H3C       COOH
    \3  2/
     C=C
    /     \
  H3C       BR
```

FORMULA   C5H7O2BR   MOL WT   179.01
SOLVENT   C2H6O S
ORIG ST   CS2   TEMP   323

165.10   109.70   146.50   22.50   26.60
 1/1   2/1   3/1   4/4   5/4

E.LIPPMAA,T.PEHK,K.ANDERSSON,C.RAPPE
ORG MAGN RESONANCE   2, 109 (1970)

384·   P 002600   Z—3—CHLOROCROTONIC ACID

```
            1
  CL       COOH
    \3  2/
     C=C
    /     \
  H3C       H
   4
```

FORMULA   C4H5O2CL   MOL WT   120.54
SOLVENT   C2H6O S
ORIG ST   CS2   TEMP   323

165.10   117.60   145.10   27.80
 1/1   2/2   3/1   4/4

E.LIPPMAA,T.PEHK,K.ANDERSSON,C.RAPPE
ORG MAGN RESONANCE   2, 109 (1970)

---

385   P 002600   E—3—CHLOROCROTONIC ACID

```
   4        1
 H3C       COOH
    \3  2/
     C=C
    /     \
  CL        H
```

FORMULA   C4H5O2CL   MOL WT   120.54
SOLVENT   C2H6O S
ORIG ST   CS2   TEMP   323

166.10   119.20   152.00   23.20
 1/1   2/2   3/1   4/4

E.LIPPMAA,T.PEHK,K.ANDERSSON,C.RAPPE
ORG MAGN RESONANCE   2, 109 (1970)

---

386   P 002600   Z—2,3—DICHLOROCROTONIC ACID

```
   4        1
  H3C      COOH
     \3  2/
      C=C
     /    \
   CL      CL
```

FORMULA   C4H4O2CL2   MOL WT   154.98
SOLVENT   C2H6O S
ORIG ST   CS2   TEMP   323

162.30	121.00	144.30	23.80
1/1	2/1	3/1	4/4

E.LIPPMAA,T.PEHK,K.ANDERSSON,C.RAPPE
ORG MAGN RESONANCE   2,   109 (1970)

---

387   P 002600   E—2,3—DICHLOROCROTONIC ACID

```
           1
   CL      COOH
     \3  2/
      C=C
     /    \
   H3C      CL
    4
```

FORMULA   C4H4O2CL2   MOL WT   154.98
SOLVENT   C2H6O S
ORIG ST   CS2   TEMP   323

162.50	119.20	133.20	24.60
1/1	2/1	3/1	4/4

E.LIPPMAA,T.PEHK,K.ANDERSSON,C.RAPPE
ORG MAGN RESONANCE   2,   109 (1970)

---

388   P 002600   Z—2,3—DIBROMOCROTONIC ACID

```
   4        1
  H3C      COOH
     \3  2/
      C=C
     /    \
   BR      BR
```

FORMULA   C4H4O2BR2   MOL WT   243.88
SOLVENT   C2H6O S
ORIG ST   CS2   TEMP   323

163.60	115.30	137.50	27.50
1/1	2/1	3/1	4/4

E.LIPPMAA,T.PEHK,K.ANDERSSON,C.RAPPE
ORG MAGN RESONANCE   2,   109 (1970)

---

389   P 002600   E—2,3—DIBROMOCROTONIC ACID

```
           1
   BR      COOH
     \3  2/
      C=C
     /    \
   H3C      BR
    4
```

FORMULA   C4H4O2BR2   MOL WT   243.88
SOLVENT   C2H6O S
ORIG ST   CS2   TEMP   323

164.80	109.20	119.80	27.80
1/1	2/1	3/1	4/4

E.LIPPMAA,T.PEHK,K.ANDERSSON,C.RAPPE
ORG MAGN RESONANCE   2,   109 (1970)

---

390   P 002600   E—2,3—DIIODOCROTONIC ACID

```
           1
   J       COOH
     \3  2/
      C=C
     /    \
   H3C      J
    4
```

FORMULA   C4H4O2I2   MOL WT   337.88
SOLVENT   C2H6O S
ORIG ST   CS2   TEMP   323

167.20	88.00	95.20	37.20
1/1	2/1	3/1	4/4

E.LIPPMAA,T.PEHK,K.ANDERSSON,C.RAPPE
ORG MAGN RESONANCE   2,   109 (1970)

391   O 003200 N,N—DIMETHYLFORMAMIDE

```
        2
  H     CH3
   \   /
    1C—N
   //   \
  O      CH3
          3
```

FORMULA	C3H7NO		MOL WT	73.10
SOLVENT	C3H7N O			
ORIG ST	TMS		TEMP	298

| 161.70 | 34.95 | 29.85 |
| 1/2 | 2/4 | 3/4 |

E.BREITMAIER,G.JUNG,W.VOELTER,L.POHL
UNPUBLISHED   (1972)

---

392   P 003200 HEPTADEUTERIO—N,N—DIMETHYLFORMAMIDE

```
        2
  D     CD3
   \   /
    1C—N
   //   \
  O      CD3
          3
```

FORMULA	C3D7NO		MOL WT	80.14
SOLVENT	C3D7N O			
ORIG ST	TMS		TEMP	298

| 161.60 | 34.10 | 29.00 |
| 1/3 | 2/7 | 3/7 |

E.BREITMAIER,G.JUNG,W.VOELTER,L.POHL
UNPUBLISHED   (1972)

---

393   P 003200 N,N—DIMETHYLACETAMIDE

```
   2      3
  H3C    CH3
    \   /
     1C—N
    //   \
   O      CH3
           4
```

FORMULA	C4H9NO		MOL WT	87.12
SOLVENT	C4H9N O			
ORIG ST	TMS		TEMP	298

| 169.05 | 20.60 | 36.80 | 33.65 |
| 1/1 | 2/4 | 3/4 | 4/4 |

E.BREITMAIER,G.JUNG,W.VOELTER,L.POHL
UNPUBLISHED   (1972)

---

394   P 003200 NONADEUTERIO—N,N—DIMETHYLACETAMIDE

```
   2      3
  D3C    CD3
    \   /
     1C—N
    //   \
   O      CD3
           4
```

FORMULA	C4D9NO		MOL WT	96.18
SOLVENT	C4D9N O			
ORIG ST	TMS		TEMP	298

| 169.05 | 19.75 | 35.95 | 32.70 |
| 1/1 | 2/7 | 3/7 | 4/7 |

E.BREITMAIER,G.JUNG,W.VOELTER,L.POHL
UNPUBLISHED   (1972)

---

395   P 003500 ACETONITRILE

```
    2   1
  CH3—C≡N
```

FORMULA	C2H3N		MOL WT	41.05
SOLVENT	C2H3N			
ORIG ST	TMS		TEMP	298

| 116.70 | 0.20 |
| 1/1 | 2/4 |

E.BREITMAIER,G.JUNG,W.VOELTER,L.POHL
UNPUBLISHED   (1972)

396 P 003500 TRIDEUTERIOACETONITRILE

```
  2   1
CD3-C≡N
```

FORMULA	C2D3N	MOL WT	44.07
SOLVENT	C2D3N		
ORIG ST	TMS	TEMP	298

```
116.55    -0.20
 1/1       2/7
```

E.BREITMAIER,G.JUNG,W.VOELTER,L.POHL
UNPUBLISHED   (1972)

---

397 P 003530 METHYL ISOCYANIDE

FORMULA	C2H3N	MOL WT	41.05
SOLVENT	C2H3N		
ORIG ST	C6H6	TEMP	AMB

```
  1   + -
CH3-N≡C 2
```

```
26.50   156.30
 1/4     2/1
```

G.E.MACIEL,D.A.BEATTY
J PHYS CHEM   69, 3920 (1965)

---

398 P 003530 ETHYL ISOCYANIDE

FORMULA	C3H5N	MOL WT	55.08
SOLVENT	C3H5N		
ORIG ST	CS2	TEMP	AMB

```
  1    2   + -
CH3-CH2-N≡C 3
```

```
14.40    36.00   156.60
 1/4      2/3      3/1
```

I.MORISHIMA,A.MIZUNO,T.YONEZAWA
CHEM COMMUN   1970, 1321 (1970)

---

399 P 003530 TERT-BUTYL ISOCYANIDE

```
     1
    H3C
      \2 + -
    H3C-C-N≡C
      /
    H3C
```

FORMULA	C5H9N	MOL WT	83.13
SOLVENT	C5H9N		
ORIG ST	CS2	TEMP	AMB

```
9.80    58.00   155.00
 1/4     2/1      3/1
```

I.MORISHIMA,A.MIZUNO,T.YONEZAWA
CHEM COMMUN   1970, 1321 (1970)

---

400 P 003600 METHYL ACETATE

```
  2   1   3
CH3-C-O-CH3
    ‖
    O
```

FORMULA	C3H6C2	MOL WT	74.08
SOLVENT	C4H8O2		
ORIG ST	CS2	TEMP	AMB

```
170.70    19.60    50.70
 1/1       2/4      3/4
```

M.CHRISTL,H.J.REICH,J.D.ROBERTS
J AM CHEM SOC   93, 3463 (1971)

401   P 003600   METHYL ACETATE

```
2   1   3
CH3-C-O-CH3
    ‖
    O
```

FORMULA	C3H6O2	MOL WT 74.08
SOLVENT	C3H6O2	
ORIG ST	TMS	TEMP 298

169.80   18.65   49.85
 1/1   2/4   3/4

E.BREITMAIER,G.JUNG,W.VOELTER,L.POHL
UNPUBLISHED   (1972)

---

402   P 003600   TRIDEUTERIOMETHYL TRIDEUTERIOACETATE

```
2   1   3
CD3-COOCD3
```

FORMULA	C3D6O2	MOL WT 80.12
SOLVENT	C3D6O2	
ORIG ST	TMS	TEMP 298

169.80   17.90   49.10
 1/1   2/7   3/7

E.BREITMAIER,G.JUNG,W.VOELTER,L.POHL
UNPUBLISHED   (1972)

---

403   P 003600   ETHYL ACETATE

```
4   3   1   2
CH3-C-O-CH2-CH3
    ‖
    O
```

FORMULA	C4H8O2	MOL WT 88.11
SOLVENT	C4H8O2	
ORIG ST	CS2	TEMP AMB

59.80   13.80   170.00   20.00
 1/3   2/4   3/1   4/4

M.CHRISTL,H.J.REICH,J.D.ROBERTS
J AM CHEM SOC   93, 3463 (1971)

---

404   P 003600   2-PROPYL ACETATE

```
4   3   1   2
CH3-C-O-CH-CH3
    ‖    |
    O    CH3
```

FORMULA	C5H10O2	MOL WT 102.13
SOLVENT	C4H8O2	
ORIG ST	CS2	TEMP AMB

66.80   20.40   169.50   21.40
 1/2   2/4   3/1   4/4

M.CHRISTL,H.J.REICH,J.D.ROBERTS
J AM CHEM SOC   93, 3463 (1971)

---

405   P 003600   2-METHYL-2-PROPYL ACETATE

```
          CH3
4   3   ‖ 2
CH3-C-O-C-CH3
    ‖   |
    O   CH3
```

FORMULA	C6H12O2	MOL WT 116.16
SOLVENT	C4H8O2	
ORIG ST	CS2	TEMP AMB

79.40   27.80   169.50   21.70
 1/1   2/4   3/1   4/4

M.CHRISTL,H.J.REICH,J.D.ROBERTS
J AM CHEM SOC   93, 3463 (1971)

406   P 004500   DIMETHYLSULFOXIDE

```
      1
     CH3
    /
O=S
    \
     CH3
```

FORMULA	C2H6OS	MOL WT 78.13
SOLVENT	C2H6O S	
ORIG ST	TMS	TEMP 298

40.80
1/4

E.BREITMAIER,G.JUNG,W.VOELTER,L.POHL
UNPUBLISHED   (1972)

---

407   P 004500   HEXADEUTERIODIMETHYLSULFOXIDE

```
      1
     CD3
    /
O=S
    \
     CD3
```

FORMULA	C2D6OS	MOL WT 84.17
SOLVENT	C2D6O S	
ORIG ST	TMS	TEMP 298

39.60
1/7

E.BREITMAIER,G.JUNG,W.VOELTER,L.POHL
UNPUBLISHED   (1972)

---

408   P 004700   SODIUM HYDROGEN CARBONATE

```
   1
 NAHCO3
```

FORMULA	CHO3NA	MOL WT 84.01
SOLVENT	D2O	
ORIG ST	TMS	TEMP AMB

161.30
1/1

W.VOELTER,E.BREITMAIER
UNPUBLISHED   (1972)

---

409   P 004700   DISODIUM CARBONATE

```
    1
 NA2CO3
```

FORMULA	CO3NA2	MOL WT 105.99
SOLVENT	D2O	
ORIG ST	TMS	TEMP AMB

169.05
1/1

W.VOELTER,E.BREITMAIER
UNPUBLISHED

---

410   P 004900   TETRAMETHYLUREA

```
   N(CH3)2
   1/
O=C
   \  2
   N(CH3)2
```

FORMULA	C5H12N2O	MOL WT 116.16
SOLVENT	C5H12N2O	
ORIG ST	TMS	TEMP 298

164.45   37.75
1/1   2/4

E.BREITMAIER,G.JUNG,W.VOELTER,L.POHL
UNPUBLISHED   (1972)

411   P 004900   DODECADEUTERICTETRAMETHYLUREA

```
        2
     N(CD3)2
      /
   O=C1
      \
     N(CD3)2
```

FORMULA	C5D12N2O	MOL WT	128.24
SOLVENT	C5D12N2O		
ORIG ST	TMS	TEMP	298

164.55   35.90
1/1   2/7

E.BREITMAIER,G.JUNG,W.VOELTER,L.POHL
UNPUBLISHED   (1972)

---

412   P 005200   METHYL ISOCYANATE

```
   2  1
 H3C-N=C=O
```

FORMULA	C2H3ON	MOL WT	57.05
SOLVENT	C2H3ON		
ORIG ST	C6H6	TEMP	AMB

120.20   25.10
1/1   2/4

G.E.MACIEL,D.A.BEATTY
J PHYS CHEM   69, 3920 (1965)

---

413   P 005200   METHYL ISOTHIOCYANATE

```
   2  1
 H3C-N=C=S
```

FORMULA	C2H3NS	MOL WT	73.12
SOLVENT	C2H3NS		
ORIG ST	C6H6	TEMP	AMB

127.40   28.00
1/4 1   2/1 4

G.E.MACIEL,D.A.BEATTY
J PHYS CHEM   69, 3920 (1965)

---

414   Q 000100   NORBORNYL CATION

```
   3       2
   C---C
  /  7  \1
 4C---C---C+
  \     /
   C---C
   5       6
```

FORMULA	C7H11	MOL WT	95.17
SOLVENT	SO2-SBF5		
ORIG ST	CS2	TEMP	203

90.70   90.70   32.10   48.50
1/1   2/3   3/3   4/2

G.A.OLAH,A.M.WHITE
J AM CHEM SOC   91, 5801 (1969)

---

415   Q 000710   CYCLOPROPANE

```
 H2C---CH2
   \  /
    CH2
    1
```

FORMULA	C3H6	MOL WT	42.08
SOLVENT	C3H6		
ORIG ST	CS2	TEMP	AMB

-3.80
1/3

J.J.BURKE,P.C.LAUTERBUR
J AM CHEM SOC   86, 1870 (1964)

416   Q 000210 METHOXYCARBONYLCYCLOPROPANE

```
3   2
C———C
 \  /
  C1
  |
  C4
 // \   5
O    O—CH3
```

FORMULA	C5H8O2			MOL WT	100.12
SOLVENT	C5H8O2/CDCL3				
ORIG ST	C4H12SI			TEMP	AMB

12.70	8.30	8.30	175.20	51.50
1/2	2/3	3/3	4/1	5/4

M.GORDON,S.H.GROVER,J.B.STOTHERS
CAN J CHEM   51, 2092 (1973)

---

417   Q 000220 CYCLOBUTANE

```
H2C——CH2
 |    |
H2C——CH2
```

FORMULA	C4H8	MOL WT	56.11
SOLVENT	C4H8		
ORIG ST	CS2	TEMP	AMB

22.10
1/3

J.J.BURKE,P.C.LAUTERBUR
J AM CHEM SOC   86, 1870 (1964)

---

418   Q 000220 CYCLOBUTENE

```
4     1
C——C
|   ||
C——C
3     2
```

FORMULA	C4H6	MOL WT	54.09
SOLVENT	C6H12		
ORIG ST	CS2	TEMP	AMB

136.00	30.20
1/2	3/3

D.E.DORMAN,M.JAUTELAT,J.D.ROBERTS
J ORG CHEM   36, 2757 (1971)

---

419   Q 000220 METHYLENECYCLOBUTANE

```
    5
   CH2
4   //
C——C1
|   |
C——C
3   2
```

FORMULA	C5H8			MOL WT	68.12
SOLVENT	C6H12				
ORIG ST	CS2			TEMP	AMB

149.20	31.10	15.80	103.90
1/1	2/3	3/3	5/3

D.E.DORMAN,M.JAUTELAT,J.D.ROBERTS
J ORG CHEM   36, 2757 (1971)

---

420   Q 000220 CYCLOBUTANONE

```
      O
4    //
C——C1
|   |
C——C
3   2
```

FORMULA	C4H6O	MOL WT	70.09
SOLVENT	C4H8O2		
ORIG ST	CS2	TEMP	AMB

207.90	46.60	8.70
1/1	2/3	3/3

F.J.WEIGERT,J.D.ROBERTS
J AM CHEM SOC   92, 1347 (1970)

421   Q 000220   METHOXYCARBONYLCYCLOBUTANE

```
        C3
       / \
    4C     C2
       \ /
        C1
        |
        C5
       ⁄ \  6
     O    O-CH3
```

FORMULA	C6H1OO2			MOL WT	114.15
SOLVENT	C6H1OO2/CDCL3				
ORIG ST	C4H12SI			TEMP	AMB

37.90	25.20	18.40	25.20	175.70	51.40
1/2	2/3	3/3	4/3	5/1	6/4

M.GORDON,S.H.GROVER,J.B.STOTHERS
CAN J CHEM   51, 2092 (1973)

---

422   Q 000300   CYCLOPENTANE

```
  H2C----CH2
   |      |
  H2C    CH2
     \  /
      CH2
       1
```

FORMULA	C5H10
SOLVENT	C5H10
ORIG ST	CS2

MOL WT	70.14
TEMP	AMB

25.30
1/3

J.J.BURKE,P.C.LAUTERBUR
J AM CHEM SOC   86, 1870 (1964)

---

423   Q 000300   METHYLCYCLOPENTANE

```
       C5
      / \
   4C    \
    |     1C-CH3
   3C    ⁄   6
      \ /
       C2
```

FORMULA	C6H12		MOL WT	84.16
SOLVENT	C4H8O2			
ORIG ST	CS2		TEMP	AMB

34.60	34.60	25.20	20.20
1/2	2/3	3/3	6/4

M.CHRISTL,H.J.REICH,J.D.ROBERTS
J AM CHEM SOC   93, 6612 (1971)

---

424   Q 000300   1,1-DIMETHYLCYCLOPENTANE

```
    C5    6
    / \  CH3
   4C  \ /
    |   C1
   3C  / \
    \ /   CH3
    C2    7
```

FORMULA	C7H14		MOL WT	98.19
SOLVENT	C4H8O2			
ORIG ST	CS2		TEMP	AMB

38.90	41.10	24.70	28.80
1/1	2/3	3/3	6/4

M.CHRISTL,H.J.REICH,J.D.ROBERTS
J AM CHEM SOC   93, 6612 (1971)

---

425   Q 000300   CIS-1,2-DIMETHYLCYCLOPENTANE

```
     5C
     / \
   4C   \  6
    |    1C-CH3
   3C   ⁄
    \ /
    2C-CH3
       7
```

FORMULA	C7H14		MOL WT	98.19
SOLVENT	C4H8O2			
ORIG ST	CS2		TEMP	AMB

37.40	33.00	23.00	14.90
1/2	3/3	4/3	6/4

M.CHRISTL,H.J.REICH,J.D.ROBERTS
J AM CHEM SOC   93, 6612 (1971)

426   Q 000300   TRANS—1,2—DIMETHYLCYCLOPENTANE

```
        C5
       /  \
    4C  \   6
     |   1C-CH3
    3C  /
     \ /
   H3C-C2
      7
```

FORMULA	C7H14			MOL WT	98.19
SOLVENT	C4H8O2				
ORIG ST	CS2			TEMP	AMB

42.50	34.80	23.10	18.50
1/2	3/3	4/3	6/4

M.CHRISTL,H.J.REICH,J.D.ROBERTS
J AM CHEM SOC   93, 6612 (1971)

---

427   Q 000300   CIS—1,3—DIMETHYLCYCLOPENTANE

```
      6
    1C-CH3
    / \
  5C    \
   |    C2
  4C   /
    \ /
    3C-CH3
      7
```

FORMULA	C7H14			MOL WT	98.19
SOLVENT	C4H8O2				
ORIG ST	CS2			TEMP	AMB

35.20	44.80	34.10	20.90
1/2	2/3	4/3	6/4

M.CHRISTL,H.J.REICH,J.D.ROBERTS
J AM CHEM SOC   93, 6612 (1971)

---

428   Q 000300   TRANS—1,3—DIMETHYLCYCLOPENTANE

```
      6
    1C-CH3
    / \
  5C    \
   |    C2
  4C   /
    \ /
  H3C-C3
      7
```

FORMULA	C7H14			MOL WT	98.19
SOLVENT	C4H8O2				
ORIG ST	CS2			TEMP	AMB

33.30	42.90	35.00	21.20
1/2	2/3	4/3	6/4

M.CHRISTL,H.J.REICH,J.D.ROBERTS
J AM CHEM SOC   93, 6612 (1971)

---

429   Q 000300   CYCLOPENTENE

```
      5
      C
     / \ 1
    /   C
  4C    ||
    \   C
     \ / 2
      C
      3
```

FORMULA	C5H8		MOL WT	68.12
SOLVENT	C6H12			
ORIG ST	CS2		TEMP	AMB

129.60	31.60	22.10
1/2	3/3	4/3

D.E.DORMAN,M.JAUTELAT,J.D.ROBERTS
J ORG CHEM   36, 2757 (1971)

---

430   Q 000300   METHYLENECYCLOPENTANE

```
    5    6
    C   CH2
   / \  //
  /    C1
 4C    |
   \   C2
    \ /
     C
     3
```

FORMULA	C6H10			MOL WT	82.15
SOLVENT	C6H12				
ORIG ST	CS2			TEMP	AMB

151.60	32.10	25.90	103.80
1/1	2/3	3/3	6/3

D.E.DORMAN,M.JAUTELAT,J.D.ROBERTS
J ORG CHEM   36, 2757 (1971)

431   Q 000300   CYCLOPENTANOL

```
        2
        C
      /   \
    3C      \
     |    1C—OH
     C     /
      \   /
        C
```

FORMULA	C5H10O	MOL WT	86.13
SOLVENT	C4H8O2		
ORIG ST	CS2	TEMP	AMB

73.30	35.00	23.40
1/2	2/3	3/3

M.CHRISTL,H.J.REICH,J.D.ROBERTS
J AM CHEM SOC   93, 3463 (1971)

---

432   Q 000300   1—METHYLCYCLOPENTANOL

```
        2
        C
      /   \  OH
    3C      \ /
     |       1C
    4C      / \
      \    /   CH3
        C      6
        5
```

FORMULA	C6H12O	MOL WT	100.16
SOLVENT	C4H8O2		
ORIG ST	CS2	TEMP	AMB

79.20	41.20	24.20	28.30
1/1	2/3	3/3	6/4

M.CHRISTL,H.J.REICH,J.D.ROBERTS
J AM CHEM SOC   93, 3463 (1971)

---

433   Q 000300   CIS—2—METHYLCYCLOPENTANOL

```
     6CH3
      |
      C2
     /  \
    3C    \
     |    1C—OH
    4C    /
      \  /
       5C
```

FORMULA	C6H12O	MOL WT	100.16
SOLVENT	C4H8O2		
ORIG ST	CS2	TEMP	AMB

75.20	39.80	34.50	22.10	31.00	13.70
1/2	2/2	3/3	4/3	5/3	6/4

M.CHRISTL,H.J.REICH,J.D.ROBERTS
J AM CHEM SOC   93, 3463 (1971)

---

434   Q 000300   TRANS—2—METHYLCYCLOPENTANOL

```
     6CH3
      |
      C2
     /  \
    3C    \
     |    1C—OH
    4C    /
      \  /
       5C
```

FORMULA	C6H12O	MOL WT	100.16
SOLVENT	C4H8O2		
ORIG ST	CS2	TEMP	AMB

79.80	42.20	33.90	21.50	31.80	18.30
1/2	2/2	3/3	4/3	5/3	6/4

M.CHRISTL,H.J.REICH,J.D.ROBERTS
J AM CHEM SOC   93, 3463 (1971)

---

435   Q 000300   CIS—3—METHYLCYCLOPENTANOL

```
     6     2
    H3C    C
      \  / \
       C3   \
       |    1C—OH
      4C    /
        \  /
         C
         5
```

FORMULA	C6H12O	MOL WT	100.16
SOLVENT	C4H8O2		
ORIG ST	CS2	TEMP	AMB

73.20	44.10	33.00	32.40	35.40	21.10
1/2	2/3	3/2	4/3	5/3	6/4

M.CHRISTL,H.J.REICH,J.D.ROBERTS
J AM CHEM SOC   93, 3463 (1971)

436   Q 000300   TRANS-3-METHYLCYCLOPENTANOL

```
   6   2
  H3C   C
    \ / \
     C3
     |    1C—OH
    4C    /
     \  /
      C
      5
```

FORMULA	C6H12O			MOL WT	100.16
SOLVENT	C4H8O2				
ORIG ST	CS2			TEMP	AMB

73.20	44.30	31.90	32.70	35.20	20.70
1/2	2/3	3/2	4/3	5/3	6/4

M.CHRISTL,H.J.REICH,J.D.ROBERTS
J AM CHEM SOC   93, 3463 (1971)

437   Q 000300   TRANS-1,2-DIMETHYLCYCLOPENTANOL

```
   7CH3
    |
    C2
   / \   OH
 3C   \ /
  |    1C
 4C   / \
  \  /   CH3
  5C    6
```

FORMULA	C7H14O			MOL WT	114.19
SOLVENT	C4H8O2				
ORIG ST	CS2			TEMP	AMB

79.00	44.30	32.40	21.10	41.30	26.00
1/1	2/2	3/3	4/3	5/3	6/4
12.70					
7/4					

M.CHRISTL,H.J.REICH,J.D.ROBERTS
J AM CHEM SOC   93, 3463 (1971)

438   Q 000300   1,3-DIMETHYLCYCLOPENTANOL

```
   7   2
  H3C   C
    \ / \   OH
     C3   \ /
     |    1C
    4C   / \
     \  /   CH3
      C    6
      5
```

FORMULA	C7H14O			MOL WT	114.19
SOLVENT	C4H8O2				
ORIG ST	CS2			TEMP	AMB

79.30	50.30	33.80	33.60	42.00	20.60
1/1	2/3	3/2	4/3	5/3	6/4
21.50					
7/4					

M.CHRISTL,H.J.REICH,J.D.ROBERTS
J AM CHEM SOC   93, 3463 (1971)

439   Q 000300   CYCLOPENTYL ACETATE

```
    2
    C
   / \
 3C   \   6 7
  |    1C—O—C—CH3
 4C   / ||
  \ /   O
   C
   5
```

FORMULA	C7H12O2			MOL WT	128.17
SOLVENT	C4H8O2				
ORIG ST	CS2			TEMP	AMB

76.50	32.60	23.70	169.60	20.50
1/2	2/3	3/3	6/1	7/4

M.CHRISTL,H.J.REICH,J.D.ROBERTS
J AM CHEM SOC   93, 3463 (1971)

440   Q 000300   1-METHYLCYCLOPENTYL ACETATE

```
    2
    C      7 8
   / \   O—C—CH3
 3C   \ /  ||
  |    1C   O
 4C   / \
  \ /   CH3
   C   6
   5
```

FORMULA	C8H14O2			MOL WT	142.20
SOLVENT	C4H8O2				
ORIG ST	CS2			TEMP	AMB

88.90	39.10	23.70	24.10	169.40	21.50
1/1	2/3	3/3	6/4	7/1	8/4

M.CHRISTL,H.J.REICH,J.D.ROBERTS
J AM CHEM SOC   93, 3463 (1971)

441   Q 000300   CIS-2-METHYLCYCLOPENTYL ACETATE

```
     6CH3
      |
      C
     /2\
3C      \      7 8
 |      1C-O-C-CH3
4C      /      ||
  \  /          O
   C
   5
```

FORMULA	C8H14O2			MOL WT	142.20
SOLVENT	C4H8O2				
ORIG ST	CS2			TEMP	AMB

77.90	38.50	31.80	22.20	32.00	13.60
1/2	2/2	3/3	4/3	5/3	6/4
169.40	20.30				
7/1	8/4				

M.CHRISTL,H.J.REICH,J.D.ROBERTS
J AM CHEM SOC   93, 3463 (1971)

442   Q 000300   TRANS-2-METHYLCYCLOPENTYL ACETATE

```
     6CH3
      |
      C
     /2\
3C      \      7 8
 |      1C-O-C-CH3
4C      /      ||
  \  /          O
   C
   5
```

FORMULA	C8H14O2			MOL WT	142.20
SOLVENT	C4H8O2				
ORIG ST	CS2			TEMP	AMB

81.90	40.20	31.40	22.50	32.20	18.00
1/2	2/2	3/3	4/3	5/3	6/4
169.40	20.50				
7/1	8/4				

M.CHRISTL,H.J.REICH,J.D.ROBERTS
J AM CHEM SOC   93, 3463 (1971)

443   Q 000300   CIS-3-METHYLCYCLOPENTYL ACETATE

```
 6    2
H3C   C
  \ / \
   C3    \      7 8
   |      1C-O-C-CH3
4C      /      ||
  \  /          O
   C
   5
```

FORMULA	C8H14O2			MOL WT	142.20
SOLVENT	C4H8O2				
ORIG ST	CS2			TEMP	AMB

76.30	41.10	33.00	32.50	32.40	20.50
1/2	2/3	3/2	4/3	5/3	6/4
169.40	20.40				
7/1	8/4				

M.CHRISTL,H.J.REICH,J.D.ROBERTS
J AM CHEM SOC   93, 3463 (1971)

444   Q 000300   TRANS-3-METHYLCYCLOPENTYL ACETATE

```
 6    2
H3C   C
  \ / \
   C3    \      7 8
   |      1C-O-C-CH3
4C      /      ||
  \  /          O
   C
   5
```

FORMULA	C8H14O2			MOL WT	142.20
SOLVENT	C4H8O2				
ORIG ST	CS2			TEMP	AMB

76.50	41.40	32.60	32.40	32.50	19.90
1/2	2/3	3/2	4/3	5/3	6/4
169.40	21.50				
7/1	8/4				

M.CHRISTL,H.J.REICH,J.D.ROBERTS
J AM CHEM SOC   93, 3463 (1971)

445   Q 000300   TRANS-1,2-DIMETHYLCYCLOPENTYL ACETATE

```
     7CH3
      |
      C        8 9
     /2\    O-C-CH3
3C      \  /   ||
 |      1C    O
4C      /  \
  \  /     CH3
   C        6
   5
```

FORMULA	C9H16O2			MOL WT	156.23
SOLVENT	C4H8O2				
ORIG ST	CS2			TEMP	AMB

88.90	45.40	31.80	20.80	36.50	22.00
1/1	2/2	3/3	4/3	5/3	6/4
12.90	169.40	21.30			
7/4	8/1	9/4			

M.CHRISTL,H.J.REICH,J.D.ROBERTS
J AM CHEM SOC   93, 3463 (1971)

446   Q 000300 (CIS-,TRANS-)1,3-DIMETHYLCYCLOPENTYL ACETATE

```
    7    2
  H3C    C        8  9
    \  / \     O-C-CH3
     C3   \ /   ||
     |    1C     O
    4C    / \
      \  /    CH3
       C     6
       5
```

FORMULA	C9H16O2			MOL WT	156.23
SOLVENT	C4H8O2				
ORIG ST	CS2			TEMP	AMB

88.60	48.00	33.00	33.00	39.50	25.20
1/1	2/3	3/2	4/3	5/3	6/4
20.70	169.40	21.50			
7/4	8/1	9/4			

M.CHRISTL,H.J.REICH,J.D.ROBERTS
J AM CHEM SOC   93, 3463 (1971)

---

447   Q 000300 (CIS-,TRANS-)1,3-DIMETHYLCYCLOPENTYL ACETATE

FORMULA	C9H16O2			MOL WT	156.23
SOLVENT	C4H8O2				
ORIG ST	CS2			TEMP	AMB

```
    7    2
  H3C    C        8  9
    \  / \     O-C-CH3
     C3   \ /   ||
     |    1C     O
    4C    / \
      \  /    CH3
       C     6
       5
```

89.40	48.10	33.00	33.00	39.20	24.90
1/1	2/3	3/2	4/3	5/3	6/4
20.30	169.40	21.50			
7/4	8/1	9/4			

M.CHRISTL,H.J.REICH,J.D.ROBERTS
J AM CHEM SOC   93, 3463 (1971)

---

448   Q 000300 CYCLOPENTANONE

```
          O
   5      //
   C---C1
   |    |
   C    C
  4 \  / 2
     C
     3
```

FORMULA	C5H8O		MOL WT	84.12
SOLVENT	C4H8O2			
ORIG ST	CS2		TEMP	AMB

213.60	36.70	22.00
1/1	2/3	3/3

F.J.WEIGERT,J.D.ROBERTS
J AM CHEM SOC   92, 1347 (1970)

---

449   Q 000300 METHOXYCARBONYLCYCLOPENTANE

```
   4C-C3
   /    \
  5C     C2
   \    /
    \  /
     C1
     |
     C6
    // \  7
   O    O-CH3
```

FORMULA	C7H12O2			MOL WT	128.17
SOLVENT	C7H12O2/CDCL3				
ORIG ST	C4H12SI			TEMP	AMB

43.70	30.00	25.80	25.80	30.00	177.00
1/2	2/3	3/3	4/3	5/3	6/1
51.40					
7/4					

M.GORDON,S.H.GROVER,J.B.STOTHERS
CAN J CHEM   51, 2092 (1973)

---

450   Q 000400 CYCLOHEXANE

```
   H2C--CH2
   /      \
  H2C      CH2
   \      /
   H2C--CH2
       1
```

FORMULA	C6H12	MOL WT	84.16
SOLVENT	C6H12		
ORIG ST	CS2	TEMP	AMB

26.60
1/3

J.J.BURKE,P.C.LAUTERBUR
J AM CHEM SOC   86, 1870 (1964)

451   Q 000400 DODECADEUTERIOCYCLOHEXANE

```
    3   2
  D2C--CD2
  /      \
D2C4     1CD2
  \      /
  D2C--CD2
    5   6
```

FORMULA   C6D12   MOL WT   96.24
SOLVENT   C6D12
ORIG ST   TMS   TEMP   298

          25.15
          1/5

E.BREITMAIER,G.JUNG,W.VOELTER,L.POHL
UNPUBLISHED   (1972)

---

452   Q 000400 METHYLCYCLOHEXANE

```
   2   6
   C--C
  /    \
4C      C-CH3
  \    /1 7
   C--C
   3   2
```

FORMULA   C7H14   MOL WT   98.19
SOLVENT   C7H14
ORIG ST   C6H6   TEMP   AMB

   33.05   35.75   26.55   26.40   22.70
   1/2   2/3   3/3   4/3   7/4

D.K.DALLING,D.M.GRANT
J AM CHEM SOC   89, 6612 (1967)

---

453   Q 000400 1,1-DIMETHYLCYCLOHEXANE

```
   5  6 7
   C--C CH3
  /    \|
4C      C1
  \    /|
   C--C CH3
   3  2 8
```

FORMULA   C8H16   MOL WT   112.22
SOLVENT   C8H16
ORIG ST   C6H6   TEMP   AMB

   30.00   39.85   22.60   26.65   28.85
   1/1   2/3   3/3   4/3   7/4

D.K.DALLING,D.M.GRANT
J AM CHEM SOC   89, 6612 (1967)

---

454   Q 000400 CIS-1,2-DIMETHYLCYCLOHEXANE

```
  4C--C5
  /    \
3C      C6
  \    /
  2C--C1
  |    |
 H3C  CH3
  8    7
```

FORMULA   C8H16   MOL WT   112.22
SOLVENT   C8H16
ORIG ST   C6H6   TEMP   AMB

   34.45   31.50   23.65   15.75
   1/2   3/3   4/3   7/4

D.K.DALLING,D.M.GRANT
J AM CHEM SOC   89, 6612 (1967)

---

455   Q 000400 TRANS-1,2-DIMETHYLCYCLOHEXANE

```
  4C--C5
  /    \
3C8CH3 C6
  \|   /
  2C--C1
   |
  7CH3
```

FORMULA   C8H16   MOL WT   112.22
SOLVENT   C8H16
ORIG ST   C6H6   TEMP   AMB

   39.55   36.05   26.85   20.20
   1/2   3/3   4/3   7/4

D.K.DALLING,D.M.GRANT
J AM CHEM SOC   89, 6612 (1967)

456 Q 000400 CIS-1,3-DIMETHYLCYCLOHEXANE

```
    4C--C5
   /      \
 3C        C6
  I\       /
 H3C C--C1
  8 2  I
      7CH3
```

FORMULA   C8H16   MOL WT   112.22
SOLVENT   C8H16
ORIG ST   C6H6   TEMP   AMB

32.80	44.70	35.35	26.45	22.80
1/2	2/3	4/3	5/3	7/4

D.K.DALLING,D.M.GRANT
J AM CHEM SOC   89, 6612 (1967)

---

457 Q 000400 TRANS-1,3-DIMETHYLCYCLOHEXANE

```
  8  4
 H3C C--C5
  I/      \
 3C        C6
   \      /
    2C--C1
      I
     7CH3
```

FORMULA   C8H16   MOL WT   112.22
SOLVENT   C8H16
ORIG ST   C6H6   TEMP   AMB

27.05	41.40	33.90	20.75	20.50
1/2	2/3	4/3	5/3	7/4

D.K.DALLING,D.M.GRANT
J AM CHEM SOC   89, 6612 (1967)

---

458 Q 000400 CIS-1,4-DIMETHYLCYCLOHEXANE

```
    4C--C5
   /I      \
 3C8CH3    C6
   \      /
    2C--C1
      I
     7CH3
```

FORMULA   C8H16   MOL WT   112.22
SOLVENT   C8H16
ORIG ST   C6H6   TEMP   AMB

30.15	30.60	20.05
1/2	2/3	7/4

D.K.DALLING,D.M.GRANT
J AM CHEM SOC   89, 6612 (1967)

---

459 Q 000400 TRANS-1,4-DIMETHYLCYCLOHEXANE

```
   8CH3
    I
   4C--C5
  /      \
 3C        C6
  \      /
   2C--C1
    I
   7CH3
```

FORMULA   C8H16   MOL WT   112.22
SOLVENT   C8H16
ORIG ST   C6H6   TEMP   AMB

32.60	35.65	22.70
1/2	2/3	7/4

D.K.DALLING,D.M.GRANT
J AM CHEM SOC   89, 6612 (1967)

---

460 Q 000400 1,1,2-TRIMETHYLCYCLOHEXANE

```
     6  7
   5C--C CH3 E
   /    \I
 4C       C1
   \    2/I
   3C--C CH3 A
    I 8
   9CH3
```

FORMULA   C9H18   MOL WT   126.24
SOLVENT   C9H18
ORIG ST   C6H6   TEMP   AMB

32.85	41.80	31.35	26.80	22.75	41.25
1/1	2/2	3/3	4/3	5/3	6/3
30.50	19.10	16.35			
7/4	8/4	9/4			

D.K.DALLING,D.M.GRANT
J AM CHEM SOC   89, 6612 (1967)

461 — Q 000400 1,1,3-TRIMETHYLCYCLOHEXANE

```
        6 7
    5C--C CH3 E
   /     \|
  4C       C1
   \     /|
   3C--C CH3 A
    |  2 8
   9CH3
```

FORMULA	C9H18			MOL WT	126.24
SOLVENT	C9H18				
ORIG ST	C6H6			TEMP	AMB

30.75	49.35	28.30	35.70	22.60	39.50
1/1	2/3	3/2	4/3	5/3	6/3
33.65	24.85	23.15			
7/4	8/4	9/4			

D.K.DALLING,D.M.GRANT
J AM CHEM SOC   89, 6612 (1967)

462 — Q 000400 1,1,4-TRIMETHYLCYCLOHEXANE

```
      5        6
    9 C------C      7
  H3C /        \  CH3
     |/          \|/
     C4           1C
      \          / \
       \        /    CH3
        C------C     8
        3      2
```

FORMULA	C9H18			MOL WT	126.24
SOLVENT	C9H18				
ORIG ST	C4H12SI			TEMP	AMB

39.50	39.50	32.90	32.81	31.38	31.38
2/3	6/3	7/4	4/2	3/3	5/3
29.79	24.56	22.39			
1/1	8/4	9/4			

D.K.DALLING,D.M.GRANT
J AM CHEM SOC   94, 5318 (1972)

463 — Q 000400 1-TRANS-2-CIS-3-TRIMETHYLCYCLOHEXANE

```
        6 7
    5C--C CH3
   /     \|
  4C9CH3  C1
   \|    /
   3C--C2
    |
   8CH3
```

FORMULA	C9H18			MOL WT	126.24
SOLVENT	C9H18				
ORIG ST	C6H6			TEMP	AMB

39.15	46.20	36.45	26.45	20.75	16.60
1/2	2/2	4/3	5/3	7/4	8/4

D.K.DALLING,D.M.GRANT
J AM CHEM SOC   89, 6612 (1967)

464 — Q 000400 1-TRANS-2-CIS-4-TRIMETHYLCYCLOHEXANE

```
   9 5  6 7
  H3C C--C CH3
   |/    \|
   4C       C1
    \      /
    3C--C2
     |
    8CH3
```

FORMULA	C9H18			MOL WT	126.24
SOLVENT	C9H18				
ORIG ST	C6H6			TEMP	AMB

38.80	33.60	40.75	26.95	31.80	29.45
1/2	2/2	3/3	4/2	5/3	6/3
20.30	20.05	19.05			
7 8/4	8 7/4	9/4			

D.K.DALLING,D.M.GRANT
J AM CHEM SOC   89, 6612 (1967)

465 — Q 000400 1-CIS-3-CIS-5-TRIMETHYLCYCLOHEXANE

```
    5C--C6
   /|    \
  4C9CH3  C1
   \    /|
    3C--C CH3
     |  2 7
    8CH3
```

FORMULA	C9H18		MOL WT	126.24
SOLVENT	C9H18			
ORIG ST	C6H6		TEMP	AMB

32.70	44.20	22.80
1/2	2/3	7/4

D.K.DALLING,D.M.GRANT
J AM CHEM SOC   89, 6612 (1967)

466   Q 000400 1—CIS—3—TRANS—5—TRIMETHYLCYCLOHEXANE

```
    9CH3
     |
    5C——C6
   /      \
 4C        C1
   \      /|
    3C——C CH3
    |  2 7
    8CH3
```

FORMULA	C9H18			MOL WT	126.24
SOLVENT	C9H18				
ORIG ST	C6H6			TEMP	AMB

26.45	45.00	40.90	28.60	23.05	18.90
1/2	2/3	4/3	5/2	7/4	9/4

D.K.DALLING,D.M.GRANT
J AM CHEM SOC   89, 6612 (1967)

---

467   Q 000400 1—TRANS—2—TRANS—3—TRIMETHYLCYCLOHEXANE

```
   5        6
   C————————C
  /          \
4C 9        8 C1
  \ CH3  H3C /|
   \|       1/ CH3
    C————————C  7
    3        2
```

FORMULA	C9H18			MOL WT	126.24
SOLVENT	C9H18				
ORIG ST	C4H12SI			TEMP	AMB

41.88	35.19	33.97	33.67	33.04	21.29
2/2	6/3	3/2	4/3	1/2	5/3
20.51	17.42	13.81			
7/4	8/4	9/4			

D.K.DALLING,D.M.GRANT
J AM CHEM SOC   94, 5318 (1972)

---

468   Q 000400 1—CIS—2—CIS—3—TRIMETHYLCYCLOHEXANE

```
   5        6
   C————————C
  /          \
 /            \
4C            1C
  \          /|
   \3      2/ CH3
    C————————C  7
    |        |
    CH3      CH3
    9        8
```

FORMULA	C9H18			MOL WT	126.24
SOLVENT	C9H18				
ORIG ST	C4H12SI			TEMP	AMB

39.81	37.51	37.51	28.48	28.48	27.19
2/2	1/2	3/2	4/3	6/3	5/3
20.41	20.41	5.33			
7/4	9/4	8/4			

D.K.DALLING,D.M.GRANT
J AM CHEM SOC   94, 5318 (1972)

---

469   Q 000400 1—CIS—2—TRANS—4—TRIMETHYLCYCLOHEXANE

```
     5        6
  9  C————————C
 H3C /          \
  |/             \
  4C              C1
   \            /|
    \          2/ CH3
     C————————C  7
     3        |
           8CH3
```

FORMULA	C9H18			MOL WT	126.24
SOLVENT	C9H18				
ORIG ST	C4H12SI			TEMP	AMB

43.15	35.84	35.25	33.91	29.15	26.29
3/3	5/3	1/2	2/2	6/3	4/2
22.78	19.71	12.76			
9/4	7/4	8/4			

D.K.DALLING,D.M.GRANT
J AM CHEM SOC   94, 5318 (1972)

---

470   Q 000400 1—CIS—2—CIS—4—TRIMETHYLCYCLOHEXANE

```
     5        6
  9  C————————C  7
C3C /          \ CH3
  |/             \|
  4C              8 C
   \          H3C /1
    \            1/
     C————————C
     3        2
```

FORMULA	C9H18			MOL WT	126.24
SOLVENT	C9H18				
ORIG ST	C4H12SI			TEMP	AMB

38.04	35.50	34.06	33.70	32.93	29.32
3/3	2/2	6/3	1/2	4/2	5/3
22.96	20.34	11.68			
9/4	8/4	7/4			

D.K.DALLING,D.M.GRANT
J AM CHEM SOC   94, 5318 (1972)

471 Q 000400 CYCLOHEXENE

```
        6
        C
    5 /   \ 1
    C       C
    |       ||
    C       C
    4 \   / 2
        C
        3
```

FORMULA C6H10   MOL WT   82.15
SOLVENT C6H12
ORIG ST CS2   TEMP   AMB

    126.20   24.50   22.10
     1/2   3/3   4/3

D.E.DORMAN,M.JAUTELAT,J.D.ROBERTS
J ORG CHEM   36, 2757 (1971)

---

472 Q 000400 METHYLENECYCLOHEXANE

```
    6    7
    C   CH2
    / \ //
   5C   C1
   |    |
   4C   C2
    \  /
     C
     3
```

FORMULA C7H12   MOL WT   96.17
SOLVENT C6H12
ORIG ST CS2   TEMP   AMB

    148.50   35.00   27.70   25.70   105.90
     1/1   2/3   3/3   4/3   7/3

D.E.DORMAN,M.JAUTELAT,J.D.ROBERTS
J ORG CHEM   36, 2757 (1971)

---

473 Q 000400 CYCLOHEXANOL

```
    3   2
    C---C
   /     \
  4C      1C—OH
   \     /
    C---C
    5   6
```

FORMULA C6H12O   MOL WT   100.16
SOLVENT C6H12O
ORIG ST CS2   TEMP   AMB

    69.50   35.50   24.40   25.90
     1/2   2/3   3/3   4/3

J.D.ROBERTS,F.J.WEIGERT,J.I.KROSCHWITZ,H.J.REICH
J AM CHEM SOC   92, 1338 (1970)

---

474 Q 000400 1-METHYLCYCLOHEXANOL

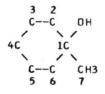

```
    3   2
    C---C   OH
   /     \ /
  4C      1C
   \     / \
    C---C   CH3
    5   6   7
```

FORMULA C7H14O   MOL WT   114.19
SOLVENT C7H14O
ORIG ST CS2   TEMP   AMB

    69.00   39.70   22.80   26.00   29.50
     1/1   2/3   3/3   4/3   7/4

J.D.ROBERTS,F.J.WEIGERT,J.I.KROSCHWITZ,H.J.REICH
J AM CHEM SOC   92, 1338 (1970)

---

475 Q 000400 CIS-2-METHYLCYCLOHEXANOL

```
        7
       CH3
    3  /
    C---C
   /   2\
  4C     1C—OH
   \     /
    C---C
    5   6
```

FORMULA C7H14O   MOL WT   114.19
SOLVENT C7H14O
ORIG ST CS2   TEMP   AMB

    71.10   35.80   29.30   24.20   21.50   31.80
     1/2   2/2   3/3   4/3   5/3   6/3
    16.20
     7/4

J.D.ROBERTS,F.J.WEIGERT,J.I.KROSCHWITZ,H.J.REICH
J AM CHEM SOC   92, 1338 (1970)

476　　　Q 000400　TRANS—2—METHYLCYCLOHEXANOL

```
        CH3
    3   2/7
    C——C
   /      \
  4C      1C—OH
   \      /
    C——C
    5   6
```

FORMULA	C7H14O			MOL WT	114.19
SOLVENT	C7H14O				
ORIG ST	CS2			TEMP	AMB

76.60	39.70	34.00	25.80	25.40	35.10
1/2	2/2	3/3	4/3	5/3	6/3
18.80					
7/4					

J.D.ROBERTS,F.J.WEIGERT,J.I.KROSCHWITZ,H.J.REICH
J AM CHEM SOC　　　　　　　　　92, 1338 (1970)

477　　　Q 000400　CIS—3—METHYLCYCLOHEXANOL

```
   H3C
   7\3  2
    C——C
   /      \
  C4      1C—OH
   \      /
    C——C
    5   6
```

FORMULA	C7H14O			MOL WT	114.19
SOLVENT	C7H14O				
ORIG ST	CS2			TEMP	AMB

70.50	44.00	31.70	34.80	24.40	34.40
1/2	2/3	3/2	4/3	5/3	6/3
22.50					
7/4					

J.D.ROBERTS,F.J.WEIGERT,J.I.KROSCHWITZ,H.J.REICH
J AM CHEM SOC　　　　　　　　　92, 1338 (1970)

478　　　Q 000400　TRANS—3—METHYLCYCLOHEXANOL

```
   H3C
   7\3  2
    C——C
   /      \
  4C      1C—OH
   \      /
    C——C
    5   6
```

FORMULA	C7H14O			MOL WT	114.19
SOLVENT	C7H14O				
ORIG ST	CS2			TEMP	AMB

66.50	41.20	26.60	34.40	20.20	32.80
1/2	2/3	3/2	4/2	5/2	6/2
20.20					
7/4					

J.D.ROBERTS,F.J.WEIGERT,J.I.KROSCHWITZ,H.J.REICH
J AM CHEM SOC　　　　　　　　　92, 1338 (1970)

479　　　Q 000400　CIS—4—METHYLCYCLOHEXANOL

```
    3   2
    C——C
   / 7    \
 H3C-C4   1C—OH
   \      /
    C——C
    5   6
```

FORMULA	C7H14O			MOL WT	114.19
SOLVENT	C7H14O				
ORIG ST	CS2			TEMP	AMB

| 65.90 | 31.40 | 28.70 | 30.60 | 20.90 |
| 1/2 | 2/3 | 3/3 | 4/2 | 7/4 |

J.D.ROBERTS,F.J.WEIGERT,J.I.KROSCHWITZ,H.J.REICH
J AM CHEM SOC　　　　　　　　　92, 1338 (1970)

480　　　Q 000400　TRANS—4—METHYLCYCLOHEXANOL

```
    3   2
    C——C
   / 7    \
 H3C-C4   1C—OH
   \      /
    C——C
    5   6
```

FORMULA	C7H14O			MOL WT	114.19
SOLVENT	C7H14O				
ORIG ST	CS2			TEMP	AMB

| 69.70 | 34.80 | 33.10 | 31.40 | 21.70 |
| 1/2 | 2/3 | 3/3 | 4/2 | 7/2 |

J.D.ROBERTS,F.J.WEIGERT,J.I.KROSCHWITZ,H.J.REICH
J AM CHEM SOC　　　　　　　　　92, 1338 (1970)

481   Q 000400   CIS-4-TERT-BUTYLCYCLOHEXANOL

```
    3   2
    C--C
8   7 /     \
(CH3)3C-C4    1C-OH
      \     /
       C--C
       5   6
```

FORMULA	C10H20O			MOL WT	156.27
SOLVENT	C10H20O				
ORIG ST	CS2			TEMP	AMB

64.70	33.00	20.70	47.90	32.10	27.10
1/2	2/3	3/3	4/2	7/1	8/4

J.D.ROBERTS,F.J.WEIGERT,J.I.KROSCHWITZ,H.J.REICH
J AM CHEM SOC   92, 1338 (1970)

---

482   Q 000400   TRANS-4-TERT-BUTYLCYCLOHEXANOL

```
    3   2
    C--C
8   7 /     \
(CH3)3C-C4    1C-OH
      \     /
       C--C
       5   6
```

FORMULA	C10H20O			MOL WT	156.27
SOLVENT	C10H20O				
ORIG ST	CS2			TEMP	AMB

70.10	35.40	25.40	47.00	31.80	27.20
1/2	2/3	3/3	4/2	7/1	8/4

J.D.ROBERTS,F.J.WEIGERT,J.I.KROSCHWITZ,H.J.REICH
J AM CHEM SOC   92, 1338 (1970)

---

483   Q 000400   CYCLOHEXANONE

```
        O
   6    //
   C--C1
  /     \
5C       C2
  \     /
   C--C
   4    3
```

FORMULA	C6H10O	MOL WT	98.15
SOLVENT	C4H8O2		
ORIG ST	CS2	TEMP	AMB

208.50	40.40	26.50	23.80
1/1	2/3	3/3	4/3

F.J.WEIGERT,J.D.ROBERTS
J AM CHEM SOC   92, 1347 (1970)

---

484   Q 000400   2-METHYLCYCLOHEXANONE

```
        O
   6    //
   C--C1
  /     \2 7
5C       C-CH3
  \     /
   C--C
   4    3
```

FORMULA	C7H12O			MOL WT	112.17
SOLVENT	C4H8O2				
ORIG ST	CS2			TEMP	AMB

210.00	44.00	35.20	24.20	27.00	40.60
1/1	2/2	3/3	4/3	5/3	6/3
13.50					
7/4					

F.J.WEIGERT,J.D.ROBERTS
J AM CHEM SOC   92, 1347 (1970)

---

485   Q 000400   3-METHYLCYCLOHEXANONE

```
        O
   6    //
   C--C1
  /     \
5C       C2
  \     /
   C--C3
   4    \
        CH3
        7
```

FORMULA	C7H12O			MOL WT	112.17
SOLVENT	C4H8O2				
ORIG ST	CS2			TEMP	AMB

208.10	48.80	32.70	32.20	24.20	39.80
1/1	2/3	3/2	4/3	5/3	6/3
20.80					
7/4					

F.J.WEIGERT,J.D.ROBERTS
J AM CHEM SOC   92, 1347 (1970)

486　　　Q 000400　**4-METHYLCYCLOHEXANONE**

```
        O
   6   ⫽
   C--C1
  /      \
5C        C2
  \      /
   4C--C
  /     3
 7CH3
```

FORMULA　C7H10O　　　　　　　MOL WT　110.16
SOLVENT　C4H8O2
ORIG ST　CS2　　　　　　　　TEMP　　　AMB

| 208.70 | 39.50 | 33.80 | 30.10 | 19.90 |
| 1/1 | 2/3 | 3/3 | 4/2 | 7/4 |

F.J.WEIGERT,J.D.ROBERTS
J AM CHEM SOC　　　　　　　92, 1347 (1970)

487　　　Q 000400　**2-TERT-BUTYLCYCLOHEXANONE**

```
        O
   6   ⫽
   C--C1
  /    \2 7 8
5C      C-C(CH3)3
  \    /
   C--C
   4   3
```

FORMULA　C10H18O　　　　　　MOL WT　154.25
SOLVENT　C4H8O2
ORIG ST　CS2　　　　　　　　TEMP　　　AMB

210.40	59.90	29.30	26.20	28.70	44.00
1/1	2/2	3/3	4/3	5/3	6/3
31.80	27.70				
7/1	8/4				

F.J.WEIGERT,J.D.ROBERTS
J AM CHEM SOC　　　　　　　92, 1347 (1970)

488　　　Q 000400　**3-TERT-BUTYLCYCLOHEXANONE**

```
        O
   6   ⫽
   C--C1
  /     \
5C       C2
  \     /
   C--C3
   4    \
       C(CH3)3
        7 8
```

FORMULA　C10H18O　　　　　　MOL WT　154.25
SOLVENT　C4H8O2
ORIG ST　CS2　　　　　　　　TEMP　　　AMB

208.70	43.00	48.90	26.50	26.00	40.70
1/1	2/3	3/2	5 4/3	4 5/3	6/3
32.30	27.20				
7/3	8/4				

F.J.WEIGERT,J.D.ROBERTS
J AM CHEM SOC　　　　　　　92, 1347 (1970)

489　　　Q 000400　**4-TERT-BUTYLCYCLOHEXANONE**

```
        O
       ⫽
   6C--C1
  /     \
5C       C2
  \     /
   4C--C3
 8  /
(CH3)3C7
```

FORMULA　C10H18O　　　　　　MOL WT　154.25
SOLVENT　C4H8O2
ORIG ST　CS2　　　　　　　　TEMP　　　AMB

| 209.00 | 41.10 | 27.70 | 46.80 | 32.50 | 27.70 |
| 1/1 | 2/3 | 3/3 | 4/2 | 7/1 | 8/4 |

F.J.WEIGERT,J.D.ROBERTS
J AM CHEM SOC　　　　　　　92, 1347 (1970)

490　　　Q 000400　**CIS-3,4-DIMETHYLCYCLOHEXANONE**

```
        O
       ⫽
   6C--C1
  /     \
5C       C2
  \     /
   4C--C3
   |    |
  H3C  CH3
   8    7
```

FORMULA　C8H14O　　　　　　　MOL WT　126.20
SOLVENT　C4H8O2
ORIG ST　CS2　　　　　　　　TEMP　　　AMB

209.30	49.10	36.60	33.40	30.60	39.00
1/1	2/3	3/2	4/2	5/3	6/3
16.20	15.90				
8 7/4	7 8/4				

F.J.WEIGERT,J.D.ROBERTS
J AM CHEM SOC　　　　　　　92, 1347 (1970)

491 — Q 000400 TRANS-3,4-DIMETHYLCYCLOHEXANONE

```
              O
              ‖
         6C--C1
        /      \
     5C8CH3    C2
      \|      /
       4C--C3
          |
        7CH3
```

FORMULA	C8H14O			MOL WT	126.20
SOLVENT	C4H8O2				
ORIG ST	CS2			TEMP	AMB

209.10	46.90	37.70	41.10	34.70	39.90
1/1	2/3	3/2	4/2	5/3	6/3
20.20	18.90				
8 7/4	7 8/4				

F.J.WEIGERT,J.D.ROBERTS
J AM CHEM SOC   92, 1347 (1970)

492 — Q 000400 CIS-3,5-DIMETHYLCYCLOHEXANONE

```
              O
              ‖
         6C--C1
        /      \
     5C        C2
      |\      /
     H3C C--C3
      8  4  |
           7CH3
```

FORMULA	C8H14O			MOL WT	126.20
SOLVENT	C4H8O2				
ORIG ST	CS2			TEMP	AMB

207.90	49.10	33.10	42.70	22.30
1/1	2/3	3/2	4/3	7/4

F.J.WEIGERT,J.D.ROBERTS
J AM CHEM SOC   92, 1347 (1970)

493 — Q 000400 TRANS-3,5-DIMETHYLCYCLOHEXANONE

```
               O
       8  6    ‖
     H3C C--C1
      |/      \
     5C        C2
       \      /
        4C--C3
           |
         7CH3
```

FORMULA	C8H14O			MOL WT	126.20
SOLVENT	C4H8O2				
ORIG ST	CS2			TEMP	AMB

208.30	48.50	29.50	39.60	20.80
1/1	2/3	3/2	4/3	7/4

F.J.WEIGERT,J.D.ROBERTS
J AM CHEM SOC   92, 1347 (1970)

494 — Q 000400 4,4-DIMETHYLCYCLOHEXANONE

```
              O
              ‖
         6C--C1
        /      \
     5C        C2
      \  4    /
     H3C-C--C3
      8   |
        7CH3
```

FORMULA	C8H14O			MOL WT	126.20
SOLVENT	C4H8O2				
ORIG ST	CS2			TEMP	AMB

209.10	37.70	39.20	29.90	27.50
1/1	2/3	3/3	4/1	7/4

F.J.WEIGERT,J.D.ROBERTS
J AM CHEM SOC   92, 1347 (1970)

495 — Q 000400 2-ACETOXYCYCLOHEXANONE

```
          O O
      6   ‖ ‖
    C--C1   C-CH3
   /    \  /7 8
  5C    2C-O
   \    /
    C--C
    4    3
```

FORMULA	C8H12O3			MOL WT	156.18
SOLVENT	C6D6				
ORIG ST	TMS			TEMP	AMB

202.60	76.80	32.90	23.50	26.80	40.30
1/1	2/2	3/3	4/3	5/3	6/3
169.10	20.20				
7/1	8/4				

J.B.STOTHERS,I.S.Y.WANG,D.OUCHI,E.W.WARNHOFF
J AM CHEM SOC   93, 6702 (1971)

496　　　Q 000400　METHOXYCARBONYLCYCLOHEXANE

```
      3 2
     C-C    O
    /   \1 7/
  4C      C-C
    \   /   \ 8
     C-C     O-CH3
     5 6
```

FORMULA	C8H14O2			MOL WT	314.12
SOLVENT	C8H14O2/CDCL3				AMB
ORIG ST	C4H12SI			TEMP	

43.10	29.00	25.40	25.80	25.40	29.00
1/2	2/3	3/3	4/3	5/3	6/3
176.30	51.20				
7/1	8/4				

M.GORDON,S.H.GROVER,J.B.STOTHERS
CAN J CHEM　　　　　　　　　　51, 2092 (1973)

497　　　Q 000400　1-METHOXYCARBONYL-1-METHYLCYCLOHEXANE

```
    3 2    7
   C-C    CH3
  /   \1/
 4C     C    O
  \   / \8/
   C-C   C
   5 6    \ 9
          O-CH3
```

FORMULA	C9H16O2			MOL WT	156.23
SOLVENT	C9H16O2/CDCL3				
ORIG ST	C4H12SI			TEMP	AMB

43.10	35.50	23.20	25.70	23.20	35.50
1/1	2/3	3/3	4/3	5/3	6/3
26.30	178.00	51.40			
7/4	8/1	9/4			

M.GORDON,S.H.GROVER,J.B.STOTHERS
CAN J CHEM　　　　　　　　　　51, 2092 (1973)

498　　　Q 000400　CIS-4-TERT-BUTYL-1-METHOXYCARBONYLCYCLOHEXANE

```
 10        3 2
 CH3      C-C    O
 11 \9 4/   \1 7/
 CH3-C-C     C-C
  12 /   \   /   \ 8
 CH3      C-C    O-CH3
          5 6
```

FORMULA	C12H22O2			MOL WT	198.31
SOLVENT	C12H22O2/CDCL3				
ORIG ST	C4H12SI			TEMP	AMB

38.90	28.00	23.80	47.90	23.80	28.00
1/2	2/3	3/3	4/2	5/3	6/3
175.40	51.20	32.40	27.40	27.40	27.40
7/1	8/4	9/1	10/4	11/4	12/4

M.GORDON,S.H.GROVER,J.B.STOTHERS
CAN J CHEM　　　　　　　　　　51, 2092 (1973)

499　　　Q 000400　TRANS-4-TERT-BUTYL-1-METHOXYCARBONYLCYCLOHEXANE

```
 10        3 2
 CH3      C-C    O
 11 \9 4/   \1 7/
 CH3-C-C     C-C
 12 /   \   /   \ 8
 CH3      C-C    O-CH3
          5 6
```

FORMULA	C12H22O2			MOL WT	198.31
SOLVENT	C12H22O2/CDCL3				
ORIG ST	C4H12SI			TEMP	AMB

43.40	29.50	26.60	47.30	26.60	29.50
1/2	2/3	3/3	4/2	5/3	6/3
176.40	51.20	32.30	27.40	27.40	27.40
7/1	8/4	9/1	10/4	11/4	12/4

M.GORDON,S.H.GROVER,J.B.STOTHERS
CAN J CHEM　　　　　　　　　　51, 2092 (1973)

500　　　Q 000400　1-METHYL-CIS-4-TERT-BUTYL-1-METHOXYCARBONYL-
　　　　　　　　　　　　　CYCLOHEXANE

```
         3 2
 CH3    C-C    CH3
   \9 4/    \1/
 CH3-C-C     C    O
  /   \   / \7/
 CH3    C-C   C
        5 6    \ 8
               O-CH3
```

FORMULA	C13H24O2			MOL WT	212.34
SOLVENT	C13H24O2/CDCL3				
ORIG ST	C4H12SI			TEMP	AMB

43.30	36.40	24.80	47.50	24.80	36.40
1/1	2/3	3/3	4/2	5/3	6/3
177.60	51.30	32.20	28.30	27.40	
7/1	8/4	9/1			

M.GORDON,S.H.GROVER,J.B.STOTHERS
CAN J CHEM　　　　　　　　　　51, 2092 (1973)

501   Q 000500 CYCLOHEPTANE

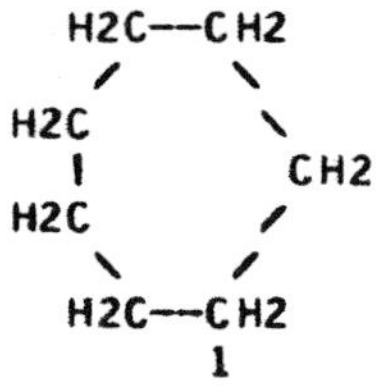

```
    H2C--CH2
   /        \
 H2C         \
  |          CH2
 H2C         /
   \        /
    H2C--CH2
        1
```

FORMULA   C7H14
SOLVENT   C7H14
ORIG ST   CS2

MOL WT   98.19

TEMP   AMB

28.20
1/3

J.J.BURKE,P.C.LAUTERBUR
J AM CHEM SOC

86, 1870 (1964)

---

502   Q 000500 CYCLOOCTANE

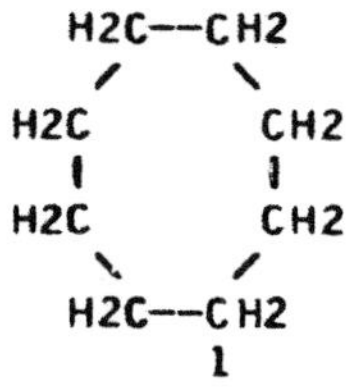

```
    H2C--CH2
   /        \
 H2C         CH2
  |           |
 H2C         CH2
   \        /
    H2C--CH2
        1
```

FORMULA   C8H16
SOLVENT   C8H16
ORIG ST   CS2

MOL WT   112.22

TEMP   AMB

26.60
1/3

J.J.BURKE,P.C.LAUTERBUR
J AM CHEM SOC

86, 1870 (1964)

---

503   Q 000500 CYCLONONANE

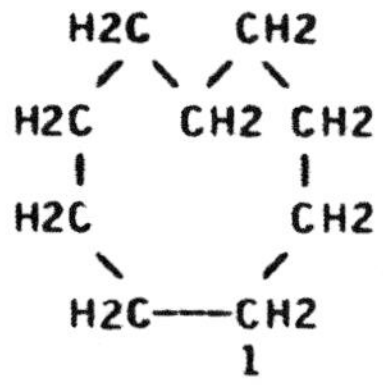

```
   H2C   CH2
  /  \  /  \
H2C  CH2 CH2
 |         |
H2C       CH2
  \       /
   H2C---CH2
        1
```

FORMULA   C9H18
SOLVENT   C9H18
ORIG ST   CS2

MOL WT   126.24

TEMP   AMB

25.80
1/3

J.J.BURKE,P.C.LAUTERBUR
J AM CHEM SOC

86, 1870 (1964)

---

504   Q 000500 CYCLODECANE

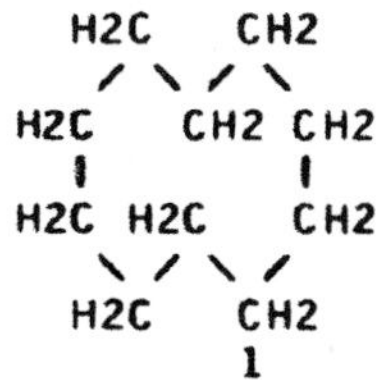

```
   H2C   CH2
  /  \  /  \
H2C  CH2 CH2
 |        |
H2C H2C  CH2
  \  / \ /
   H2C  CH2
        1
```

FORMULA   C10H20
SOLVENT   C10H20
ORIG ST   CS2

MOL WT   140.27

TEMP   AMB

25.00
1/3

J.J.BURKE,P.C.LAUTERBUR
J AM CHEM SOC

86, 1870 (1964)

---

505   Q 000500 CYCLOHEPTENE

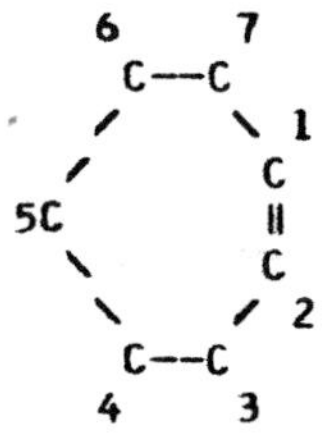

```
   6    7
    C--C
   /    \ 1
  /      C
 /       ||
5C       C
  \     / 2
   C--C
   4   3
```

FORMULA   C7H12
SOLVENT   C6H12
ORIG ST   CS2

MOL WT   96.17

TEMP   AMB

131.50   28.40   26.80   31.50
1/2   3/3   4/3   5/3

D.E.DORMAN,M.JAUTELAT,J.D.ROBERTS
J ORG CHEM

36, 2757 (1971)

506   Q 000500   CIS–CYCLOOCTENE

```
    4           7
    C           C
   /  \       /  \
 3C    5C---C6    C8
   \            /
    2C======C1
   /           \
  H             H
```

FORMULA	C8H14		MOL WT	110.20
SOLVENT	C6H12			
ORIG ST	CS2		TEMP	AMB

129.20	24.80	25.80	28.60
1/2	3/3	4/3	5/3

D.E.DORMAN,M.JAUTELAT,J.D.ROBERTS
J ORG CHEM   36, 2757 (1971)

---

507   Q 000500   TRANS–CYCLOOCTENE

```
        7C
       /  \
  H  6C    C8
   \  |    /
    2C===C1
   /  |   \
 3C   C5   H
   \  /
    C4
```

FORMULA	C8H14		MOL WT	110.20
SOLVENT	C6H12			
ORIG ST	CS2		TEMP	AMB

132.80	34.30	28.70
1/2	3,4/3	5/3

D.E.DORMAN,M.JAUTELAT,J.D.ROBERTS
J ORG CHEM   36, 2757 (1971)

---

508   Q 000500   CYCLOHEPTATRIENE

```
    2  1
    C=C
   /    \
 3C      \
  ||      C7
 4C      /
   \    /
    C=C
    5  6
```

FORMULA	C7H8		MOL WT	92.14
SOLVENT	CCL4			
ORIG ST	TMS		TEMP	AMB

120.40	126.80	131.00	28.10
1/2	2/2	3/2	7/3

H.GUENTHER,T.KELLER
CHEM BER   103, 3231 (1970)

---

509   Q 000500   1,6–DIMETHYLCYCLOHEPTATRIENE

```
      8CH3
    2 1/
    C=C
   /    \
 3C      \
  ||      C7
 4C      /
   \    /
    C=C
    5 6\
       9CH3
```

FORMULA	C9H12		MOL WT	120.20
SOLVENT	CCL4			
ORIG ST	TMS		TEMP	AMB

130.60	122.20	128.80	40.10	24.60
1/1	2/2	3/2	7/3	8/4

H.GUENTHER,T.KELLER
CHEM BER   103, 3231 (1970)

---

510   Q 000500   7–TERT–BUTYLCYCLOHEPTATRIENE

```
    2  1
    C=C
   /    \
 3C      \  8 9
  ||      7C-C(CH3)3
 4C      /
   \    /
    C=C
    5  6
```

FORMULA	C11H16		MOL WT	148.25
SOLVENT	CCL4			
ORIG ST	TMS		TEMP	AMB

123.00	124.60	130.80	49.40	31.10	27.30
1–6/2	1–6/2	1–6/2	7/2	8/1	9/4

H.GUENTHER,T.KELLER
CHEM BER   103, 3231 (1970)

511   Q 000500   3,4—BENZO—CYCLOHEPTATRIENE

```
     8    2 1
     C   C=C
    / \ / / \
  9C   C3    \
   |    H      C7
  10C   C4    /
    \\ / \  /
     C   C=C
    11   5 6
```

FORMULA C11H10   MOL WT   142.20
SOLVENT CCL4
ORIG ST TMS   TEMP   AMB

125.90   127.70   130.30   130.80   137.20   26.60
                                      3/1   7/3

H.GUENTHER,T.KELLER
CHEM BER   103, 3231 (1970)

---

512   Q 000500 CYCLOHEPTANOL

```
    3 2
    C—C
   /    \
  4C      \1
   |       C—OH
  5C      /
    \    /
     C—C
     6 7
```

FORMULA C7H14O   MOL WT   114.19
SOLVENT C7H14O
ORIG ST CS2   TEMP   AMB

72.40   37.70   23.30   28.60
1/2   2/3   3/3   4/3

J.D.ROBERTS,F.J.WEIGERT,J.I.KROSCHWITZ,H.J.REICH
J AM CHEM SOC   92, 1338 (1970)

---

513   Q 000500 CYCLOOCTANOL

```
    3 2
    C—C
   /    \1
  4C      C—OH
   |      |
  5C      C 8
    \    /
     C—C
     6 7
```

FORMULA C8H16O   MOL WT   128.22
SOLVENT C8H16O
ORIG ST CS2   TEMP   AMB

71.30   34.70   23.00   25.50   27.80
1/2   2/3   3/3   4/3   5/3

J.D.ROBERTS,F.J.WEIGERT,J.I.KROSCHWITZ,H.J.REICH
J AM CHEM SOC   92, 1338 (1970)

---

514   Q 000500 CYCLOHEPTANONE

```
   6    7
   C——C   O
  /     \ //
 /       C1
5C       |
 \       C
  \    / 2
   C——C
   4    3
```

FORMULA C7H12O   MOL WT   112.17
SOLVENT C4H8O2
ORIG ST CS2   TEMP   AMB

211.40   42.40   29.40   23.20
1/1   2/3   3/3   4/3

F.J.WEIGERT,J.D.ROBERTS
J AM CHEM SOC   92, 1347 (1970)

---

515   Q 000500 CYCLOOCTANONE

```
   7    8
   C——C   O
  6/    \ //
  C       C1
  |       |
  C       C
 5 \    / 2
   C——C
   4    3
```

FORMULA C8H14O   MOL WT   126.20
SOLVENT C4H8O2
ORIG ST CS2   TEMP   AMB

215.60   40.90   26.50   24.80   24.00
1/1   2/3   3/3   4/3   5/3

F.J.WEIGERT,J.D.ROBERTS
J AM CHEM SOC   92, 1347 (1970)

516   Q 000500   CYCLODECANONE

```
    8   10
    C    C    O
 7 / \9/ \ //
   C    C    C1
   |         |
   C    C    C
 6 \ /4\ / 2
    C    C
    5    3
```

FORMULA	C10H18O			MOL WT	154.25
SOLVENT	C4H8O2				
ORIG ST	C S2			TEMP	AMB

| 212.10 | 41.00 | 24.30 | 24.20 | 22.60 | 24.40 |
| 1/1 | 2/3 | 3/3 | 4/3 | 5/3 | 6/3 |

F.J.WEIGERT,J.D.ROBERTS
J AM CHEM SOC   92, 1347 (1970)

---

517   Q 000600   QUADRICYCLENE

```
    3C----C2
   /|    |\
 4C----C----C1
   \| 7 |/
    5C----C6
```

FORMULA	C7H8		MOL WT	92.14
SOLVENT	C4H8O2			
ORIG ST	C S2		TEMP	AMB

| 22.90 | 14.70 | 31.90 |
| 1/2 | 2/2 | 7/3 |

J.B.GRUTZNER,M.JAUTELAT,J.B.DENCE,R.A.SMITH,
J.D.ROBERTS
J AM CHEM SOC   92, 7107 (1971)

---

518   Q 000600   TRICYCLENE

```
    3C----C2
   /     |\
 4C----C----C1
   \  7 |/
    5C----C6
```

FORMULA	C7H10		MOL WT	94.16
SOLVENT	C4H8O2			
ORIG ST	C S2		TEMP	AMB

| 9.60 | 32.90 | 29.40 |
| 1/2 | 3/3 | 4/2 |

J.B.GRUTZNER,M.JAUTELAT,J.B.DENCE,R.A.SMITH,
J.D.ROBERTS
J AM CHEM SOC   92, 7107 (1971)

---

519   Q 000600   NORBORNANE

```
    3C----C2
   /     \
 4C----C----C1
   \  7  /
    5C----C6
```

FORMULA	C7H12		MOL WT	96.17
SOLVENT	C4H8O2			
ORIG ST	C S2		TEMP	AMB

| 36.50 | 29.80 | 38.40 |
| 1/2 | 2/3 | 7/3 |

J.B.GRUTZNER,M.JAUTELAT,J.B.DENCE,R.A.SMITH,
J.D.ROBERTS
J AM CHEM SOC   92, 7107 (1971)

---

520   Q 000600   BICYCLO(2.2.2)OCTANE

```
   6  5
   C-C
  1/   \4
  C-C-C-C
   \   /
    C-C
    2  3
```

FORMULA	C8H14			MOL WT	110.20
SOLVENT	CCL4				
ORIG ST	C6H12			TEMP	AMB

| 23.55 | 25.65 | 25.65 | 23.55 | 25.65 | 25.65 |
| 1/2 | 2/3 | 3/3 | 4/2 | 5/3 | 6/3 |

G.E.MACIEL,H.C.DORN
J AM CHEM SOC   93, 1268 (1971)

521   Q 000600   1-METHYLNORBORNANE

```
    3C---C2
   /      \
 4C---C--C-CH3
   \  7 /1 8
    5C---C6
```

FORMULA	C8H14			MOL WT	110.20
SOLVENT	C4H8O2				
ORIG ST	CS2			TEMP	AMB

43.80	36.80	31.30	37.90	45.30	20.70
1/1	2/3	3/3	4/2	7/3	8/4

J.B.GRUTZNER,M.JAUTELAT,J.B.DENCE,R.A.SMITH,
J.D.ROBERTS
J AM CHEM SOC   92, 7107 (1971)

---

522   Q 000600   EXO-2-METHYLNORBORNANE

```
      8CH3
       |
    3C---C2
   /      \
 4C---C---C1
   \  7 /
    5C---C6
```

FORMULA	C8H14			MOL WT	110.20
SOLVENT	C4H8O2				
ORIG ST	CS2			TEMP	AMB

43.20	36.50	39.90	37.00	30.00	28.70
1/2	2/2	3/3	4/2	5/3	6/3
34.70	22.00				
7/3	8/4				

J.B.GRUTZNER,M.JAUTELAT,J.B.DENCE,R.A.SMITH,
J.D.ROBERTS
J AM CHEM SOC   92, 7107 (1971)

---

523   Q 000600   ENDO-2-METHYLNORBORNANE

```
      2 8
    3C---C-CH3
   /      \
 4C---C---C1
   \  7 /
    5C---C6
```

FORMULA	C8H14			MOL WT	110.20
SOLVENT	C4H8O2				
ORIG ST	CS2			TEMP	AMB

41.90	34.30	40.40	37.90	30.30	22.10
1/2	2/2	3/3	4/2	5/3	6/3
38.60	17.10				
7/3	8/4				

J.B.GRUTZNER,M.JAUTELAT,J.B.DENCE,R.A.SMITH,
J.D.ROBERTS
J AM CHEM SOC   92, 7107 (1971)

---

524   Q 000600   7-METHYLNORBORNANE

```
    3C---C2
   / 8CH3\
 4C---C---C1
   \  7 /
    5C---C6
```

FORMULA	C8H14			MOL WT	110.20
SOLVENT	C4H8O2				
ORIG ST	CS2			TEMP	AMB

40.70	26.90	40.70	30.70	44.00	12.40
1/2	2/3	4/2	5/3	7/2	8/4

J.B.GRUTZNER,M.JAUTELAT,J.B.DENCE,R.A.SMITH,
J.D.ROBERTS
J AM CHEM SOC   92, 7107 (1971)

---

525   Q 000600   NORBORNENE

```
    3C===C2
   /      \
 4C---C---C1
   \  7 /
    5C---C6
```

FORMULA	C7H10			MOL WT	94.16
SOLVENT	C4H8O2				
ORIG ST	CS2			TEMP	AMB

41.90	135.20	25.20	48.50
1/2	2/2	5/3	7/3

J.B.GRUTZNER,M.JAUTELAT,J.B.DENCE,R.A.SMITH,
J.D.ROBERTS
J AM CHEM SOC   92, 7107 (1971)

526　　　　　　　　Q 000600　1—METHYLNORBORNENE

```
3C===C2
  /      \
4C---C---C-CH3
  \ 7 /1 8
  5C---C6
```

FORMULA　C8H12　　　　　　　MOL WT　108.18
SOLVENT　C4H8O2
ORIG ST　CS2　　　　　　　　　TEMP　　　AMB

49.60	139.70	135.50	43.00	27.70	32.30
1/1	2/2	3/2	4/2	5/3	6/3
54.40	17.70				
7/3	8/4				

J.B.GRUTZNER,M.JAUTELAT,J.B.DENCE,R.A.SMITH,
J.D.ROBERTS
J AM CHEM SOC　　　　　　　92, 7107 (1971)

527　　　　　　　　Q 000600　EXO—5—METHYLNORBORNENE

```
3C===C2
  /      \
4C---C---C1
  \ 7 /
  5C----C6
  |
  8CH3
```

FORMULA　C8H12　　　　　　　MOL WT　108.18
SOLVENT　C4H8O2
ORIG ST　CS2　　　　　　　　　TEMP　　　AMB

42.40	136.90	135.90	48.40	32.70	34.70
1/2	2/2	3/2	4/2	5/2	6/3
44.70	21.40				
7/3	8/4				

J.B.GRUTZNER,M.JAUTELAT,J.B.DENCE,R.A.SMITH,
J.D.ROBERTS
J AM CHEM SOC　　　　　　　92, 7107 (1971)

528　　　　　　　　Q 000600　ENDO—5—METHYLNORBORNENE

```
3C===C2
  /      \
4C---C---C1
  \ 7 /
H3C-C---C6
  8   5
```

FORMULA　C8H12　　　　　　　MOL WT　108.18
SOLVENT　C4H8O2
ORIG ST　CS2　　　　　　　　　TEMP　　　AMB

43.30	136.90	132.20	47.50	32.70	33.90
1/2	2/2	3/2	4/2	5/2	6/3
50.20	19.20				
7/3	8/4				

J.B.GRUTZNER,M.JAUTELAT,J.B.DENCE,R.A.SMITH,
J.D.ROBERTS
J AM CHEM SOC　　　　　　　92, 7107 (1971)

529　　　　　　　　Q 000600　SYN—7—METHYLNORBORNENE

```
3C===C2
  / 8CH3\
4C---C---C1
  \ 7 /
  5C---C6
```

FORMULA　C8H12　　　　　　　MOL WT　108.18
SOLVENT　C4H8O2
ORIG ST　CS2　　　　　　　　　TEMP　　　AMB

47.50	132.10	25.60	54.40	12.20
1/2	2/2	5/3	7/3	8/4

J.B.GRUTZNER,M.JAUTELAT,J.B.DENCE,R.A.SMITH,
J.D.ROBERTS
J AM CHEM SOC　　　　　　　92, 7107 (1971)

530　　　　　　　　Q 000600　ANTI—7—METHYLNORBORNENE

```
3C===C2
  / 7 \
4C---C---C1
  \ 8CH3/
  5C---C6
```

FORMULA　C8H12　　　　　　　MOL WT　108.18
SOLVENT　C4H8O2
ORIG ST　CS2　　　　　　　　　TEMP　　　AMB

45.70	137.50	21.50	53.00	14.10
1/2	2/2	5/3	7/3	8/4

J.B.GRUTZNER,M.JAUTELAT,J.B.DENCE,R.A.SMITH,
J.D.ROBERTS
J AM CHEM SOC　　　　　　　92, 7107 (1971)

---

531   Q 000600   NORBORNADIENE

```
  3C===C2
   /      \
4C---C---C1
   \  7  /
  5C===C6
```

FORMULA	C7H8		MOL WT	92.14
SOLVENT	C4H8O2			
ORIG ST	CS2		TEMP	AMB

| 50.60 | 143.10 | 75.10 |
| 1/2 | 2/2 | 7/3 |

J.B.GRUTZNER,M.JAUTELAT,J.B.DENCE,R.A.SMITH,
J.D.ROBERTS
J AM CHEM SOC   92, 7107 (1971)

---

532   Q 000600   EXO-2-FLUORONORBORNANE

```
  6 5
  C-C
 / 7 \
1C--C--C4
 \     /
  2C-C3
   |
   F
```

FORMULA	C7H11F		MOL WT	114.16
SOLVENT	C7H11F/C4H8O2			
ORIG ST	CS2		TEMP	AMB

42.10	95.60	39.80	34.60	28.00	22.30
1/2	2/2	3/3	4/2	5/3	6/3
35.00					
7/3					

J.B.GRUTZNER,M.JAUTELAT,J.B.DENCE,R.A.SMITH,
J.D.ROBERTS
J AM CHEM SOC   92, 7107 (1970)

---

533   Q 000600   2,2-DIFLUORONORBORNANE

```
  6 5
  C-C
1/ 7 \
C--C--C4
 \2  /
F-C-C3
  |
  F
```

FORMULA	C7H10F2		MOL WT	132.15
SOLVENT	C7H10F2/C4H8O2			
ORIG ST	CS2		TEMP	AMB

44.90	131.10	42.70	36.20	27.40	20.80
1/2	2/1	3/3	4/2	5/3	6/3
36.90					
7/3					

J.B.GRUTZNER,M.JAUTELAT,J.B.DENCE,R.A.SMITH,
J.D.ROBERTS
J AM CHEM SOC   92, 7107 (1970)

---

534   Q 000600   1-METHYL-2,2-DIFLUORONORBORNANE

```
    6 5
    C-C
 8 1/ 7 \4
CH3-C--C--C
   \2  /
   F-C-C3
     |
     F
```

FORMULA	C8H12F2		MOL WT	146.18
SOLVENT	C8H12F2/C4H8O2			
ORIG ST	CS2		TEMP	AMB

48.70	130.20	43.30	35.30	29.60	28.80
1/1	2/1	3/3	4/2	5/3	6/3
43.90	12.20				
7/3	8/4				

J.B.GRUTZNER,M.JAUTELAT,J.B.DENCE,R.A.SMITH,
J.D.ROBERTS
J AM CHEM SOC   92, 7107 (1970)

---

535   Q 000600   EXO-3-METHYL-2,2-DIFLUORONORBORNANE

```
   6 5
   C-C
  / 7 \
1C--C--C4
  \2  /
 F-C-C3
   |  \8
   F   CH3
```

FORMULA	C8H12F2		MOL WT	146.18
SOLVENT	C8H12F2/C4H8O2			
ORIG ST	CS2		TEMP	AMB

44.90	130.90	46.80	43.60	28.60	21.00
1/2	2/1	3/2	4/2	5/3	6/3
34.20	11.90				
7/3	8/4				

J.B.GRUTZNER,M.JAUTELAT,J.B.DENCE,R.A.SMITH,
J.D.ROBERTS
J AM CHEM SOC   92, 7107 (1970)

536   Q 000600 ENDO-3-METHYL-2,2-DIFLUORONORBORNANE

```
    6 5
    C-C
   / 7 \
 1C--C--C4
   \2 /
 F-C-C3
   |  \8
   F   CH3
```

FORMULA	C8H12F2			MOL WT	146.18
SOLVENT	C8H12F2/C4H8O2				
ORIG ST	CS2			TEMP	AMB

44.00	129.30	45.60	41.20	20.10	20.90
1/2	2/1	3/2	4/2	5/3	6/3
36.00	9.00				
7/3	8/4				

J.B.GRUTZNER,M.JAUTELAT,J.B.DENCE,R.A.SMITH,
J.D.ROBERTS
J AM CHEM SOC   92, 7107 (1970)

537   Q 000600 EXO-5-METHYL-2,2-DIFLUORONORBORNANE

```
      8
      CH3
    6 5/
    C-C
   / 7 \
 1C--C--C4
   \2 /
 F-C-C3
   |
   F
```

FORMULA	C8H12F2			MOL WT	146.18
SOLVENT	C8H12F2/C4H8O2				
ORIG ST	CS2			TEMP	AMB

45.60	131.00	43.50	42.50	34.60	30.60
1/2	2/1	3/3	4/2	5/2	6/3
33.40	21.50				
7/3	8/4				

J.B.GRUTZNER,M.JAUTELAT,J.B.DENCE,R.A.SMITH,
J.D.ROBERTS
J AM CHEM SOC   92, 7107 (1970)

538   Q 000600 ENDO-5-METHYL-2,2-DIFLUORONORBORNANE

```
      8
      CH3
    6 5/
    C-C
   / 7 \
 1C--C--C4
   \2 /
 F-C-C3
   |
   F
```

FORMULA	C8H12F2			MOL WT	146.18
SOLVENT	C8H12F2/C4H8O2				
ORIG ST	CS2			TEMP	AMB

46.00	131.00	35.40	41.30	32.20	29.20
1/2	2/1	3/3	4/2	5/2	6/3
38.50	16.10				
7/3	8/4				

J.B.GRUTZNER,M.JAUTELAT,J.B.DENCE,R.A.SMITH,
J.D.ROBERTS
J AM CHEM SOC   92, 7107 (1970)

539   Q 000600 EXO-6-METHYL-2,2-DIFLUORONORBORNANE

```
    8CH3
    | 5
    6C-C
   / 7 \
 1C--C--C4
   \2 /
 F-C-C3
   |
   F
```

FORMULA	C8H12F2			MOL WT	146.18
SOLVENT	C8H12F2/C4H8O2				
ORIG ST	CS2			TEMP	AMB

51.40	131.00	41.90	36.50	37.80	27.10
1/2	2/1	3/3	4/2	5/3	6/2
33.40	20.50				
7/3	8/4				

J.B.GRUTZNER,M.JAUTELAT,J.B.DENCE,R.A.SMITH,
J.D.ROBERTS
J AM CHEM SOC   92, 7107 (1970)

540   Q 000600 ENDO-6-METHYL-2,2-DIFLUORONORBORNANE

```
    8
    CH3
    |
    6C-C5
   / 7 \
 1C--C--C4
   \2 /
 F-C-C3
   |
   F
```

FORMULA	C8H12F2			MOL WT	146.18
SOLVENT	C8H12F2/C4H8O2				
ORIG ST	CS2			TEMP	AMB

49.50	131.50	43.50	36.10	36.30	32.30
1/2	2/1	3/3	4/2	5/3	6/2
38.70	17.80				
7/3	8/4				

J.B.GRUTZNER,M.JAUTELAT,J.B.DENCE,R.A.SMITH,
J.D.ROBERTS
J AM CHEM SOC   92, 7107 (1970)

541   Q 000600   SYN-7-METHYL-2,2-DIFLUORONORBORNANE

```
      6 5
      C-C
     /  R  \
   1/   R   \
   C---C---C4
     \  7  /
      \2 /
      F-C-C3
    8    |
  R  -CH3   F
```

FORMULA	C8H12F2		MOL WT	146.18	
SOLVENT	C8H12F2/C4H8O2				AMB
ORIG ST	CS2		TEMP		

48.80	131.40	40.30	41.10	27.70	22.00
1/2	2/1	3/3	4/2	5/3	6/3
45.20	12.20				
7/2	8/4				

J.B.GRUTZNER,M.JAUTELAT,J.B.DENCE,R.A.SMITH,
J.D.ROBERTS
J AM CHEM SOC   92, 7107 (1970)

542   Q 000600   ANTI-7-METHYL-2,2-DIFLUORONORBORNANE

```
      6 5
      C-C
     /  R  \
    /   R   \
   1C---C---C4
     \  7  /
      \2 /
      F-C-C3
    8    |
  R  -CH3   F
```

FORMULA	C8H12F2		MOL WT	146.18	
SOLVENT	C8H12F2/C4H8O2				
ORIG ST	CS2		TEMP		AMB

49.10	130.60	44.10	40.10	24.50	17.90
1/2	2/1	3/3	4/2	5/3	6/3
42.10	11.50				
7/2	8/4				

J.B.GRUTZNER,M.JAUTELAT,J.B.DENCE,R.A.SMITH,
J.D.ROBERTS
J AM CHEM SOC   92, 7107 (1970)

543   Q 000600   EXO-2-HYDROXYNORBORNANE

```
   3     2
   C-----C-OH
  /       \
 4C---C---C1
   \  7  /
    C-----C
    5     6
```

FORMULA	C7H12O		MOL WT	112.17	
SOLVENT	C4H8O2				
ORIG ST	CS2		TEMP		AMB

44.20	74.10	42.10	35.50	28.50	24.60
1/2	2/2	3/3	4/2	5/3	6/3
34.30					
7/3					

J.B.GRUTZNER,M.JAUTELAT,J.B.DENCE,R.A.SMITH,
J.D.ROBERTS
J AM CHEM SOC   92, 7107 (1970)

544   Q 000600   ENDO-2-HYDROXYNORBORNANE

```
          OH
   3     2/
   C-----C
  /       \
 4C---C---C1
   \  7  /
    C-----C
    5     6
```

FORMULA	C7H12O		MOL WT	112.17	
SOLVENT	C4H8O2				
ORIG ST	CS2		TEMP		AMB

42.80	72.20	39.30	37.40	30.00	20.10
1/2	2/2	3/3	4/2	5/3	6/3
37.50					
7/3					

J.B.GRUTZNER,M.JAUTELAT,J.B.DENCE,R.A.SMITH,
J.D.ROBERTS
J AM CHEM SOC   92, 7107 (1970)

545   Q 000600   1-METHYL-2-NORBORNANOL(ENDO)

```
          OH
   3     2/
   C-----C
  /       \
 4C---C---C-CH3
   \  7  /1 8
    C-----C
    5     6
```

FORMULA	C8H14O		MOL WT	126.20	
SOLVENT	C4H8O2				
ORIG ST	CS2		TEMP		AMB

47.90	76.80	40.80	37.10	31.50	27.10
1/1	2/2	3/3	4/2	5/3	6/3
44.60	18.50				
7/3	8/4				

J.B.GRUTZNER,M.JAUTELAT,J.B.DENCE,R.A.SMITH,
J.D.ROBERTS
J AM CHEM SOC   92, 7107 (1970)

546   Q 000600 EXO—3—METHYL—2—NORBORNANOL(ENDO)

```
  H3C        OH
   8\3    2/
     C———C
    /      \
 4C———C———C 1
    \  7  /
     C———C
     5   6
```

FORMULA	C8H140			MOL WT	126.20
SOLVENT	C4H802				
ORIG ST	CS2			TEMP	AMB
43.50	45.70	44.10	30.20	19.90	34.30
1/2	3/2	4/2	5/3	6/3	7/3
19.50					
8/4					

J.B.GRUTZNER,M.JAUTELAT,J.B.DENCE,R.A.SMITH,
J.D.ROBERTS
J AM CHEM SOC   92, 7107 (1970)

---

547   Q 000600 ENDO—3—METHYL—2—NORBORNANOL(ENDO)

```
  H3C        OH
   8\3    2/
     C———C
    /      \
 4C———C———C 1
    \  7  /
     C———C
     5   6
```

FORMULA	C8H140			MOL WT	126.20
SOLVENT	C4H802				
ORIG ST	CS2			TEMP	AMB
43.90	71.40	37.10	42.60	21.90	19.80
1/2	2/2	3/2	4/2	5/3	6/3
36.80	10.20				
7/3	8/4				

J.B.GRUTZNER,M.JAUTELAT,J.B.DENCE,R.A.SMITH,
J.D.ROBERTS
J AM CHEM SOC   92, 7107 (1970)

---

548   Q 000600 1—METHYL—2—NORBORNANOL(EXO)

```
            OH
    3    2/
     C———C
    /      \
 4C———C———C—CH3
    \  7  /1 8
     C———C
     5   6
```

FORMULA	C8H140			MOL WT	126.20
SOLVENT	C4H802				
ORIG ST	CS2			TEMP	AMB
47.60	76.60	43.50	36.10	30.60	33.40
1/1	2/2	3/3	4/2	5/3	6/3
40.30	16.30				
7/3	8/4				

J.B.GRUTZNER,M.JAUTELAT,J.B.DENCE,R.A.SMITH,
J.D.ROBERTS
J AM CHEM SOC   92, 7107 (1970)

---

549   Q 000600 EXO—3—METHYL—2—NORBORNANOL(EXO)

```
  H3C        OH
   8\3    2/
     C———C
    /      \
 4C———C———C 1
    \  7  /
     C———C
     5   6
```

FORMULA	C8H140			MOL WT	126.20
SOLVENT	C4H802				
ORIG ST	CS2			TEMP	AMB
45.10	43.50	43.30	29.40	24.70	31.90
1/2	3/2	4/2	5/3	6/3	7/3
19.60					
8/4					

J.B.GRUTZNER,M.JAUTELAT,J.B.DENCE,R.A.SMITH,
J.D.ROBERTS
J AM CHEM SOC   92, 7107 (1970)

---

550   Q 000600 ENDO—3—METHYL—2—NORBORNANOL(EXO)

```
  H3C        OH
   8\3    2/
     C———C
    /      \
 4C———C———C 1
    \  7  /
     C———C
     5   6
```

FORMULA	C8H140			MOL WT	126.20
SOLVENT	C4H802				
ORIG ST	CS2			TEMP	AMB
45.60	46.40	41.10	21.20	25.20	37.00
1/2	3/2	4/2	5/3	6/3	7/3
14.60					
8/4					

J.B.GRUTZNER,M.JAUTELAT,J.B.DENCE,R.A.SMITH,
J.D.ROBERTS
J AM CHEM SOC   92, 7107 (1970)

551   Q 000600 EXO—2—AMINONORBORNANE

```
  NH2
   I  3
  2C—C
  1/ 7 \
  C——C——C4
   \    /
    C—C
    6  5
```

FORMULA	C7H13N			MOL WT	111.19
SOLVENT	C7H13N				
ORIG ST	C6H6			TEMP	AMB

45.40	55.10	42.20	36.10	28.60	26.70
1/2	2/2	3/3	4/2	5/3	6/3
34.00					
7/3					

W.J.HORSLEY,H.STERNLICHT
J AM CHEM SOC   90, 3738 (1968)

---

552   Q 000600 ENDO—2—AMINONORBORNANE

```
  NH2
   I  3
  2C—C
  / 7 \
 1C——C——C4
   \    /
    C—C
    6  5
```

FORMULA	C7H13N			MOL WT	111.19
SOLVENT	C7H13N				
ORIG ST	C6H6			TEMP	AMB

43.30	53.10	40.30	37.70	30.40	20.30
1/2	2/2	3/3	4/2	5/3	6/3
38.70					
7/3					

W.J.HORSLEY,H.STERNLICHT
J AM CHEM SOC   90, 3738 (1968)

---

553   Q 000600 2—NORBORNANONE

```
       O
  3    //
  C———C2
  / 7 \
 4C———C——C1
   \    /
    C———C
    5    6
```

FORMULA	C7H10O			MOL WT	110.16
SOLVENT	CDCL3				
ORIG ST	TMS			TEMP	298

49.75	216.75	45.10	35.40	27.30	24.15
1/2	2/1	3/3	4/2	5/3	6/3
37.65					
7/3					

E.BREITMAIER,K.H.SPOHN
UNPUBLISHED   (1973)

---

554   Q 000600 1—METHYL—2—NORBORNANONE

```
       O
  3    2//
  C———C
  / 7 \1 8
 4C———C——C—CH3
   \    /
    C———C
    5    6
```

FORMULA	C8H12O			MOL WT	124.18
SOLVENT	C4H8O2				
ORIG ST	CS2			TEMP	AMB

53.30	215.90	45.20	34.40	29.00	31.50
1/1	2/1	3/3	4/2	5/3	6/3
43.90	13.70				
7/2	8/4				

J.B.GRUTZNER,M.JAUTELAT,J.B.DENCE,R.A.SMITH,
J.D.ROBERTS
J AM CHEM SOC   92, 7107 (1970)

---

555   Q 000600 EXO—3—METHYL—2—NORBORNANONE

```
 8CH3   O
 3 I    2//
  C——C
  / 7 \
 4C———C———C1
   \    /
    C——C
    5    6
```

FORMULA	C8H12O			MOL WT	124.18
SOLVENT	C4H8O2				
ORIG ST	CS2			TEMP	AMB

49.30	217.60	47.90	41.60	28.10	23.60
1/2	2/1	3/2	4/2	5/3	6/3
34.10	13.80				
7/3	8/4				

J.B.GRUTZNER,M.JAUTELAT,J.B.DENCE,R.A.SMITH,
J.D.ROBERTS
J AM CHEM SOC   92, 7107 (1970)

556　　　　Q 000600　ENDO—3—METHYL—2—NORBORNANONE

```
              O
  8  3     2//
 H3C-C----C
    /  7  \
  4C---C---C1
    \     /
     C---C
    5     6
```

FORMULA	C8H12O			MOL WT	124.18
SOLVENT	C4H8O2				
ORIG ST	C S2			TEMP	AMB

50.10	217.20	48.00	40.60	20.90	25.30
1/2	2/1	3/2	4/2	5/3	6/3
37.00	10.40				
7/3	8/4				

J.B.GRUTZNER,M.JAUTELAT,J.B.DENCE,R.A.SMITH,
J.D.ROBERTS
J AM CHEM SOC　　　　　92, 7107 (1970)

557　　　　Q 000600　EXO—5—METHYL—2—NORBORNANONE

```
     O
  3     2//
  C----C
  /  7  \
4C---C---C1
  \     /
 5C---C
  |     6
 8CH3
```

FORMULA	C8H12O			MOL WT	124.18
SOLVENT	C4H8O2				
ORIG ST	C S2			TEMP	AMB

50.40	215.20	45.10	42.00	33.30	34.60
1/2	2/1	3/3	4/2	5/2	6/3
33.90	21.70				
7/3	8/4				

J.B.GRUTZNER,M.JAUTELAT,J.B.DENCE,R.A.SMITH,
J.D.ROBERTS
J AM CHEM SOC　　　　　92, 7107 (1970)

558　　　　Q 000600　ENDO—5—METHYL—2—NORBORNANONE

```
     O
  3     2//
  C----C
  /  7  \
4C---C---C1
  \     /
H3C-C----C
 8  5     6
```

FORMULA	C8H12O			MOL WT	124.18
SOLVENT	C4H8O2				
ORIG ST	C S2			TEMP	AMB

51.10	214.60	38.40	40.60	32.70	33.20
1/2	2/1	3/3	4/2	5/2	6/3
39.00	16.90				
7/3	8/4				

J.B.GRUTZNER,M.JAUTELAT,J.B.DENCE,R.A.SMITH,
J.D.ROBERTS
J AM CHEM SOC　　　　　92, 7107 (1970)

559　　　　Q 000600　EXO—6—METHYL—2—NORBORNANONE

```
     O
  3     2//
  C----C
  /  7  \
4C---C---C1
  \     /
   C---C6
  5    |
     8CH3
```

FORMULA	C8H12O			MOL WT	124.18
SOLVENT	C4H8O2				
ORIG ST	C S2			TEMP	AMB

56.40	215.50	43.70	36.10	37.50	31.00
1/2	2/1	3/3	4/2	5/3	6/2
33.90	20.60				
7/3	8/4				

J.B.GRUTZNER,M.JAUTELAT,J.B.DENCE,R.A.SMITH
J.D.ROBERTS
J AM CHEM SOC　　　　　92, 7107 (1970)

560　　　　Q 000600　ENDO—6—METHYL—2—NORBORNANONE

```
     O
  3     2//
  C----C
  /  7  \
4C---C---C1
  \     /
   C---C-CH3
  5   6 8
```

FORMULA	C8H12O			MOL WT	124.18
SOLVENT	C4H8O2				
ORIG ST	C S2			TEMP	AMB

55.80	213.50	45.60	35.80	38.60	32.40
1/2	2/1	3/3	4/2	5/3	6/2
36.00	18.50				
7/3	8/4				

J.B.GRUTZNER,M.JAUTELAT,J.B.DENCE,R.A.SMITH,
J.D.ROBERTS
J AM CHEM SOC　　　　　92, 7107 (1970)

561   Q 000600   SYN—7—METHYL—2—NORBORNANONE

```
            O
   3      2//
   C---C
  / 8CH3\
4C---C---C1
  \  7  /
   C---C
  5     6
```

FORMULA	C8H12O			MOL WT	124.18
SOLVENT	C4H8O2				
ORIG ST	CS2			TEMP	AMB
54.90	215.60	40.00	39.70	28.80	24.20
1/2	2/1	3/3	4/2	5/3	6/3
43.60	12.60				
7/2	8/4				

J.B.GRUTZNER,M.JAUTELAT,J.B.DENCE,R.A.SMITH,
J.D.ROBERTS
J AM CHEM SOC   92, 7107 (1970)

562   Q 000600   ANTI—7—METHYL—2—NORBORNANONE

```
            O
   3      2//
   C---C
  /  7  \
4C---C---C1
  \H3C8 /
   C---C
  5     6
```

FORMULA	C8H12O			MOL WT	124.18
SOLVENT	C4H8O2				
ORIG ST	CS2			TEMP	AMB
54.00	214.80	47.00	39.90	24.60	21.00
1/2	2/1	3/3	4/2	5/3	6/3
42.50	11.80				
7/2	8/4				

J.B.GRUTZNER,M.JAUTELAT,J.B.DENCE,R.A.SMITH,
J.D.ROBERTS
J AM CHEM SOC   92, 7107 (1970)

563   Q 000600   2,3—BENZO—NORCARADIENE—CARBOXYLIC ACID

```
        12
        COOH
       1 /
  8C    C-C7
  //  \ /  \||
 9C    C2  C6
  |    ||   |
10C    C3  C5
  \\  / \  //
 11C     C4
```

FORMULA	C12H10O2			MOL WT	186.21
SOLVENT	CHCL3				
ORIG ST	TMS			TEMP	AMB
22.90	28.60	31.50	131.10	132.70	125.90
			2,3/1	2,3/1	
126.60	127.20	128.00	129.00	182.00	
				12/1	

H.GUENTHER,T.KELLER
CHEM BER   103, 3231 (1970)

564   Q 000600   1—FLUOROBICYCLO(2.2.2)OCTANE

```
   6 5
   C-C
  1/  \4
F-C-C-C-C
  \   /
   C-C
   2 3
```

FORMULA	C8H13F			MOL WT	128.19
SOLVENT	CCL4				
ORIG ST	C6H12			TEMP	AMB
92.00	30.85	26.95	23.80	26.95	30.85
1/1	2/3	3/3	4/2	5/3	6/3

G.E.MACIEL,H.C.DORN
J AM CHEM SOC   93, 1268 (1971)

565   Q 000600   1—CHLOROBICYCLO(2.2.2)OCTANE

```
    6 5
    C-C
   1/  \4
CL-C-C-C-C
   \   /
    C-C
    2 3
```

FORMULA	C8H13CL			MOL WT	144.65
SOLVENT	CCL4				
ORIG ST	C6H12			TEMP	AMB
56.80	35.80	27.80	22.90	27.80	35.80
1/1	2/3	3/3	4/2	5/3	6/3

G.E.MACIEL,H.C.DORN
J AM CHEM SOC   93, 1268 (1971)

566   Q 000600 1-BROMOBICYCLO(2.2.2)OCTANE

```
    6 5
    C-C
  1/   \4
BR-C-C-C-C
   \   /
    C-C
    2 3
```

FORMULA C8H 3BR   MOL WT 189.10
SOLVENT CCL4
ORIG ST C6H12   TEMP   AMB

62.45	37.15	28.70	22.35	28.70	37.15
1/1	2/3	3/3	4/2	5/3	6/3

G.E.MACIEL,H.C.DORN
J AM CHEM SOC   93, 1268 (1971)

567   Q 000600 1—METHOXYBICYCLO(2.2.2)OCTANE

```
       6 5
       C-C
     1/   \4
CH3O-C-C-C-C
      \   /
       C-C
       2 3
```

FORMULA C9H16O   MOL WT 140.23
SOLVENT CCL4
ORIG ST C6H12   TEMP   AMB

71.90	28.90	26.50	23.85	26.50	28.90
1/1	2/3	3/3	4/2	5/3	6/3

G.E.MACIEL,H.C.DORN
J AM CHEM SOC   93, 1268 (1971)

568   Q 000600 TRICYCLO(4,3,1,0)—DECADIENE-2,4

```
    2   9
    C   C
   ⁄ \ ⁄ \
3C  1C   \
 |  |\    \
 |  |  C10 C8
 |  1⁄   ⁄
4C  6C  ⁄
 \⁄ \ ⁄
  C5  C7
```

FORMULA C10H12   MOL WT 132.21
SOLVENT CCL4
ORIG ST TMS   TEMP   AMB

37.70	129.00	119.20	32.30	19.70	15.70
1/1	2/2	3/2	7/3	8/3	10/3

H.GUENTHER,T.KELLER
CHEM BER   103, 3231 (1970)

569   Q 000600 DICHLORO-TRICYCLO(4,3,1,0)—DECADIENE-(2,4)

```
    2   9
    C   C
   ⁄ \ ⁄ \
3C  1C   \
 |  |\    \
 |  | CCL2C8
 |  1⁄10 ⁄
4C  6C  ⁄
 \⁄ \ ⁄
  C5  C7
```

FORMULA C10H10CL2   MOL WT 201.10
SOLVENT CCL4
ORIG ST TMS   TEMP   AMB

49.40	123.00	124.30	35.70	25.40
1/1	2,3/2	2,3/2	7/3	8/3

H.GUENTHER,T.KELLER
CHEM BER   103, 3231 (1970)

570   Q 000600 DIBROMO-TRICYCLO(4,3,1,0)—DECADIENE-(2,4)

```
    2   9
    C   C
   ⁄ \ ⁄ \
3C  1C   \
 |  |\10  \
 |  | CBR2C8
 |  1⁄   ⁄
4C  6C  ⁄
 \⁄ \ ⁄
  C5  C7
```

FORMULA C10H10BR2   MOL WT 290.00
SOLVENT CCL4
ORIG ST TMS   TEMP   AMB

47.30	123.90	124.40	37.90	25.80	49.20
1/1	2,3/2	2,3/2	7/3	8/3	10/1

H.GUENTHER,T.KELLER
CHEM BER   103, 3231 (1970)

---

571   Q 000700   BENZENONIUM ION

```
    5   6
    C--C
  4// + \
  C   H   C
   \     /1
    C==C
    3   2
```

FORMULA   C6H7   MOL WT   79.12
SOLVENT   HF-SO2CLF-SBF5
ORIG ST   CS2   TEMP   195

144.50
1/-

G.A.OLAH,R.H.SCHLOSBERG,R.D.PORTER,Y.K.MO,
D.P.KELLY,G.D.MATESCU
J AM CHEM. SOC   94, 2034 (1972)

---

572   Q 000800   BENZENE

```
   5 6
   C-C
 4C   C1
   \ /
   C=C
   3 2
```

FORMULA   C6H6   MOL WT   78.11
SOLVENT   C6H6
ORIG ST   CS2   TEMP   AMB

127.50	127.50	127.50	127.50	127.50	127.50
1/2	2/2	3/2	4/2	5/2	6/2

P.C.LAUTERBUR
J AM CHEM SOC   83, 1838 (1961)

---

573   Q 000800   BENZENE

```
    6C
   // \
  5C    C1
  |     ||
  4C    C2
   \ /
    C3
```

FORMULA   C6H6   MOL WT   78.11
SOLVENT   C6H6
ORIG ST   TMS   TEMP   298

128.40
1/2

E.BREITMAIER,G.JUNG,W.VOELTER,L.POHL
UNPUBLISHED   (1972)

---

574   Q 000800   HEXADEUTERIOBENZENE

```
     D
    6C
  D // \ D
  5C    C1
  |     ||
  4C    C2
  D \ / D
    C3
     D
```

FORMULA   C6D6   MOL WT   84.15
SOLVENT   C6D6
ORIG ST   TMS   TEMP   298

127.85
1/3

E.BREITMAIER,G.JUNG,W.VOELTER,L.POHL
UNPUBLISHED   (1972)

---

575   Q 000800   TOLUENE

```
   6   7
   C   CH3
  // \ /
 5C   1C
 |    ||
 4C   C2
  \ /
   C
   3
```

FORMULA   C7H8   MOL WT   92.14
SOLVENT   CS2
ORIG ST   C6H6   TEMP   AMB

137.60	129.10	128.30	125.45
1/1	2/2	3/2	4/2

T.D.ALGER,D.M.GRANT,E.G.PAUL
J AM CHEM SOC   88, 5397 (1966)

576   Q 000800   TOLUENE

```
  5 6
  C-C
 ⁄⁄   ⟍1
4C     C-CH3
  ⟍  ⁄ 7
  C=C
  3 2
```

FORMULA	C7H8			MOL WT	92.14
SOLVENT	C7H8				
ORIG ST	C4H12SI			TEMP	280

137.70	129.30	128.50	125.60	128.50	129.30
1/1	2/2	3/2	4/2	5/2	6/2
21.30					
7/4					

D.LAUER,E.L.MOTELL,D.D.TRAFICANTE,G.E.MACIEL
J AM CHEM SOC   94, 5335 (1972)

577   Q 000800   TOLUENE

```
       7
  6C  CH3
 ⁄⁄ ⟍ ⁄
5C   C1
 |    ||
4C   C2
 ⟍ ⁄
  C3
```

FORMULA	C7H8			MOL WT	92.14
SOLVENT	C7H8				
ORIG ST	TMS			TEMP	298

136.70	128.20	127.40	124.50	20.30
1/1	2/2	3/2	4/2	7/4

E.BREITMAIER,G.JUNG,W.VOELTER,L.POHL
UNPUBLISHED   (1972)

578   Q 000800   OCTADEUTERIOTOLUENE

```
   D   7
  6C  CD3
 D ⁄⁄ ⟍ ⁄
 5C   C1
  |    ||
 4C   C2
 D ⟍ ⁄ D
   C3
    D
```

FORMULA	C7D8			MOL WT	100.19
SOLVENT	C7D8				
ORIG ST	TMS			TEMP	298

136.40	127.85	126.75	123.85	19.20
1/1	2/3	3/3	4/3	7/7

E.BREITMAIER,G.JUNG,W.VOELTER,L.POHL
UNPUBLISHED   (1972)

579   Q 000800   ORTHO-XYLENE

```
  5 6
  C-C
 ⁄⁄   ⟍1
4C     C-CH3
  ⟍  ⁄ 7
  C=C2
  3 |
   CH3
```

FORMULA	C8H10			MOL WT	106.17
SOLVENT	C8H10				
ORIG ST	CS2			TEMP	AMB

135.90	135.90	128.90	125.30	125.30	128.90
1/1	2/1	3/2	4/2	5/2	6/2
18.90					
7/4					

P.C.LAUTERBUR
J AM CHEM SOC   83, 1838 (1961)

580   Q 000800   PARA-XYLENE

```
     5 6
     C-C
    4⁄⁄   ⟍
H3C-C     C-CH3
    ⟍  ⁄1 7
    C=C
    3 2
```

FORMULA	C8H10			MOL WT	106.17
SOLVENT	C8H10				
ORIG ST	CS2			TEMP	AMB

134.50	128.00	128.00	134.50	128.00	123.00
1/1	2/2	3/2	4/1	5/2	6/2
20.40					
7/4					

P.C.LAUTERBUR
J AM CHEM SOC   83, 1838 (1961)

581   Q 000800   MESITYLENE

```
        CH3
        | 6
      5C-C
       /   \1
    4C       C-CH3
      \   /  7
      3C=C2
        |
        CH3
```

FORMULA	C9H12			MOL WT	120.20
SOLVENT	C9H12				
ORIG ST	CS2			TEMP	AMB

136.10	126.40	136.10	126.40	136.10	126.40
1/1	2/2	3/1	4/2	5/1	6/2
20.30					
7/4					

P.C.LAUTERBUR
J AM CHEM SOC   83, 1838 (1961)

582   Q 000800   DURENE

```
        CH3
        | 6
      5C-C
       /   \1
  H3C-C       C-CH3
     4\   /  7
       C=C2
      3  \
          CH3
```

FORMULA	C10H14			MOL WT	134.22
SOLVENT	C10H14				
ORIG ST	CS2			TEMP	AMB

132.90	132.90	130.50	132.90	132.90	
1/1	2/1	3/2	4/1	5/1	6/2
18.90					
7/4					

P.C.LAUTERBUR
J AM CHEM SOC   83, 1838 (1961)

583   Q 000600   HEXAMETHYLBENZENE

```
    H3C     CH3
      \5   /
       C-C6
       /   \1
  H3C-C       C-CH3
     4\   /  7
       C=C2
      /3  \
    H3C     CH3
```

FORMULA	C12H18			MOL WT	162.28
SOLVENT	C12H18				
ORIG ST	CS2			TEMP	AMB

132.10	132.10	132.10	132.10	132.10	132.10
1/1	2/1	3/1	4/1	5/1	6/1
17.60					
7/4					

P.C.LAUTERBUR
J AM CHEM SOC   83, 1838 (1961)

584   Q 000800   ETHYLBENZENE

```
    5 6
     C-C
     /   \1
   4C       C-CH2-CH3
     \   /  7    8
      C=C
      3 2
```

FORMULA	C8H10			MOL WT	106.17
SOLVENT	C8H10				
ORIG ST	C4H12SI			TEMP	280

144.10	128.00	128.50	125.90	128.50	128.00
1/1	2/2	3/2	4/2	5/2	6/2
29.20	15.80				
7/3	8/4				

D.LAUER,E.L.MOTELL,D.D.TRAFICANTE,G.E.MACIEL
J AM CHEM SOC   94, 5335 (1972)

585   Q 000800   ISOPROPYLBENZENE

```
    5 6      8
     C-C     CH3
     /   \  /
   4C       C-CH
     \   /1 7\
      C=C     CH3
      3 2
```

FORMULA	C9H12			MOL WT	120.20
SOLVENT	C9H12				
ORIG ST	C4H12SI			TEMP	280

148.60	126.50	128.50	126.00	128.50	126.50
1/1	2/2	3/2	4/2	5/2	6/2
34.40	24.10				
7/2	8/4				

D.LAUER,E.L.MOTELL,D.D.TRAFICANTE,G.E.MACIEL
J AM CHEM SOC   94, 5335 (1972)

586   Q 000800   TERT—BUTYLBENZENE

```
      5 6      8
      C-C     CH3
     ╱  ╲    ╱
   4C      C-C-CH3
     ╲  ╱1 7╲
      C=C     CH3
      3 2
```

FORMULA	C10H14			MOL WT	134.22
SOLVENT	C10H14				
ORIG ST	C4H12SI			TEMP	280

150.50	125.10	128.10	125.40	128.10	125.10
1/1	2/2	3/2	4/2	5/2	6/2
34.50	31.40				
7/1	8/4				

D.LAUER,E.L.MOTELL,D.D.TRAFICANTE,G.E.MACIEL
J AM CHEM SOC   94, 5335 (1972)

---

587   Q 000800   BIPHENYL

```
           2 3
   C-C     C-C
  ╱  ╲   ╱  ╲
 C    C-C1    C4
  ╲  ╱   ╲  ╱
   C=C     C=C
           6 5
```

FORMULA	C12H10		MOL WT	154.21
SOLVENT	CS2			
ORIG ST	C6H6		TEMP	AMB

141.50	127.35	128.95	127.50
1/1	2/2	3/2	4/2

T.D.ALGER,D.M.GRANT,E.G.PAUL
J AM CHEM SOC   88, 5397 (1966)

---

588   Q 000800   STYRENE

```
    5 6
    C-C
   ╱  ╲
 4C      C-CH=CH2
   ╲  ╱1 7 8
    C=C
    3 2
```

FORMULA	C8H8			MOL WT	104.15
SOLVENT	C8H8				
ORIG ST	CS2			TEMP	AMB

136.10	136.10	126.70	125.00	126.70	135.10
1/1	2/2	3/2	4/2	5/2	6/2
135.50	112.00				
7/2	8/3				

K.S.DHAMI,J.B.STOTHERS
CAN J CHEM   43, 510 (1965)

---

589   Q 000800   META—METHYLSTYRENE

```
    5 6
    C-C
   ╱  ╲
 4C      C-CH=CH2
   ╲  ╱1 8 9
   3C=C2
     ｜
     CH3
     7
```

FORMULA	C9H10			MOL WT	118.18
SOLVENT	C9H10				
ORIG ST	CS2			TEMP	AMB

136.20	127.20	136.20	127.20	127.20	122.50
1/1	2/2	3/1	4/2	5/2	6/2
20.00	136.10	111.40			
7/4	8/2	9/3			

K.S.DHAMI,J.B.STOTHERS
CANAD J CHEM   43, 510 (1965)

---

590   Q 000800   ORTHO—METHYLSTYRENE

```
    5 6
    C-C
   ╱  ╲1
 4C      C-CH=CH2
   ╲  ╱ 8 9
    C=C2
    3 ｜
      CH3
      7
```

FORMULA	C9H10			MOL WT	118.18
SOLVENT	C9H10				
ORIG ST	CS2			TEMP	AMB

133.40	134.30	127.40	125.00	125.00	127.40
1/1	2/1	3/1	4/2	5/2	6/2
18.50	135.20	113.40			
7/4	8/2	9/3			

K.S.DHAMI,J.B.STOTHERS
CANAD J CHEM   43, 510 (1965)

591   Q 000800 PARA—METHYLSTYRENE

```
                              FORMULA   C9H10                 MOL WT   118.18
       5 6                    SOLVENT   C9H10
       C—C                    ORIG ST   CS2                   TEMP       AMB
      ⁄⁄   ⁖
 H3C—C      C—CH=CH2          136.50   127.70   127.70   136.50   127.70   127.70
   7 4⟍   ⁄1 8  9              1/1      2/2      3/2      4/1      5/2      6/2
       C=C                     20.10   136.30   112.80
       3 2                     7/4      8/2      9/3
```

K.S.DHAMI,J.B.STOTHERS
CAN J CHEM   43, 510 (1965)

---

592   Q 000800 2,4—DIMETHYLSTYRENE

```
                              FORMULA   C10H12                MOL WT   132.21
       5 6                    SOLVENT   C10H12
       C—C                    ORIG ST   CS2                   TEMP       AMB
      4⁄⁄   ⟍1
 CH3—C      C—CH=CH2          133.80   133.80   129.80   133.80   125.00   129.80
   ⟍   ⁄ 8  9                  1/1      2/1      3/2      4/1      5/2      6/2
       C=C2                    19.60   134.40   112.10
       3 ⎮                     7/4      8/2      9/3
       CH3
       7
```

K.S.DHAMI,J.B.STOTHERS
CANAD J CHEM   43, 510 (1965)

---

593   Q 000800 2,5—DIMETHYLSTYRENE

```
       CH3                    FORMULA   C10H12                MOL WT   132.21
       ⎮ 6                    SOLVENT   C10H12
       5C—C                   ORIG ST   CS2                   TEMP       AMB
      ⁄⁄   ⟍1
      4C      C—CH=CH2        133.80   133.80   128.30   126.10   133.80   128.30
       ⟍   ⁄ 8  9              1/1      2/1      3/2      4/2      5/1      6/2
       C=C2                    19.00   133.70   112.50
       3 ⎮                     7/4      8/2      9/3
       CH3
       7
```

K.S.DHAMI,J.B.STOTHERS
CANAD J CHEM   43, 510 (1965)

---

594   Q 000800 2,6—DIMETHYLSTYRENE

```
       CH3                    FORMULA   C10H12                MOL WT   132.21
       5 ⎮                    SOLVENT   C10H12
       C—C6                   ORIG ST   CS2                   TEMP       AMB
      ⁄⁄   ⟍1
      4C      C—CH=CH2        135.70   134.00   127.10   127.10   127.10   134.00
       ⟍   ⁄ 8  9              1/1      2/1      3/2      4/2      5/2      6/1
       C=C2                    20.10   134.20   118.20
       3 ⎮                     7/4      8/2      9/3
       CH3
       7
```

K.S.DHAMI,J.B.STOTHERS
CANAD J CHEM   43, 510 (1965)

---

595   Q 000800 2,4,6—TRIMETHYLSTYRENE

```
       CH3                    FORMULA   C11H14                MOL WT   146.23
       5 ⎮                    SOLVENT   C11H14
       C—C6                   ORIG ST   CS2                   TEMP       AMB
      ⁄⁄   ⟍
 H3C—C      C—CH=CH2          134.00   134.00   128.50   134.00   128.50   134.00
   4⟍   ⁄1 8  9                1/1      2/1      3/2      4/1      5/2      6/1
       C=C2                    20.00   134.50   117.80
       3 ⎮                     7/4      8/2      9/3
       CH3
       7
```

K.S.DHAMI,J.B.STOTHERS
CANAD J CHEM   +3, 510 (1965)

596   Q 000400 2,3,5,6—TETRAMETHYLSTYRENE

H3C   CH3
  \   /
   5C—C6   FORMULA C12H16   MOL WT   160.26
   ‖   ‖   SOLVENT C12H16
  4C   C—CH=CH2   ORIG ST CS2   TEMP   AMB
   \   /1 9 10
   3C=C2   136.90   131.50   131.50   129.70   131.50   131.50
  /   \   1/1   2/1   3/1   4/2   5/1   6/1
H3C   CH3   19.40   15.20   133.90   118.30
  8   7   9/2   10/3

                   K.S.DHAMI,J.B.STOTHERS
                   CANAD J CHEM   43,   510 (1965)

---

597   Q 000800 2,4,6—TRIISOPROPYLSTYRENE

   CH3—CH—CH3   FORMULA C17H26   MOL WT   230.40
        5 | SOLVENT C17H26
CH3   C—C6   ORIG ST CS2   TEMP   AMB
  \   4‖   ‖1 7 8
  C—C   C—CH=CH2 132.90   144.90   119.20   144.90   119.20   144.90
  /   \3 2/   1/1   2/1   3/2   4/1   5/2   6/1
CH3   C=C   134.50   117.90   29.20   23.00   25.10
 11 | 10   7/2   8/3   9/3
   CH3—CH—CH3
        9
                   K.S.DHAMI,J.B.STOTHERS
                   CANAD J CHEM   43,   510 (1965)

---

598   Q 000800 ALPHA—METHYLSTYRENE

  5 6
  C—C   CH3   FORMULA C9H10   MOL WT   118.18
  ‖   ‖1 | SOLVENT C9H10
4C   C—C=CH2   ORIG ST CS2   TEMP   AMB
  \   / 7 8
   C=C   140.40   126.70   126.70   124.70   126.70   126.70
   3 2   1/1   2/2   3/2   4/2   5/2   6/2
                   141.90   111.20
                    7/1   8/3

                   K.S.DHAMI,J.B.STOTHERS
                   CANAD J CHEM   43,   510 (1965)

---

599   Q 000800 ALPHA—ETHYLSTYRENE

                   FORMULA C10H12   MOL WT   132.21
                   SOLVENT C10H12
  5 6   ORIG ST CS2   TEMP   AMB
  C—C   CH2—CH3
  ‖   ‖1 | 140.50   126.40   126.50   125.40   126.50   126.50
4C   C—C=CH2   1/1   2/2   3/2   4/2   5/2   6/2
  \   / 7 8   148.80   109.70
   C=C   7/1   8/3
   3 2
                   K.S.DHAMI,J.B.STOTHERS
                   CANAD J CHEM   43,   510 (1965)

---

600   Q 000900 FLUOROBENZENE

                   FORMULA C6H5F   MOL WT   96.11
  5 6   SOLVENT C6H5F
  C—C   ORIG ST C6H6   TEMP   AMB
  ‖   ‖
4C   C—F   162.50   113.10   128.30   123.00   128.30   113.10
  \   /1   1/1   2/2   3/2   4/2   5/2   6/2
   C=C
   3 2   H.SPIESECKE,W.G.SCHNEIDER
                   J CHEM PHYS   35,   731 (1961)

601   Q 000900 CHLOROBENZENE

```
                     FORMULA   C6H5CL              MOL WT   112.56
       5 6           SOLVENT   C6H5CL
       C-C           ORIG ST   C6H6                TEMP     AMB
      //   \\
    4C      C-CL     133.80  127.60  128.40  125.40  128.40  127.60
      \    /1         1/1     2/2     3/2     4/2     5/2     6/2
       C=C
       3 2           H.SPIESECKE,W.G.SCHNEIDER
                     J CHEM PHYS                  35,  731 (1961)
```

602   Q 000900 BROMOBENZENE

```
                     FORMULA   C6H5BR              MOL WT   157.01
       5 6           SOLVENT   C6H5BR
       C-C           ORIG ST   C6H6                TEMP     AMB
      //   \\
    4C      C-BR     122.00  130.70  129.60  126.40  129.60  130.70
      \    /1         1/1     2/2     3/2     4/2     5/2     6/2
       C=C
       3 2           H.SPIESECKE,W.G.SCHNEIDER
                     J CHEM PHYS                  35,  731 (1961)
```

603   Q 000900 BROMOBENZENE

```
                     FORMULA   C6H5BR              MOL WT   157.01
      6C    BR       SOLVENT   C6H5BR
     //  \  /        ORIG ST   TMS                 TEMP     298
    5C    C1
    |     ||         122.35  131.20  129.80  126.55
    4C    C2          1/1     2/2     3/2     4/2
     \\  /
      C3            E.BREITMAIER,G.JUNG,W.VOELTER,L.POHL
                    UNPUBLISHED                      (1972)
```

604   Q 000900 PENTADEUTERIOBROMOBENZENE

```
        D            FORMULA   C6D5BR              MOL WT   162.04
      6C    BR       SOLVENT   C6D5BR
    D //  \  /        ORIG ST   TMS                 TEMP     298
    5C    C1
    |     ||         122.05  130.85  129.15  126.00
    4C    C2          1/1     2/3     3/3     4/3
    D \\  / D
      C3            E.BREITMAIER,G.JUNG,W.VOELTER,L.POHL
        D           UNPUBLISHED                      (1972)
```

605   Q 000900 IODOBENZENE

```
                     FORMULA   C6H5I               MOL WT   204.01
       5 6           SOLVENT   C6H5I
       C-C           ORIG ST   C6H6                TEMP     AMB
      //   \\
    4C      C-J      95.10   137.30  130.00  127.00  130.00  137.30
      \    /1         1/1     2/2     3/2     4/2     5/2     6/2
       C=C
       3 2           H.SPIESECKE,W.G.SCHNEIDER
                     J CHEM PHYS                  35,  731 (1961)
```

606   Q 000900   META–DIFLUOROBENZENE

```
   5  6
   C–C
  ⫽   ⫶1
4C      C–F
   ⫶   ⫽
  3C=C2
   ⎮
   F
```

FORMULA   C6H4F2   MOL WT   114.10
SOLVENT   C6H4F2
ORIG ST   C6H6   TEMP   AMB

162.00	102.20	162.00	109.80	129.60	109.80
1/1	2/2	3/1	4/2	5/2	6/2

A.R.TARPLEY,J.H.GOLDSTEIN
J PHYS CHEM   76,   515 (1972)

---

607   Q 000900   META–DICHLOROBENZENE

```
   5  6
   C–C
  ⫽   ⫶1
4C      C–CL
   ⫶   ⫽
  3C=C2
   ⎮
   CL
```

FORMULA   C6H4CL2   MOL WT   147.00
SOLVENT   C6H4CL2
ORIG ST   C6H6   TEMP   AMB

133.80	127.40	133.80	125.80	129.70	125.80
1/1	2/2	3/1	4/2	5/2	6/2

A.R.TARPLEY,J.H.GOLDSTEIN
J PHYS CHEM   76,   515 (1972)

---

608   Q 000900   META–DIBROMOBENZENE

```
   5  6
   C–C
  ⫽   ⫶
4C      C–BR
   ⫶   ⫽1
  3C=C2
   ⎮
   BR
```

FORMULA   C6H4BR2   MOL WT   235.91
SOLVENT   C6H4BR2
ORIG ST   C6H6   TEMP   AMB

122.00	132.90	122.00	129.30	130.40	129.30
1/1	2/2	3/1	4/2	5/2	6/2

A.R.TARPLEY,J.H.GOLDSTEIN
J PHYS CHEM   76,   515 (1972)

---

609   Q 000900   META–DIIODOBENZENE

```
   5  6
   C–C
  ⫽   ⫶
4C      C–J
   ⫶   ⫽1
  3C=C2
   ⎮
   J
```

FORMULA   C6H4I2   MOL WT   329.91
SOLVENT   C6H4I2
ORIG ST   C6H6   TEMP   AMB

94.70	143.90	94.70	135.90	131.10	135.90
1/1	2/2	3/1	4/2	5/2	6/2

A.R.TARPLEY,J.H.GOLDSTEIN
J PHYS CHEM   76,   515 (1972)

---

610   Q 000900   ORTHO–DIFLUOROBENZENE

```
   5  6
   C–C
  ⫽   ⫶1
4C      C–F
   ⫶   ⫽
   C=C2
  3 ⎮
    F
```

FORMULA   C6H4F2   MOL WT   114.10
SOLVENT   C6H4F2
ORIG ST   C6H6   TEMP   AMB

149.20	149.20	115.90	123.50	123.50	115.90
1/1	2/1	3/2	4/2	5/2	6/2

A.R.TARPLEY,J.H.GOLDSTEIN
J PHYS CHEM   76,   515 (1972)

611 Q 000900 ORTHO—DICHLOROBENZENE

```
    5 6
    C—C
   ⁄    ⟍1
 4C      C—CL
   ⟍   ⁄
    C=C2
    3 |
      CL
```

FORMULA	C6H4CL2		MOL WT	147.00
SOLVENT	C6H4CL2			
ORIG ST	C6H6		TEMP	AMB

| 131.00 | 131.00 | 129.30 | 126.80 | 126.80 | 129.30 |
| 1/1 | 2/1 | 3/2 | 4/2 | 5/2 | 6/2 |

A.R.TARPLEY,J.H.GOLDSTEIN
J PHYS CHEM   76, 515 (1972)

612 Q 000900 ORTHO—DIBROMOBENZENE

```
    5 6
    C—C
   ⁄    ⟍1
 4C      C—BR
   ⟍   ⁄
    C=C2
      |
      BR
```

FORMULA	C6H4BR2		MOL WT	235.91
SOLVENT	C6H4BR2			
ORIG ST	C6H6		TEMP	AMB

| 123.50 | 123.50 | 132.70 | 127.70 | 127.70 | 132.70 |
| 1/1 | 2/1 | 3/2 | 4/2 | 5/2 | 6/2 |

A.R.TARPLEY,J.H.GOLDSTEIN
J PHYS CHEM   76, 515 (1972)

613 Q 000900 ORTHO—DIIODOBENZENE

```
    5 6
    C—C
   ⁄    ⟍1
 4C      C—J
   ⟍   ⁄
    C=C
    3 2⟍
        J
```

FORMULA	C6H4I2		MOL WT	329.91
SOLVENT	C6H4I2			
ORIG ST	C6H6		TEMP	AMB

| 107.50 | 107.50 | 138.50 | 128.50 | 128.50 | 138.50 |
| 1/1 | 2/1 | 3/2 | 4/2 | 5/2 | 6/2 |

A.R.TARPLEY,J.H.GOLDSTEIN
J PHYS CHEM   76, 515 (1972)

614 Q 000900 META—CHLOROSTYRENE

```
    5 6
    C—C
   ⁄    ⟍
 4C      C—CH=CH2
   ⟍   ⁄1 7  8
    3C=C2
      |
      CL
```

FORMULA	C8H7CL		MOL WT	138.60
SOLVENT	C8H7CL			
ORIG ST	CS2		TEMP	AMB

137.50	125.60	133.40	125.60	128.00	123.40
1/1	2/2	3/1	4/2	5/2	6/2
133.40	113.80				
7/2	8/3				

K.S.DHAMI,J.B.STOTHERS
CANAD J CHEM   43, 510 (1965)

615 Q 000900 ORTHO—CHLOROSTYRENE

```
    5 6
    C—C
   ⁄    ⟍1
 4C      C—CH=CH2
   ⟍   ⁄ 7  8
    C=C2
    3 |
      CL
```

FORMULA	C8H7CL		MOL WT	138.60
SOLVENT	C8H7CL			
ORIG ST	CS2		TEMP	AMB

133.90	131.30	128.30	126.50	126.50	128.30
1/1	2/1	3/2	4/2	5/2	6/2
134.30	114.80				
7/2	8/3				

K.S.DHAMI,J.B.STOTHERS
CANAD J CHEM   43, 510 (1965)

616   Q 000900   PARA—CHLOROSTYRENE

```
      5 6
      C-C
     ⫽   ⫺
CL-C      C-CH=CH2
  4⧵   ⁄1 7  8
      C=C
      3 2
```

FORMULA	C8H7CL			MOL WT	138.60
SOLVENT	C8H7CL				
ORIG ST	CS2			TEMP	AMB

136.30	127.80	127.80	133.20	127.80	127.80
1/1	2/2	3/2	4/1	5/2	6/2
135.50	113.60				
7/2	8/3				

K.S.DHAMI,J.B.STOTHERS
CANAD J CHEM   43, 510 (1965)

---

617   Q 000900   META—BROMOSTYRENE

```
      5 6
      C-C
     ⫽   ⫺
4C        C-CH=CH2
   ⧵   ⁄1 7  8
  3C=C2
   I
   BR
```

FORMULA	C8H7BR			MOL WT	183.05
SOLVENT	C8H7BR				
ORIG ST	CS2			TEMP	AMB

138.00	128.90	123.40	128.90	128.90	124.10
1/1	2/2	3/1	4/2	5/2	6/2
131.90	114.20				
7/2	8/3				

K.S.DHAMI,J.B.STOTHERS
CANAD J CHEM   43, 510 (1965)

---

618   Q 000900   ORTHO—BROMOSTYRENE

```
      5 6
      C-C
     ⫽   ⫺1
4C        C-CH=CH2
   ⧵   ⁄ 7  8
    C=C2
    3 I
      BR
```

FORMULA	C8H7BR			MOL WT	183.05
SOLVENT	C8H7BR				
ORIG ST	CS2			TEMP	AMB

136.30	122.40	131.70	127.50	127.50	127.50
1/1	2/1	3/2	4/2	5/2	6/2
136.30	116.00				
7/2	8/3				

K.S.DHAMI,J.B.STOTHERS
CANAD J CHEM   43, 510 (1965)

---

619   Q 000900   PARA—BROMOSTYRENE

```
      5 6
      C-C
     ⫽   ⫺
BR-C      C-CH=CH2
  4⧵   ⁄1 7  8
      C=C
      3 2
```

FORMULA	C8H7BR			MOL WT	183.05
SOLVENT	C8H7BR				
ORIG ST	CS2			TEMP	AMB

136.20	127.10	130.80	121.90	130.80	127.10
1/1	2/2	3/2	4/1	5/2	6/2
135.00	113.90				
7/2	8/3				

K.S.DHAMI,J.B.STOTHERS
CANAD J CHEM   43, 510 (1965)

---

620   Q 001000   NITROBENZENE

```
      5 6
      C-C
     ⫽   ⫺
4C        C-NO2
   ⧵   ⁄1
    C=C
    3 2
```

FORMULA	C6H5NO2			MOL WT	123.11
SOLVENT	C6H5NO2				
ORIG ST	C6H6			TEMP	AMB

| 147.00 | 122.10 | 128.20 | 133.40 | 128.20 | 122.10 |
| 1/1 | 2/2 | 3/2 | 4/2 | 5/2 | 6/2 |

H.SPIESECKE,W.G.SCHNEIDER
J CHEM PHYS   35, 731 (1961)

621 Q 001000 NITROBENZENE

```
    6C   NO2
   ∥ ╲ ╱
  5C   C1
  │    ‖
  4C   C2
   ╲ ╱
    C3
```

FORMULA	C6H5NO2			MOL WT	123.11
SOLVENT	C6H5N O2				
ORIG ST	TMS			TEMP	298

147.15	122.45	128.60	133.90
1/1	2/2	3/2	4/2

E.BREITMAIER,G.JUNG,W.VOELTER,L.POHL
UNPUBLISHED   (1972)

622 Q 001000 PENTADEUTERIONITROBENZENE

```
      D
    6C   NO2
 D ∥ ╲ ╱
  5C   C1
  │    ‖
  4C   C2
 D ╲ ╱ D
    C3
    D
```

FORMULA	C6D5NO2			MOL WT	128.14
SOLVENT	C6D5N O2				
ORIG ST	TMS			TEMP	298

147.05	121.90	127.95	133.35
1/1	2/3	3/3	4/3

E.BREITMAIER,G.JUNG,W.VOELTER,L.POHL
UNPUBLISHED   (1972)

623 Q 001000 META-NITROSTYRENE

```
   5  6
   C—C
  ∥    ╲
 4C     C—CH=CH2
   ╲   ╱1 7  8
   3C=C2
    │
    NO2
```

FORMULA	C8H7NO2				MOL WT	149.15
SOLVENT	C8H7NO2					
ORIG ST	CS2				TEMP	AMB

136.40	120.60	147.20	120.60	128.40	133.70
1/1	2/2	3/1	4/2	5/2	6/2
133.70	115.40				
7/2	8/3				

K.S.DHAMI,J.B.STOTHERS
CANAD J CHEM   43, 510 (1965)

624 Q 001000 PARA-NITROSTYRENE

```
    5  6
    C—C
   ∥    ╲
O2N—C     C—CH=CH2
   4╲   ╱1 7  8
    C=C
    3  2
```

FORMULA	C8H7NO2				MOL WT	149.15
SOLVENT	C4H8O2					
ORIG ST	CS2				TEMP	AMB

143.60	126.00	123.10	146.50	123.10	126.00
1/1	2/2	3/2	4/1	5/2	6/2
134.70	117.80				
7/2	8/3				

K.S.DHAMI,J.B.STOTHERS
CANAD J CHEM   43, 510 (1965)

625 Q 001200 ANILINE

```
    5  6
    C—C
   ∥    ╲
  4C     C—NH2
    ╲   ╱1
    C=C
    3  2
```

FORMULA	C6H7N				MOL WT	93.13
SOLVENT	C6H7N					
ORIG ST	C6H6				TEMP	AMB

146.60	115.00	128.70	117.90	128.70	115.00
1/1	2/2	3/2	4/2	5/2	6/2

H.SPIESECKE,W.G.SCHNEIDER
J CHEM PHYS   35,   731 (1961)

626   Q 001200   PARA–DIMETHYLAMINOSTYRENE

```
        5 6
H3C    C-C
   \   //  \\
    N-C      C-CH=CH2
   /   \   /1 8 9
H3C     C=C
 7      3 2
```

FORMULA	C10H13N			MOL WT	147.22
SOLVENT	C10H13N				
ORIG ST	CS2			TEMP	AMB

124.30	125.70	111.50	149.10	111.50	125.70
1/1	2/2	3/2	4/1	5/2	6/2
39.10	136.10	107.50			
7/4	8/2	9/3			

K.S.DHAMI,J.B.STOTHERS
CANAD J CHEM   43, 510 (1965)

---

627   Q 001800   PHENOL

```
   5 6
   C-C
  //   \\
4C       C-OH
  \     /1
   C=C
   3 2
```

FORMULA	C6H6O			MOL WT	94.11
SOLVENT	CHCL3				
ORIG ST	CS2			TEMP	AMB

155.10	115.70	130.10	121.40	130.10	115.70
1/1	2/2	3/2	4/2	5/2	6/2

P.C.LAUTERBUR
J AM CHEM SOC   83, 1846 (1961)

---

628   Q 001800   META–CRESOL

```
   5 6
   C-C
  //   \\
4C       C-OH
  \     /1
  3C=C2
   |
  CH3
   7
```

FORMULA	C7H8O			MOL WT	108.14
SOLVENT	C7H8O				
ORIG ST	CS2			TEMP	AMB

154.90	116.10	139.30	122.20	130.30	112.70
1/1	2/2	3/1	4/2	5/2	6/2
20.90					
7/4					

P.C.LAUTERBUR
J AM CHEM SOC   83, 1846 (1961)

---

629   Q 001800   ORTHO–CRESOL

```
   5 6
   C-C
  //   \\
4C       C-OH
  \     /1
   C=C2
   3 |
    CH3
    7
```

FORMULA	C7H8O			MOL WT	108.14
SOLVENT	C7H8O				
ORIG ST	CS2			TEMP	AMB

153.50	124.00	131.00	121.40	127.70	115.90
1/1	2/1	3/2	4/2	5/2	6/2
16.70					
7/4					

P.C.LAUTERBUR
J AM CHEM SOC   83, 1846 (1961)

---

630   Q 001800   PARA–CRESOL

```
    5 6
    C-C
   //   \\
H3C-C     C-OH
 7 4\    /1
    C=C
    3 2
```

FORMULA	C7H8O			MOL WT	108.14
SOLVENT	C7H8O				
ORIG ST	CS2			TEMP	AMB

152.60	115.30	130.20	130.50	130.20	115.30
1/1	2/2	3/2	4/1	5/2	6/2
20.60					
7/4					

P.C.LAUTERBUR
J AM CHEM SOC   83, 1846 (1961)

---

631   Q 001800   2,6-DIMETHYLPHENOL

```
        CH3
      5 |
       C-C6
   4C      C-OH
     \   /1
      C=C2
    3 |
      CH3
      7
```

FORMULA	C8H10O			MOL WT	122.17
SOLVENT	CHCL3				
ORIG ST	CS2			TEMP	AMB

152.30	123.60	128.80	120.60	128.80	123.60
1/1	2/1	3/2	4/2	5/2	6/1
15.40					
7/4					

P.C.LAUTERBUR
J AM CHEM SOC   83, 1846 (1961)

---

632   Q 001800   3,5-DIMETHYLPHENOL

```
        CH3
        |
      5C-C6
   4C      C-OH
     \   /1
      3C=C2
        |
        CH3
        7
```

FORMULA	C8H10O			MOL WT	122.17
SOLVENT	CHCL3				
ORIG ST	CS2			TEMP	AMB

154.50	112.80	138.90	121.90	138.90	112.80
1/1	2/2	3/1	4/2	5/1	6/2
20.40					
7/4					

P.C.LAUTERBUR
J AM CHEM SOC   83, 1846 (1961)

---

633   Q 002700   ANISOLE

```
     5 6
      C-C
   4C      C-OCH3
     \   /1 7
      C=C
     3 2
```

FORMULA	C7H8O			MOL WT	108.14
SOLVENT	C7H8O				
ORIG ST	CS2			TEMP	AMB

159.80	113.50	129.50	120.50	129.50	113.50
1/1	2/2	3/2	4/2	5/2	6/2
54.10					
7/4					

P.C.LAUTERBUR
J AM CHEM SOC   83, 1846 (1961)

---

634   Q 002700   PARA-METHOXYSTYRENE

```
        5 6
         C-C
  H3CO-C      C-CH=CH2
   7    \   /1 8  9
         C=C
        3 2
```

FORMULA	C9H10O			MOL WT	134.18
SOLVENT	C9H10O				
ORIG ST	CS2			TEMP	AMB

130.10	126.50	113.30	158.70	113.30	126.50
1/1	2/2	3/2	4/1	5/2	6/2
53.80	135.30	110.20			
7/4	8/2	9/3			

K.S.DHAMI,J.B.STOTHERS
CAN J CHEM   43, 510 (1965)

---

635   Q 003500   ACETOPHENONE

```
     5 6
      C-C    O
   4C      C-C-CH3
     \   / 7
      C=C
     3 2
```

FORMULA	C8H8O			MOL WT	120.15
SOLVENT	C8H8O				
ORIG ST	CS2			TEMP	AMB

136.30	128.10	128.10	131.30	128.10	128.10
1/1	2/2	3/2	4/2	5/2	6/2
195.70	24.60				
7/1	8/4				

K.S.DHAMI,J.B.STOTHERS
CAN J CHEM   43, 479 (1965)

636 Q 003500 META—METHYLACETOPHENONE

```
    9
   CH3
    | 2
   3C—C    O
   ∥    ∖1 ∥ 8
  4C      C—C—CH3
   ∖    ∕ 7
    C=C 6
    5
```

FORMULA C9H10O
SOLVENT C9H10O
ORIG ST CS2

MOL WT 134.18

TEMP AMB

136.60	127.00	136.60	132.20	127.00	124.20
1/1	2/2	3/1	4/2	5/2	6/2
195.20	24.80	20.20			
7/1	8/4	9/4			

K.S.DHAMI,J.B.STOTHERS
CAN J CHEM   43, 479 (1965)

637 Q 003500 PARA—METHYLACETOPHENONE

FORMULA C9H10O
SOLVENT C9H10O
ORIG ST CS2

MOL WT 134.18

TEMP AMB

```
    5 6
    C—C    O
  7 4∥   ∖1 ∥ 9
 H3C—C     C—C—CH3
    ∖   ∕ 8
     C=C
     3 2
```

133.40	128.20	128.20	142.70	128.20	128.20
1/1	2/2	3/2	4/1	5/2	6/2
20.90	195.70	25.60			
7/4	8/1	9/4			

K.S.DHAMI,J.B.STOTHERS
CAN J CHEM   43, 479 (1965)

638 Q 003500 ORTHO—ETHYLACETOPHENONE

```
    9    10
   CH2—CH3
    3 |
   C—C2    O
   ∥    ∖1 ∥ 8
  4C      C—C—CH3
   ∖    ∕ 7
    5C=C 6
```

FORMULA C10H12O
SOLVENT C10H12O
ORIG ST CS2

MOL WT 148.21

TEMP AMB

135.50	142.70	130.00	123.80	130.00	199.40
1/1	2/1	4/2	5/2	6/2	7/1
28.20	26.00	14.90			
8/4	9/3	10/4			

K.S.DHAMI,J.B.STOTHERS
CAN J CHEM   43, 479 (1965)

639 Q 003500 PARA—ETHYLACETOPHENONE

FORMULA C10H12O
SOLVENT C10H12O
ORIG ST CS2

MOL WT 148.21

TEMP AMB

```
         5 6
         C—C    O
 10  9  4∥   ∖1 ∥ 8
CH3—CH2—C     C—C—CH3
         ∖   ∕ 7
          C=C
          3 2
```

132.90	127.60	127.60	148.60	127.60	127.60
1/1	2/2	3/2	4/1	5/2	6/2
195.70	25.20	27.90	14.60		
7/1	8/4	9/3	10/4		

K.S.DHAMI,J.B.STOTHERS
CAN J CHEM   43, 479 (1965)

640 Q 003500 ORTHO—ISOPROPYLACETOPHENONE

```
  H3C   CH3
    ∖ ∕10
    9CH
    3 |
   C—C2    O
   ∥   ∖1 ∥ 8
  4C      C—C—CH3
   ∖   ∕ 7
    5C=C 6
```

FORMULA C11H14O
SOLVENT C11H14O
ORIG ST CS2

MOL WT 162.23

TEMP AMB

137.40	145.90	124.40	129.50	124.40	126.20
1/1	2/1	3/2	4/2	5/2	6/2
200.50	28.20	28.10	22.50		
7/1	8/4	9/2	10/4		

K.S.DHAMI,J.B.STOTHERS
CAN J CHEM   43, 479 (1965)

641   Q 003500   PARA—ISOPROPYLACETOPHENONE

```
     10      5 6
  H3C      C—C    O
    \9  4/    \1  || 8
    HC—C      C—C—CH3
    /     \    /  7
  H3C       C=C
            3 2
```

FORMULA	C11H14O			MOL WT	162.23
SOLVENT	C11H14O				
ORIG ST	CS2			TEMP	AMB

135.10	127.80	126.10	153.70	126.10	127.80
1/1	2/2	3/2	4/1	5/2	6/2
195.90	25.10	33.50	22.60		
7/1	8/4	9/2	10/4		

K.S.DHAMI,J.B.STOTHERS
CAN J CHEM   43, 479 (1965)

642   Q 003500   PARA—TERT—BUTYLACETOPHENONE

```
     10      5 6
  H3C      C—C    O
    \9  4/    \1  || 8
  H3C—C—C      C—C—CH3
    /     \    /  7
  H3C       C=C
            3 2
```

FORMULA	C12H16O			MOL WT	176.26
SOLVENT	C12H16O				
ORIG ST	CS2			TEMP	AMB

133.00	127.30	124.20	154.70	124.20	127.30
1/1	2/2	3/2	4/1	5/2	6/2
194.90	25.40	34.20	30.10		
7/1	8/4	9/1	10/4		

K.S.DHAMI,J.B.STOTHERS
CAN J CHEM   43, 479 (1965)

643   Q 003500   META—CHLOROACETOPHENONE

```
    CL
   3| 2
    C—C    O
   //    \1  || 8
  4C      C—C—CH3
   \     /  7
    5C=C6
```

FORMULA	C8H7OCL			MOL WT	154.60
SOLVENT	C8H7OCL				
ORIG ST	CS2			TEMP	AMB

137.70	128.80	133.80	132.20	128.80	126.50
1/1	2/2	3/1	4/2	5/2	6/2
195.10	25.50				
7/1	8/4				

K.S.DHAMI,J.B.STOTHERS
CAN J CHEM   43, 479 (1965)

644   Q 003500   ORTHO—CHLOROACETOPHENONE

```
       CL
      3 |
     C—C2   O
    //   \1  || 8
  4C      C—C—CH3
    \     /  7
     5C=C6
```

FORMULA	C8H7OCL			MOL WT	154.60
SOLVENT	C8H7OCL				
ORIG ST	CS2			TEMP	AMB

136.80	131.30	126.20	129.90	126.20	126.20
1/1	2/1	3/2	4/2	5/2	6/2
198.40	29.20				
7/1	8/4				

K.S.DHAMI,J.B.STOTHERS
CAN J CHEM   43, 479 (1965)

645   Q 003500   PARA—CHLOROACETOPHENONE

```
      5 6
    C—C    O
   4/   \1  || 8
  CL—C      C—C—CH3
    \     /  7
     C=C
     3 2
```

FORMULA	C8H7OCL			MOL WT	154.60
SOLVENT	C8H7OCL				
ORIG ST	CS2			TEMP	AMB

134.30	128.80	128.80	137.90	128.80	128.80
1/1	2/2	3/2	4/1	5/2	6/2
195.50	24.50				
7/1	8/4				

K.S.DHAMI,J.B.STOTHERS
CAN J CHEM   43, 479 (1965)

646   Q 003500 META—BROMOACETOPHENONE

```
   BR
    | 2
 3C—C    O
   ∥   ∖1 ∥ 8
 4C      C—C—CH3
   ∖  ∕  7
   5C=C6
```

FORMULA	C8H7OBR			MOL WT	199.05
SOLVENT	C8H7OBR				
ORIG ST	CS2			TEMP	AMB

137.50	129.60	121.30	135.20	129.60	126.50
1/1	2/2	3/1	4/2	5/2	6/2
195.10	25.80				
7/1	8/4				

K.S.DHAMI,J.B.STOTHERS
CAN J CHEM   43, 479 (1965)

---

647   Q 003500 ORTHO—BROMOACETOPHENONE

```
    BR
  3 |
  C—C2  O
  ∕  ∖1 ∥ 8
 4C    C—C—CH3
  ∖  ∕  7
  5C=C6
```

FORMULA	C8H7OBR			MOL WT	199.05
SOLVENT	C8H7OBR				
ORIG ST	CS2			TEMP	AMB

139.90	122.00	131.50	131.50	127.40	127.40
1/1	2/1	3/2	4/2	5/2	6/2
199.00	29.40				
7/1	8/4				

K.S.DHAMI,J.B.STOTHERS
CAN J CHEM   43, 479 (1965)

---

648   Q 003500 PARA—BROMOACETOPHENONE

```
  5 6
  C—C    O
 4∕  ∖1 ∥ 8
BR—C    C—C—CH3
  ∖  ∕  7
   C=C
   3 2
```

FORMULA	C8H7OBR			MOL WT	199.05
SOLVENT	C8H7OBR				
ORIG ST	CS2			TEMP	AMB

134.40	130.50	130.50	126.30	130.50	130.50
1/1	2/2	3/2	4/1	5/2	6/2
196.30	26.20				
7/1	8/4				

K.S.DHAMI,J.B.STOTHERS
CAN J CHEM   43, 479 (1965)

---

649   Q 003500 ORTHO—IODOACETOPHENONE

```
    J
  3 |
  C—C2  O
  ∕  ∖1 ∥ 8
 4C    C—C—CH3
  ∖  ∕  7
  5C=C6
```

FORMULA	C8H7OI			MOL WT	246.05
SOLVENT	CHCL3				
ORIG ST	CS2			TEMP	AMB

145.10	90.30	138.10	131.40	128.00	128.00
1/1	2/1	3/2	4/2	5/2	6/2
200.50	28.70				
7/1	8/4				

K.S.DHAMI,J.B.STOTHERS
CAN J CHEM   43, 479 (1965)

---

650   Q 003500 ORTHO—NITROACETOPHENONE

```
    NO2
  3 |
  C—C2  O
  ∕  ∖1 ∥ 8
 4C    C—C—CH3
  ∖  ∕  7
  5C=C6
```

FORMULA	C8H7O3N			MOL WT	165.15
SOLVENT	C8H7O3N				
ORIG ST	CS2			TEMP	AMB

135.40	144.70	122.50	129.80	133.00	126.30
1/1	2/1	3/2	4/2	5/2	6/2
198.00	28.10				
7/1	8/4				

K.S.DHAMI,J.B.STOTHERS
CAN J CHEM   43, 479 (1965)

651   Q 003500   PARA—NITROACETOPHENONE

```
    5 6
    C—C    O
   4//   \\1 ‖ 8
 O2N—C      C—C—CH3
    \   /  7
     C=C
     3 2
```

FORMULA	C8H7O3N			MOL WT	165.15
SOLVENT	C8H7O3N				
ORIG ST	CS2			TEMP	AMB
140.80	129.00	123.80	150.10	123.80	129.00
1/1	2/2	3/2	4/1	5/2	6/2
195.80	26.60				
7/1	8/4				

K.S.DHAMI,J.B.STOTHERS
CAN J CHEM   43, 479 (1965)

652   Q 003500   ORTHO—HYDROXYACETOPHENONE

```
     OH
    3 |
    C—C2   O
   //  \\1 ‖ 8
  4C      C—C—CH3
    \   /  7
     C=C
     5 6
```

FORMULA	C8H8O2			MOL WT	136.15
SOLVENT	C8H8O2				
ORIG ST	CS2			TEMP	AMB
118.90	161.50	118.30	135.50	118.30	129.70
1/1	2/1	3/2	4/2	5/2	6/2
204.10	25.40				
7/1	8/4				

K.S.DHAMI,J.B.STOTHERS
CAN J CHEM   43, 479 (1965)

653   Q 003500   PARA—HYDROXYACETOPHENONE

```
    3 2
    C—C    O
   4//   \\1 ‖ 8
 HO—C      C—C—CH3
    \   /  7
     C=C
     5 6
```

FORMULA	C8H8O2			MOL WT	136.15
SOLVENT	C4H8O2				
ORIG ST	CS2			TEMP	AMB
129.60	130.90	115.20	161.80	115.20	130.90
1/1	2/2	3/2	4/1	5/2	6/2
197.10	24.80				
7/1	8/4				

K.S.DHAMI,J.B.STOTHERS
CAN J CHEM   43, 479 (1965)

654   Q 003500   META—METHOXYACETOPHENONE

```
  9
 CH3O
    \3 2
     C—C    O
    //  \\1 ‖ 8
   4C      C—C—CH3
    \   /  7
    5C=C 6
```

FORMULA	C9H10O2			MOL WT	150.18
SOLVENT	C9H10O2				
ORIG ST	CS2			TEMP	AMB
137.40	111.40	158.50	118.50	128.40	118.50
1/1	2/2	3/1	4/2	5/2	6/2
195.80	25.20	54.00			
7/1	8/4	9/4			

K.S.DHAMI,J.B.STOTHERS
CAN J CHEM   43, 479 (1965)

655   Q 003500   ORTHO—METHOXYACETOPHENONE

```
    9
   OCH3
  3 |
  C—C2   O
 //  \\1 ‖ 8
4C      C—C—CH3
  \   /  7
  5C=C 6
```

FORMULA	C9H10O2			MOL WT	150.18
SOLVENT	C9H10O2				
ORIG ST	CS2			TEMP	AMB
127.40	158.20	111.10	132.80	119.40	129.30
1/1	2/1	3/2	4/2	5/2	6/2
197.50	30.70	54.30			
7/1	8/4	9/4			

K.S.DHAMI,J.B.STOTHERS
CAN J CHEM   43, 479 (1965)

656   Q 003500 PARA—METHOXYACETOPHENONE

```
        5 6
        C—C    0
   9   4/    \1 ‖ 8
  CH3O—C      C—C—CH3
        \   /  7
         C=C
         3 2
```

FORMULA	C9H10O2			MOL WT	150.18
SOLVENT	CHCL3				
ORIG ST	CS2			TEMP	AMB

129.50	129.80	113.00	162.80	113.00	129.80
1/1	2/2	3/2	4/1	5/2	6/2
195.40	25.20	54.60			
7/1	8/4	9/4			

K.S.DHAMI,J.B.STOTHERS
CAN J CHEM   43, 479 (1965)

---

657   Q 003500 ORTHO—ETHOXYACETOPHENONE

```
     CH2—CH3
      /
      O
   3  |
   C—C2   0
  /   \1 ‖ 8
 4C     C—C—CH3
  \   /  7
   5C=C 6
```

FORMULA	C10H12O2			MOL WT	164.21
SOLVENT	CHCL3				
ORIG ST	CS2			TEMP	AMB

128.00	158.20	112.30	133.30	119.80	130.30
1/1	2/1	3/2	4/2	5/2	6/2
198.40	31.60				
7/1	8/4				

K.S.DHAMI,J.B.STOTHERS
CAN J CHEM   43, 479 (1965)

---

658   Q 003500 ORTHO—AMINOACETOPHENONE

```
     NH2
   3  |
   C—C2   0
  /   \1 ‖ 8
 4C     C—C—CH3
  \   /  7
   C=C
   5 6
```

FORMULA	C8H9ON			MOL WT	135.17
SOLVENT	C8H9ON				
ORIG ST	CS2			TEMP	AMB

117.20	149.80	114.70	133.30	116.80	131.40
1/1	2/1	3/2	4/2	5/2	6/2
200.00	26.80				
7/1	8/4				

K.S.DHAMI,J.B.STOTHERS
CAN J CHEM   43, 479 (1965)

---

659   Q 003500 PARA—N—DIMETHYLAMINOACETOPHENONE

```
  9      3 2
 H3C     C—C    0
   \   4/    \1 ‖ 8
    N—C      C—C—CH3
   /   \   /  7
 H3C     C=C
         5 6
```

FORMULA	C10H13ON			MOL WT	163.22
SOLVENT	C10H13ON				
ORIG ST	CS2			TEMP	AMB

124.80	129.90	109.80	152.70	109.80	129.90
1/1	2/2	3/2	4/1	5/2	6/2
195.10	25.00	39.00			
7/1	8/4	9/4			

K.S.DHAMI,J.B.STOTHERS
CAN J CHEM   43, 479 (1965)

---

660   Q 003500 2,3—DIMETHYLACETOPHENONE

```
   10      9
  H3C     CH3
    \3  2/
     C—C    0
  /    \1 ‖ 8
 4C      C—C—CH3
  \    /  7
   C=C
   5 6
```

FORMULA	C10H12O			MOL WT	148.21
SOLVENT	C10H12O				
ORIG ST	CS2			TEMP	AMB

139.10	134.00	136.70	131.30	123.90	123.90
1/1	2/1	3/1	4/2	5/2	6/2
200.30	28.80	19.50	15.30		
7/1	8/4				

K.S.DHAMI,J.B.STOTHERS
CAN J CHEM   43, 479 (1965)

661   Q 003500   2,4-DIMETHYLACETOPHENONE

```
         9
        CH3            FORMULA  C10H12O              MOL WT  148.21
     3  /             SOLVENT  C10H12O                      AMB
     C-C2  O          ORIG ST  CS2                  TEMP
 10 4/    \1 ‖ 8
H3C-C      C-C-CH3      140.50  133.80  129.40  137.30  124.90  129.40
    \     / 7            1/1     2/1     3/2     4/1     5/2     6/2
     C=C                198.30   27.60   19.50   19.50
     5  6                7/1     8/4     9/4    10/4
```

K.S.DHAMI,J.B.STOTHERS
CAN J CHEM   43, 479 (1965)

---

662   Q 003500   2,5-DIMETHYLACETOPHENONE

```
         9
        CH3            FORMULA  C10H12O              MOL WT  148.21
     3  /             SOLVENT  C10H12O
     C-C2  O          ORIG ST  CS2                  TEMP      AMB
    //    \1 ‖ 8
   4C      C-C-CH3      135.40  133.30  128.30  128.30  133.30  128.30
    \     / 7            1/1     2/1     3/2     4/2     5/1     6/2
     5C=C6              198.20   28.10   19.70   19.70
    /                    7/1     8/4     9/4    10/4
  H3C10
```

K.S.DHAMI,J.B.STOTHERS
CAN J CHEM   43, 479 (1965)

---

663   Q 003500   2,6-DIMETHYLACETOPHENONE

```
         9
        CH3            FORMULA  C10H12O              MOL WT  148.21
    3 2/              SOLVENT  C10H12O
     C-C   O          ORIG ST  CS2                  TEMP      AMB
    //    \1 ‖ 8
   4C      C-C-CH3      141.70  131.50  126.90  126.90  126.90  131.50
    \     / 7            1/1     2/1     3/2     4/2     5/2     6/1
     C=C6              205.40   30.50   17.70   17.70
     5  \10             7/1     8/4     9/4    10/4
        CH3
```

K.S.DHAMI,J.B.STOTHERS
CAN J CHEM   43, 479 (1965)

---

664   Q 003500   2,4,5-TRIMETHYLACETOPHENONE

```
         9
        CH3            FORMULA  C11H14O              MOL WT  162.23
    3 2/              SOLVENT  C11H14O
     C-C   O          ORIG ST  CS2                  TEMP      AMB
 10 4/    \1 ‖ 8
H3C-C      C-C-CH3      132.90  134.60  130.70  138.60  134.60  132.30
    \     / 7            1/1     2/1     3/2     4/1     5/1     6/2
     5C=C6             198.00   27.80   18.00   18.00   18.00
    /                    7/1     8/4     9/4    10/4   11/4
  H3C11
```

K.S.DHAMI,J.B.STOTHERS
CAN J CHEM   43, 479 (1965)

---

665   Q 003500   2,4,6-TRIMETHYLACETOPHENONE

```
         9
        CH3            FORMULA  C11H14O              MOL WT  162.23
    3 2/              SOLVENT  C11H14O                      AMB
     C-C   O          ORIG ST  CS2                  TEMP
    4/    \1 ‖ 8
H3C-C      C-C-CH3      139.40  131.70  128.10  137.10  128.10  131.70
  10 \     / 7           1/1     2/1     3/2     4/1     5/2     6/1
     C=C6              205.90   30.80   18.50   18.50   18.50
     5  \11             7/1     8/4     9/4    10/4   11/4
        CH3
```

K.S.DHAMI,J.B.STOTHERS
CAN J CHEM   43, 479 (1965)

666   Q 003500   2,3,4,6-TETRAMETHYLACETOPHENONE

```
    10     9
  H3C    CH3          FORMULA   C12H16O              MOL WT   176.26
    \3 2/             SOLVENT   C12H16O
    C-C    O          ORIG ST   C S2                 TEMP       AMB
  4/    \1 ‖ 8
  H3C-C    C-C-CH3     134.60   132.60   140.20   140.20   132.60   206.00
  11  \    / 7          1/1      2/1      3/1      4/1      6/1      7/1
       C=C6            30.80    18.90    23.20
      5 \12            8/4
        CH3
                       K.S.DHAMI,J.B.STOTHERS
                       CAN J CHEM                      43,   479 (1965)
```

667   Q 003500   2,3,5,6-TETRAMETHYLACETOPHENONE

```
    10     9
  H3C    CH3          FORMULA   C12H16O              MOL WT   176.26
    \3 2/             SOLVENT   C S2
    C-C    O          ORIG ST   C S2                 TEMP       AMB
    //   \1 ‖ 8
   4C      C-C-CH3     144.20   127.70   133.90   131.70   133.90   127.70
    \    / 7            1/1      2/1      3/1      4/2      5/1      6/1
     5C=C6             206.70    33.10    16.50    20.40
    /    \12            7/1      8/4
  H3C 11   CH3
                       K.S.DHAMI,J.B.STOTHERS
                       CAN J CHEM                      43,   479 (1965)
```

668   Q 003500   2,3,4,5,6-PENTAMETHYLACETOPHENONE

```
    10     9
  H3C    CH3          FORMULA   C13H18O              MOL WT   190.29
    \3 2/             SOLVENT   C S2
    C-C    O          ORIG ST   C S2                 TEMP       AMB
    4/   \1 ‖ 8
  H3C-C    C-C-CH3     142.10   127.40   133.30   133.30   133.30   127.40
  11  \    / 7          1/1      2/1      3/1      4/1      5/1      6/1
      5C=C6            206.60    34.40    18.10    18.10    18.10    18.10
    /    \              7/1      8/4      9/4     10/4     11/4     12/4
  H3C    CH3           18.40
   12     13           13/4
                       K.S.DHAMI,J.B.STOTHERS
                       CAN J CHEM                      43,   479 (1965)
```

669   Q 003500   2,6-DIETHYLACETOPHENONE

```
      9    10
     CH2-CH3           FORMULA   C12H16O              MOL WT   176.26
   3 2/               SOLVENT   C12H16O
   C-C    O           ORIG ST   C S2                 TEMP       AMB
   //   \1 ‖ 8
  4C      C-C-CH3     141.40   137.70   125.30   128.10   125.30   137.70
   \    / 7            1/1      2/1      3/2      4/2      5/2      6/1
    C=C6              205.50    31.00    25.40    15.10    25.40    15.10
   5 \11  12           7/1      8/4      9/3     10/4     11/3     12/4
     CH2-CH3
                       K.S.DHAMI,J.B.STOTHERS
                       CAN J CHEM                      43,   479 (1965)
```

670   Q 003500   2,6-DIISOPROPYLACETOPHENONE

```
   11   10
  H3C   CH3         FORMULA    C14H20O              MOL WT   204.31
    \9/             SOLVENT    CS2
     CH             ORIG ST    CS2                  TEMP       AMB
    3 |
   C-C2   O         141.20   143.00   123.20   129.20   123.20   143.00
   ⁄   ⧵1 ‖ 8        1/1      2/1      3/2      4/2      5/2      6/1
 4C      C-C-CH3    206.00    31.70    34.00    25.70    25.70    34.00
   ⧵   ⁄  7          7/1      8/4      9/2     10/4     11/4     12/2
    C=C6            25.70    25.70
   5 |12            13/4     14/4
     CH
   ⁄  ⧵14
  H3C   CH3         K.S.DHAMI,J.B.STOTHERS
   13              CAN J CHEM                       43,   479 (1965)
```

671   Q 003500   2,4,6-TRIISOPROPYLACETOPHENONE

```
   11   10
  H3C   CH3         FORMULA    C17H26O              MOL WT   246.40
    \9/             SOLVENT    C4H8O2
     CH             ORIG ST    CS2                  TEMP       AMB
 13  3 |
 H3C    C-C2   O    138.80   142.70   120.10   148.80   120.10   142.70
  \H 4⁄  ⧵1 ‖ 8      1/1      2/1      3/2      4/1      5/2      6/1
 12C-C      C-C-CH3  206.30    31.70    32.90    23.60    23.60    32.90
  ⁄   ⧵    ⁄  7       7/1      8/4      9/2     10/4     11/4     12/2
 H3C14   C=C6        23.60    23.60    32.90    23.60    23.60
   5 |              13/4     14/4     15/2     16/4     17/4
   HC15
   ⁄  ⧵17
  H3C   CH3         K.S.DHAMI,J.B.STOTHERS
   16              CAN J CHEM                       43,   479 (1965)
```

672   Q 003500   2,6-DIMETHYL-4-TERT-BUTYLACETOPHENONE

```
      9             FORMULA    C14H20O              MOL WT   204.31
     CH3            SOLVENT    CS2
 11    3 2⁄         ORIG ST    CS2                  TEMP       AMB
 H3C   C-C   O
 12⧵  4⁄  ⧵1 ‖ 8    140.40   132.00   125.50   150.90   125.50   132.00
 H3C-C-C    C-C-CH3  1/1      2/1      3/2      4/1      5/2      6/1
  ⁄10 ⧵   ⁄  7      205.80    32.50    17.80    34.30    17.80
 H3C      C=C6       7/1      8/4      9/4     10/1     14/4
  13    5  ⧵14
         CH3        K.S.DHAMI,J.B.STOTHERS
                   CAN J CHEM                       43,   479 (1965)
```

673   Q 003500   2,4-DICHLOROACETOPHENONE

```
                    FORMULA    C8H6OCL2             MOL WT   189.04
     CL             SOLVENT    C8H6OCL2
   3 2⁄             ORIG ST    CS2                  TEMP       AMB
  C-C   O
  4⁄  ⧵1 ‖ 8        131.70   135.70   129.40   135.70   126.40   129.40
 CL-C     C-C-CH3    1/1      2/1      3/2      4/1      5/2      6/2
   ⧵   ⁄  7         196.40    29.60
    C=C              7/1      8/4
   5 6
                    K.S.DHAMI,J.B.STOTHERS
                   CAN J CHEM                       43,   479 (1965)
```

674   Q 003500 2,6–DICHLOROACETOPHENONE

```
                    FORMULA   C8H6OCL2              MOL WT  189.04
        CL          SOLVENT   C4H8O2
      3 |2          ORIG ST   CS2                   TEMP      AMB
      C-C   O
     4⁄   ⫰1 ‖ 8      139.40  129.10  128.00  129.80  128.00  129.10
    4C      C-C-CH3     1/1     2/1     3/2     4/2     5/2     6/1
      ⫲   ⁄  7        197.70   29.90
       C=C6           7/1     8/4
      5 |
        CL            K.S.DHAMI,J.B.STOTHERS
                      CAN J CHEM                    43,  479 (1965)
```

675   Q 003500 2,4,6–TRIBROMOACETOPHENONE

```
                    FORMULA   C8H5OBR3              MOL WT  356.84
        BR          SOLVENT   CHCL3
      3 |           ORIG ST   CS2                   TEMP      AMB
      C-C2  O
     4⁄   ⫰1 ‖ 8      142.00  118.50  134.00  123.30  134.00  118.50
   BR-C      C-C-CH3    1/1     2/1     3/2     4/1     5/2     6/1
     ⫲   ⁄  7        199.70   30.10
      5C=C6           7/1     8/4
       |
       BR             K.S.DHAMI,J.B.STOTHERS
                      CAN J CHEM                    43,  479 (1965)
```

676   Q 003500 2,4–DIHYDROXYACETOPHENONE

```
                    FORMULA   C8H8O3               MOL WT  152.15
        OH          SOLVENT   C4H8O2
      3 2⁄          ORIG ST   CS2                   TEMP      AMB
      C-C   O
     4⁄   ⫰1 ‖ 8      113.90  165.10  103.50  165.10  108.60  133.90
   HO-C      C-C-CH3    1/1     2/1     3/2     4/1     5/2     6/2
     ⫲   ⁄  7        202.60   23.60
       C=C           7/1     8/4
       5 6
                      K.S.DHAMI,J.B.STOTHERS
                      CAN J CHEM                    43,  479 (1965)
```

677   Q 003500 2,6–DIHYDROXYACETOPHENONE

```
                    FORMULA   C8H8O3               MOL WT  152.15
        OH          SOLVENT   C4H8O2
      3 |           ORIG ST   CS2                   TEMP      AMB
      C-C2  O
     ⁄   ⫰1 ‖ 8       108.00  161.40  106.50  134.50  106.50  161.40
    4C      C-C-CH3    1/1     2/1     3/2     4/2     5/2     6/1
     ⫲   ⁄  7        204.50   31.90
      5C=C6           7/1     8/4
       |
       OH             K.S.DHAMI,J.B.STOTHERS
                      CAN J CHEM                    43,  479 (1965)
```

678   Q 003500 2,4,6–TRIHYDROXYACETOPHENONE

```
                    FORMULA   C8H8O4               MOL WT  168.15
        OH          SOLVENT   C4H8O2
      3 |           ORIG ST   CS2                   TEMP      AMB
      C-C2  O
     4⁄   ⫰1 ‖ 8      104.00  165.10   94.50  165.10   94.50  165.10
   HO-C      C-C-CH3    1/1     2/1     3/2     4/1     5/2     6/1
     ⫲   ⁄  7        202.90   32.10
      5C=C6           7/1     8/4
       |
       OH             K.S.DHAMI,J.B.STOTHERS
                      CAN J CHEM                    43,  479 (1965)
```

679　　Q 003500　2,4-DIMETHOXYACETOPHENONE

```
        9
      OCH3
    3 2/
    C-C   O
 10   4/   ⟍1 ∥ 8
 CH30-C      C-C-CH3
    ⟍   /   7
      C=C
      5 6
```

FORMULA	C10H1203			MOL WT	180.21
SOLVENT	CHCL3				
ORIG ST	CS2			TEMP	AMB

119.80	160.20	96.80	163.30	104.50	131.20
1/1	2/1	3/2	4/1	5/2	6/2
195.30	30.70	54.60	54.60		
7/1	8/4	9/4	10/4		

K.S.DHAMI,J.B.STOTHERS
CAN J CHEM　　　　　　　　　　43,　479 (1965)

680　　Q 003500　2,5-DIMETHOXYACETOPHENONE

```
        9
      OCH3
    3 2/
    C-C   O
   /   ⟍1 ∥ 8
  4C      C-C-CH3
   ⟍   /   7
      C=C
  10  /5 6
 CH30
```

FORMULA	C10H1203			MOL WT	180.21
SOLVENT	CHCL3				
ORIG ST	CS2			TEMP	AMB

127.20	152.40	112.60	118.40	152.40	112.60
1/1	2/1	3/2	4/2	5/1	6/2
197.00	30.30	54.20	54.20		
7/1	8/4	9/4	10/4		

K.S.DHAMI,J.B.STOTHERS
CAN J CHEM　　　　　　　　　　43,　479 (1965)

681　　Q 003500　2,6-DIMETHOXYACETOPHENONE

```
        9
      OCH3
    3 2/
    C-C   O
   /   ⟍1 ∥ 8
  4C      C-C-CH3
   ⟍   /   7
   5C=C6
    ⟍ 10
     OCH3
```

FORMULA	C10H1203			MOL WT	180.21
SOLVENT	CS2				
ORIG ST	CS2			TEMP	AMB

141.20	156.30	104.10	131.10	104.10	156.30
1/1	2/1	3/2	4/2	5/2	6/1
199.30	31.30	55.20	55.20		
7/1	8/4	9/4	10/4		

K.S.DHAMI,J.B.STOTHERS
CAN J CHEM　　　　　　　　　　43,　479 (1965)

682　　Q 003500　2-HYDROXY-6-METHOXYACETOPHENONE

```
      OH
    3 |
    C-C2   O
   /   ⟍1 ∥
  4C      C-C-CH3
   ⟍   /   7 8
   5C=C6
    ⟍ 9
     OCH3
```

FORMULA	C9H1003			MOL WT	166.18
SOLVENT	CHCL3				
ORIG ST	CS2			TEMP	AMB

110.70	164.00	109.90	135.80	100.90	160.80
1/1	2/1	3/2	4/2	5/2	6/1
204.40	33.20	55.20			
7/1	8/4	9/4			

K.S.DHAMI,J.B.STOTHERS
CAN J CHEM　　　　　　　　　　43,　479 (1965)

683　　Q 003500　PROPIOPHENONE

```
    3 2
    C-C   O
   /   ⟍1 ∥ 8   9
  4C      C-C-CH2-CH3
   ⟍   /   7
   5C=C6
```

FORMULA	C9H100			MOL WT	134.18
SOLVENT	C9H100				
ORIG ST	CS2			TEMP	AMB

136.00	126.90	126.90	130.80	126.90	126.90
1/1	2/2	3/2	4/2	5/2	6/2
198.10	30.30	6.70			
7/1	8/3	9/4			

K.S.DHAMI,J.B.STOTHERS
CAN J CHEM　　　　　　　　　　43,　478 (1965)

684　　　Q 003500　2-METHYLPROPIOPHENONE

```
        10
        CH3              FORMULA  C10H12O              MOL WT  148.21
       3 |              SOLVENT  C10H12O
       C—C2  O          ORIG ST  CS2                   TEMP        AMB
      4⁄    ⍀1 ‖ 8   9
      C       C—C—CH2—CH3    136.50  136.50  130.60  128.00  125.00  130.60
       ⍀   ⁄ 7               1/1     2/1     3/2     4/2     5/2     6/2
        5C=C6                202.20  33.20   7.40    20.40
                             7/1     8/3     9/4     10/4
```

K.S.DHAMI,J.B.STOTHERS
CAN J CHEM　　　　　　　　　　43,　498 (1965)

685　　　Q 003500　2,4,6-TRIMETHYLPROPIOPHENONE

```
         10
         CH3             FORMULA  C12H16O              MOL WT  176.26
        3 |             SOLVENT  C12H16O
        C—C2  O         ORIG ST  CS2                   TEMP        AMB
   11  4⁄    ⍀1 ‖ 8   9
   CH3—C       C—C—CH2—CH3    138.80  131.00  127.20  136.30  127.20  131.00
        ⍀   ⁄ 7               1/1     2/1     3/2     4/1     5/2     6/1
        C=C6                  207.50  36.30   7.20    17.10   18.90
        5 |                   7/1     8/3     9/4
        CH3
        12
```

K.S.DHAMI,J.B.STOTHERS
CAN J CHEM　　　　　　　　　　43,　498 (1965)

686　　　Q 003500　2,3,5,6-TETRAMETHYLPROPIOPHENONE

```
   11    10
   H3C    CH3           FORMULA  C13H18O              MOL WT  190.29
    ⍀3  ⁄               SOLVENT  CS2
    C—C2  O             ORIG ST  CS2                   TEMP        AMB
   ⁄    ⍀1 ‖ 8   9
   4C      C—C—CH2—CH3         143.30  127.60  133.80  130.60  133.80  127.60
    ⍀   ⁄ 7                    1/1     2/1     3/1     4/2     5/1     6/1
    5C=C6                      209.20  38.10   15.00   19.10
   ⁄    ⍀                      7/1     8/3     9/4
   H3C    CH3
```

K.S.DHAMI,J.B.STOTHERS
CAN J CHEM　　　　　　　　　　43,　498 (1965)

687　　　Q 003500　2,3,4,5,6-PENTAMETHYLPROPIOPHENONE

```
         10
   H3C    CH3           FORMULA  C14H20O              MOL WT  204.31
    ⍀3 2⁄               SOLVENT  CS2
    C—C    O            ORIG ST  CS2                   TEMP        AMB
   4⁄    ⍀1 ‖ 8   9
   H3C—C      C—C—CH2—CH3      141.40  127.20  133.30  133.30  133.30  127.20
    ⍀   ⁄ 7                    1/1     2/1     3/1     4/1     5/1     6/1
    5C=C6                      209.40  37.80   17.40
   ⁄    ⍀                      7/1     8/3     9/4
   H3C    CH3
```

K.S.DHAMI,J.B.STOTHERS
CAN J CHEM　　　　　　　　　　43,　498 (1965)

688　　　Q 003500　2,4,6-TRIISOPROPYLPROPIOPHENONE

```
        H
      H3C—C—CH3         FORMULA  C18H28O              MOL WT  260.42
        3 |             SOLVENT  CS2
   H3C    C—C2  O       ORIG ST  CS2                   TEMP        AMB
    ⍀  4⁄    ⍀1 ‖ 8   9
    HC—C       C—C—CH2—CH3     138.70  143.50  121.20  148.90  121.20  143.50
   ⁄   ⍀   ⁄ 7                 1/1     2/1     3/2     4/1     5/2     6/1
   H3C   5C=C6                 208.80  39.40   15.70   24.10   32.50
         |                     7/1     8/3
      H3C—C—CH3
        H
```

K.S.DHAMI,J.B.STOTHERS
CAN J CHEM　　　　　　　　　　43,　498 (1965)

689   Q 003500   4—METHOXYPROPIOPHENONE

```
        3 2      O
        C-C
  10   4/    \1 || 8   9
 CH3O-C       C-C-CH2-CH3
       \   /  7
        C=C
        5 6
```

FORMULA	C10H12O2			MOL WT	164.21
SOLVENT	C10H12O2				
ORIG ST	CS2			TEMP	AMB
129.20	129.10	112.60	162.30	112.60	129.10
1/1	2/2	3/2	4/1	5/2	6/2
197.20	30.20	7.10	54.40		
7/1	8/3	9/4	10/4		

K.S.DHAMI,J.B.STOTHERS
CAN J CHEM   43,   498 (1965)

---

690   Q 003500   ISOBUTYROPHENONE

```
        3 2        9
        C-C   O   CH3
       //   \1 || 8/
  4C        C-C-CH
       \   /  7   \10
        C=C        CH3
        5 6
```

FORMULA	C10H12O			MOL WT	148.21
SOLVENT	C10H12O				
ORIG ST	CS2			TEMP	AMB
135.80	127.90	127.90	132.40	127.90	127.90
1/1	2/2	3/2	4/2	5/2	6/2
202.80	34.60	18.10	18.10		
7/1	8/2	9/4	10/4		

K.S.DHAMI,J.B.STOTHERS
CAN J CHEM   43,   498 (1965)

---

691   Q 003500   2—METHYLISOBUTYROPHENONE

```
       11
       CH3
     3  |         9
     C-C2   O    CH3
    //   \1 || 8/
 4C        C-C-CH
    \   /  7   \10
     C=C        CH3
     5 6
```

FORMULA	C11H14O			MOL WT	162.23
SOLVENT	C11H14O				
ORIG ST	CS2			TEMP	AMB
136.40	136.40	130.70	127.40	125.50	130.70
1/1	2/1	3/2	4/2	5/2	6/2
206.40	37.30	17.90	17.90	19.90	
7/1	8/2	9/4	10/4	11/4	

K.S.DHAMI,J.B.STOTHERS
CAN J CHEM   43,   498 (1965)

---

692   Q 003500   2,4,6—TRIMETHYLISOBUTYROPHENONE

```
        CH3
      3  |          9
      C-C2   O     CH3
    4/   \1 || 8/
 H3C-C        C-C-CH
     \   /  7   \10
      C=C6       CH3
      5 |
        CH3
```

FORMULA	C13H18O			MOL WT	190.29
SOLVENT	C13H18O				
ORIG ST	CS2			TEMP	AMB
139.10	132.30	127.80	136.80	127.80	132.30
1/1	2/1	3/2	4/1	5/2	6/1
210.70	41.10	17.60	17.60	19.30	
7/1	8/2	9/4	10/4		

K.S.DHAMI,J.B.STOTHERS
CAN J CHEM   43,   498 (1965)

---

693   Q 003500   2,3,5,6—TETRAMETHYLISOBUTYROPHENONE

```
 H3C      CH3
    \3 2/       9
     C-C    O  CH3
    //   \1 || 8/
 4C        C-C-CH
    \   /  7   \10
    5C=C6       CH3
    /    \
 H3C      CH3
```

FORMULA	C14H20O			MOL WT	204.31
SOLVENT	CS2				
ORIG ST	CS2			TEMP	AMB
143.10	129.40	134.90	132.40	134.90	129.40
1/1	2/1	3/1	4/2	5/1	6/1
212.30	44.50	17.50	17.50	20.10	
7/1	8/2	9/4	10/4		

K.S.DHAMI,J.B.STOTHERS
CAN J CHEM   43,   498 (1965)

694   Q 003500   2,3,4,5,6-PENTAMETHYLISOBUTYROPHENONE

```
  H3C      CH3
    \3 2/        9
     C-C    O   CH3
    4/    \1 ‖ 8/
 H3C-C      C-C-CH
    \    7  \10
     C=C6      CH3
    /5  \
  H3C      CH3
```

FORMULA	C15H22O			MOL WT	218.34
SOLVENT	CS2,CHCL3				
ORIG ST	CS2			TEMP	AMB

140.20	128.10	132.70	132.70	132.70	128.10
1/1	2/1	3/1	4/1	5/1	6/1
212.60	43.50	18.00	18.00		
7/1	8/2	9/4	10/4		

K.S.DHAMI,J.B.STOTHERS
CAN J CHEM   43, 498 (1965)

---

695   Q 003500   2,4,6-TRIISOPROPYLISOBUTYROPHENONE

```
          H
       H3C-C-CH3
        3 12        9
  H3C   C-C    O   CH3
    \  4/    \1 ‖ 8/
     HC-C      C-C-CH
    /   \    / 7  \10
  H3C   5C=C6      CH3
          |
       H3C-C-CH3
          H
```

FORMULA	C19H30O			MOL WT	274.45
SOLVENT	CS2,CHCL3				
ORIG ST	CS2			TEMP	AMB

137.80	144.30	121.10	149.00	121.10	144.30
1/1	2/1	3/2	4/1	5/2	6/1
212.00	42.60	16.80	16.80		
7/1	8/2	9/4	10/4		

K.S.DHAMI,J.B.STOTHERS
CAN J CHEM   43, 498 (1965)

---

696   Q 003500   4-METHOXYISOBUTYROPHENONE

```
    3 2        9
     C-C    O   CH3
 11 4/    \1 ‖ 8/
 CH3O-C      C-C-CH
    \    7  \10
     C=C      CH3
    5 6
```

FORMULA	C11H14O2			MOL WT	178.23
SOLVENT	C11H14O2				
ORIG ST	CS2			TEMP	AMB

128.20	129.60	112.90	162.40	112.90	129.60
1/1	2/2	3/2	4/1	5/2	6/2
201.00	34.30	18.80	18.80	54.40	
7/1	8/2	9/4	10/4	11/4	

K.S.DHAMI,J.B.STOTHERS
CAN J CHEM   43, 498 (1965)

---

697   Q 003500   PIVALOPHENONE

```
    3 2        9
     C-C    O   CH3
    /    \1 ‖ 8/10
 4C      C-C-C-CH3
    \    / 7  \11
     C=C      CH3
    5 6
```

FORMULA	C11H14O			MOL WT	162.23
SOLVENT	C11H14O				
ORIG ST	CS2			TEMP	AMB

137.80	127.30	127.30	130.10	127.30	127.30
1/1	2/2	3/2	4/2	5/2	6/2
206.90	43.50	27.90	27.90	27.90	
7/1	8/1	9/4	10/4	11/4	

K.S.DHAMI,J.B.STOTHERS
CAN J CHEM   43, 498 (1965)

---

698   Q 003500   2-METHYLPIVALOPHENONE

```
     12
     CH3
    3 |        9
     C-C2   O   CH3
    /    \1 ‖ 8/10
 4C      C-C-C-CH3
    \    / 7  \11
     C=C      CH3
    5 6
```

FORMULA	C12H16O			MOL WT	176.26
SOLVENT	C12H16O				
ORIG ST	CS2			TEMP	AMB

140.20	133.40	127.20	129.70	124.30	127.20
1/1	2/1	3/2	4/2	5/2	6/2
211.70	43.90	26.50	26.50	26.50	18.20
7/1	8/1	9/4	10/4	11/4	12/4

K.S.DHAMI,J.B.STOTHERS
CAN J CHEM   43, 498 (1965)

699   Q 003500 2,4,6-TRIMETHYLPIVALOPHENONE

```
       9CH3
        |   10 11 12
        C   C-C(CH3)3
       //6\ / \
     5C  1C   O
      |   ||
      C4  2C
     / \ / \
  H3C   C   CH3
   8    3   7
```

FORMULA	C14H20O			MOL WT	204.31
SOLVENT	C14H20O				
ORIG ST	CS2			TEMP	AMB
138.60	130.70	127.60	135.80	127.60	130.70
1/1	2/1	3/2	4/1	5/2	6/1
19.30	215.50	43.30	27.50		
7/4	10/1	11/1	12/4		

K.S.DHAMI,J.B.STOTHERS
CAN J CHEM   43, 498 (1965)

---

700   Q 003500 2,3,4,6-TETRAMETHYLPIVALOPHENONE

```
      10CH3
        |   11 12 13
        C   C-C(CH3)3
       //6\ / \
     5C  1C   O
      |   ||
      C4  2C
     / \3/ \
  H3C   C   CH3
   9    |   7
      8CH3
```

FORMULA	C15H22O			MOL WT	218.34
SOLVENT	C15H22O				
ORIG ST	CS2			TEMP	AMB
157.50	128.20	130.30	130.30	127.80	133.30
1/1	2/1	3/1	4/1	5/2	6/1
13.90	215.40	43.30	26.80		
7/4	11/1	12/1	13/4		

K.S.DHAMI,J.B.STOTHERS
CAN J CHEM   43, 498 (1965)

---

701   Q 003500 4-METHOXYPIVALOPHENONE

```
      3 2         9
      C-C    O   CH3
  12  4/   \1 ||  8/10
CH3O-C       C-C-C-CH3
      \   / 7  \11
       C=C        CH3
       5 6
```

FORMULA	C12H16O2			MOL WT	192.26
SOLVENT	C12H16O2				
ORIG ST	CS2			TEMP	AMB
128.90	130.00	112.40	161.00	112.40	130.00
1/1	2/2	3/2	4/1	5/2	6/2
203.50	42.80	27.70	27.70	27.70	54.30
7/1	8/1	9/4	10/4	11/4	12/4

K.S.DHAMI,J.B.STOTHERS
CAN J CHEM   43, 498 (1965)

---

702   Q 003500 2-METHYL-4-METHOXYPIVALOPHENONE

```
      6   9 10 11
      C   C-C(CH3)3
     / \ / \
   5C  1C   O
    |   ||
    C4  2C
 8 / \ / \
CH3O  C   CH3
      3   7
```

FORMULA	C13H18O2			MOL WT	206.29
SOLVENT	CS2				
ORIG ST	CS2			TEMP	AMB
139.80	131.80	116.10	155.20	111.90	126.50
1/1	2/1	3/2	4/1	5/2	6/2
54.70	211.30	44.10	27.40		
8/4	9/1	10/1	11/4		

K.S.DHAMI,J.B.STOTHERS
CAN J CHEM   43, 498 (1965)

---

703   Q 003500 2-METHYL-5-METHOXYPIVALOPHENONE

```
        CH3
      3 |         9
      C-C2    O   CH3
     /   \1 ||  8/10
    4C       C-C-C-CH3
     \   / 7  \11
      5C=C6       CH3
   12 /
 CH3O
```

FORMULA	C13H18O2			MOL WT	206.29
SOLVENT	CS2				
ORIG ST	CS2			TEMP	AMB
129.90	132.10	127.40	111.20	153.20	111.20
1/1	2/1	3/2	4/2	5/1	6/2
211.70	44.30	27.90	27.90	27.90	55.80
7/1	8/1	9/4	10/4	11/4	12/4

K.S.DHAMI,J.B.STOTHERS
CAN J CHEM   43, 498 (1965)

704   Q 003900   PARA—BENZOQUINONE

```
        6
        C   O
       // \ //
     5C   1C
      |    |
     C4   C2
      // \ //
    O    C
         3
```

FORMULA	C6H4O2		MOL WT	108.10
SOLVENT	CDCL3			
ORIG ST	TMS		TEMP	AMB

187.00   136.40
1/1   2/2

S.BERGER,A.RIEKER
TETRAHEDRON   28, 3123 (1972)

---

705   Q 003900   2—METHYL—PARA—BENZOQUINONE

```
        6
        C   O
       // \ //
     5C   1C
      |    |
     C4   2C
      // \ //
    O    C    CH3
         3    7
```

FORMULA	C7H6O2		MOL WT	122.12
SOLVENT	CDCL3			
ORIG ST	TMS		TEMP	AMB

187.50	145.90	133.30	187.70	136.60	136.50
1/1	2/1	3/2	4/1	5/2	6/2
15.80					
7/4					

S.BERGER,A.RIEKER
TETRAHEDRON   28, 3123 (1972)

---

706   Q 003900   2,6—DIMETHYL—PARA—BENZOQUINONE

```
      8CH3
        |
        C   O
       //6\ //
     5C   1C
      |    |
     C4   2C
      // \3// \7
    O    C    CH3
```

FORMULA	C8H8O2		MOL WT	136.15
SOLVENT	CDCL3			
ORIG ST	TMS		TEMP	AMB

| 187.60 | 145.80 | 133.80 | 188.30 | 15.80 |
| 1/1 | 2/1 | 3/2 | 4/1 | 7/4 |

S.BERGER,A.RIEKER
TETRAHEDRON   28, 3123 (1972)

---

707   Q 003900   DUROQUINONE

```
        CH3
         |
   H3C   C   O
      \ //6\ //
     C5   1C
      |    |
     C4   2C
      // \3// \
    O    C    CH3
         |    7
        CH3
```

FORMULA	C10H12O2		MOL WT	164.21
SOLVENT	CDCL3			
ORIG ST	TMS		TEMP	AMB

| 187.40 | 140.40 | 12.40 |
| 1/1 | 2/1 | 7/4 |

S.BERGER,A.RIEKER
TETRAHEDRON   28, 3123 (1972)

---

708   Q 003900   2,6—DIISOPROPYL—PARA—BENZOQUINONE

```
            6
  CH3)2HC   C   O
        \ // \ //
       C5   1C
        |    |
       C4   2C
        // \ // \7  8
      O    C    CH(CH3)2
           3
```

FORMULA	C12H16O2		MOL WT	192.26
SOLVENT	CDCL3			
ORIG ST	TMS		TEMP	AMB

| 186.80 | 155.30 | 129.80 | 188.60 | 27.00 | 21.50 |
| 1/1 | 2/1 | 3/2 | 4/1 | 7/2 | 8/4 |

S.BERGER,A.RIEKER
TETRAHEDRON   28, 3123 (1972)

709   Q 003900   2,5-DI-TERT-BUTYL-PARA-BENZOQUINONE

```
           6
(CH3)3C   C    O
      \ // \ //
       C5  1C
       |   |
       C4  2C
      // \ // \7 8
    O   C   C(CH3)3
        3
```

FORMULA	C14H20O2			MOL WT	220.31
SOLVENT	CDCL3				
ORIG ST	TMS			TEMP	AMB

188.20	154.20	135.50	34.50	29.00
1/1	2/1	3/2	7/1	8/4

S.BERGER,A.RIEKER
TETRAHEDRON   28, 3123 (1972)

---

710   Q 003900   2,6-DI-TERT-BUTYL-PARA-BENZOQUINONE

```
        C(CH3)3
        |
        C    O
       // 6 \ //
      5C   1C
      |    |
      C4   2C
     // \ // \7 8
    O   3C   C(CH3)3
```

FORMULA	C14H20O2			MOL WT	220.31
SOLVENT	CDCL3				
ORIG ST	TMS			TEMP	AMB

187.70	157.70	130.10	188.60	35.50	29.30
1/1	2/1	3/2	4/1	7/1	8/4

S.BERGER,A.RIEKER
TETRAHEDRON   28, 3123 (1972)

---

711   Q 003900   2,5-DIPHENYL-PARA-BENZOQUINONE

```
           6
  C6H5    C    O
      \ // \ //  8 9
       C5  1C   C-C
       |   |   //   \
       C4  2C-C7    C10
      // \ // \    /
    O   C    C=C
        3   12 11
```

FORMULA	C18H12O2			MOL WT	260.30
SOLVENT	CDCL3				
ORIG ST	TMS			TEMP	AMB

187.00	147.70	132.60	133.20	129.50	130.10
1/1	2/1	3/2	7/1	8/2	9/2
128.60					
10/2					

S.BERGER,A.RIEKER
TETRAHEDRON   28, 3123 (1972)

---

712   Q 003900   2,6-DIPHENYL-PARA-BENZOQUINONE

```
        C6H5
        |
        C    O
       // 6 \ //
      5C   1C   C-C
      |    |   //   \
      4C   2C-C7    C10
     // \ // \     /
    O   C    C=C
        3    8 9
```

FORMULA	C18H12O2			MOL WT	260.30
SOLVENT	CDCL3				
ORIG ST	TMS			TEMP	AMB

186.00	146.40	132.50	187.50	133.10	129.90
1/1	2/1	3/2	4/1	7/1	8/2
129.40	128.30				
9/2	10/2				

S.BERGER,A.RIEKER
TETRAHEDRON   28, 3123 (1972)

---

713   Q 003900   2,3,5,6-TETRAPHENYL-PARA-BENZOQUINONE

```
        C6H5
        |
  C6H5  C    O
     \ // 6 \ // 8 9
      C5  1C   C-C
      |   |   //  \
      C4  2C-C7    C10
     // \ 3 / \   /
    O   C    C=C
        |
        C6H5
```

FORMULA	C30H20O2			MOL WT	412.49
SOLVENT	CDCL3				
ORIG ST	TMS			TEMP	AMB

186.90	143.30	132.90	130.90	128.40	127.70
1/1	2/1	7/1	8/2	9/2	10/2

S.BERGER,A.RIEKER
TETRAHEDRON   28, 3123 (1972)

714   Q 003900   2-PENTACHLOROPHENOXY-6-TERT-BUTYL-PARA-BENZOQUINONE

```
      7C(CH3)3
      │ 8
      C    O  CL      CL
     ⁄6\  ⁄       ⁄
   C5  1C    10C-C11
   │    │     ⁄     ＼
   C4  2C-O-C9  12C-CL
   ⁄＼  ⁄       ＼   ⁄
  O   C      14C=C13
      3        ⁄   ＼
             CL    CL
```

FORMULA   C16H11O2CL5   MOL WT   412.53
SOLVENT   CDCL3
ORIG ST   TMS   TEMP   AMB

179.50	155.00	109.80	186.90	131.90	154.50
1/1	2/1	3/2	4/1	5/2	6/1
35.50	29.10	145.30	132.20	127.10	132.70
7/1	8/4	9/1	10/1	11/1	12/1

S.BERGER, A.RIEKER
TETRAHEDRON   28, 3123 (1972)

---

715   Q 003900   2-CHLORO-PARA-BENZOQUINONE

```
       6
       C    O
      ⁄＼  ⁄
    5C  1C
    │    │
    C4  2C
   ⁄＼  ⁄＼
  O   C   CL
      3
```

FORMULA   C6H3O2CL   MOL WT   142.54
SOLVENT   CDCL3
ORIG ST   TMS   TEMP   AMB

179.20	144.10	133.70	184.90	136.80	136.00
1/1	2/1	3/2	4/1	5/2	6/2

S.BERGER, A.RIEKER
TETRAHEDRON   28, 3123 (1972)

---

716   Q 003900   2,5-DICHLORO-PARA-BENZOQUINONE

```
       6
  CL   C    O
   ＼  ⁄＼  ⁄
    C5  1C
    │    │
    C4  2C
   ⁄＼  ⁄＼
  O   C   CL
      3
```

FORMULA   C6H2O2CL2   MOL WT   176.99
SOLVENT   C2H5OH
ORIG ST   TMS   TEMP   348

176.70	143.80	132.80
1/1	2/1	3/2

S.BERGER, A.RIEKER
TETRAHEDRON   28, 3123 (1972)

---

717   Q 003900   2,6-DIMETHYL-3,5-DICHLORO-PARA-BENZOQUINONE

```
      CH3
      │
  CL   C    O
   ＼  ⁄6\  ⁄
    C5  1C
    │    │
    C4  2C
   ⁄  ＼3＼
  O   C   CH3
      │    7
      CL
```

FORMULA   C8H6O2CL2   MOL WT   205.04
SOLVENT   CDCL3
ORIG ST   TMS   TEMP   AMB

182.50	142.70	139.90	172.30	13.40
1/1	2/1	3/1	4/1	7/4

S.BERGER, A.RIEKER
TETRAHEDRON   28, 3123 (1972)

---

718   Q 003900   2,3-DICHLORO-5,6-DICYANO-PARA-BENZOQUINONE

```
      C≡N
   7  │
  N≡C   C    O
   ＼  ⁄6\  ⁄
    C5  1C
    │    │
    C4  2C
   ⁄  ＼3⁄＼
  O   C   CL
      │
      CL
```

FORMULA   C8N2O2CL2   MOL WT   227.01
SOLVENT   CD3OD
ORIG ST   TMS   TEMP   AMB

170.10	142.10	142.10	170.10	132.90	132.90
1/1	2/1	3/1	4/1	5/1	6/1
124.80					
7/1					

S.BERGER, A.RIEKER
TETRAHEDRON   28, 3123 (1972)

719   Q 003900   2,3,5,6-TETRACHLORO-PARA-BENZOQUINONE

```
        CL
        I
   CL   C    O
    \  //6\ //
     C5  1C
     I   I
     C4  2C
    //  \3/ \
   O    C    CL
        I
        CL
```

FORMULA   C6O2CL4   MOL WT   245.88
SOLVENT   C2D6O S
ORIG ST   TMS   TEMP   323

169.40   139.40
1/1   2/1

S.BERGER,A.RIEKER
TETRAHEDRON   28, 3123 (1972)

---

720   Q 003900   2,6-DIAZIRIDINO-PARA-BENZOQUINONE

```
   C
   I\   6
   I N-C    O
  I/ // \ // 7
  C C5  1C   C
    I   I  /I
    C4  2C-N I
   // \ //  \I
  O   3C    8C
```

FORMULA   C10H10N2O2   MOL WT   190.20
SOLVENT   CDCL3
ORIG ST   TMS   TEMP   AMB

180.00   154.80   117.20   187.20   27.40
1/1   2/1   3/2   4/1   7/4

S.BERGER,A.RIEKER
TETRAHEDRON   28, 3123 (1972)

---

721   Q 003900   ORTHO-BENZOQUINONE

```
     O
     II
     C    O
    /1\ //
  6C   2C
   II   I
  5C   C3
    \4/
     C
```

FORMULA   C6H4O2   MOL WT   108.10
SOLVENT   CDCL3
ORIG ST   TMS   TEMP   223

180.20   140.00   130.40
1/1   3/2   4/2

S.BERGER,A.RIEKER
TETRAHEDRON   28, 3123 (1972)

---

722   Q 003900   4,6-DI-TERT-BUTYL-ORTHO-BENZOQUINONE

```
        O
  10  9 II
 (CH3)3C  C    O
    \ /1\ //
     C6 2C
     II  I
     5C  C3
      \4/
       C
       I 8
     7C(CH3)3
```

FORMULA   C14H20O2   MOL WT   220.31
SOLVENT   CDCL3
ORIG ST   TMS   TEMP   AMB

179.60   180.60   121.60   149.40   133.10   162.80
1/1   2/1   3/2   4/1   5/2   6/1

35.00   27.40   35.60   28.80
7/1   8/4   9/1   10/4

S.BERGER,A.RIEKER
TETRAHEDRON   28, 3123 (1972)

---

723   Q 003900   3-PHENYL-4,6-DI-T-BUTYL-ORTHO-BENZOQUINONE

```
        O
 16   15 II
 (CH3)3C  C    O
    \ /1\ // 8 9
     C6 2C  C-C
     II  I //   \
     5C  3C-C7   C10
      \4/  \    /
       C    C=C
       I    12 11
     13C(CH3)3
        14
```

FORMULA   C20H24O2   MOL WT   1854.14
SOLVENT   CDCL3
ORIG ST   TMS   TEMP   AMB

179.00   182.50   135.60   147.90   137.50   155.70
1/1   2/1   3/1   4/1   5/2   6/1

137.00   130.00   127.60   127.80   35.50   28.60
7/1   8/2   9/2   10/2   13/1   14/4

37.50   29.00
15/1   16/4

S.BERGER,A.RIEKER
TETRAHEDRON   28, 3123 (1972)

724   Q 003900   3-CHLORO-4,6-DI-TERT-BUTYL-ORTHO-BENZOQUINONE

```
        O
10    9  ‖
(CH3)3C   C    O
      \ /1\ ⁄
      C6 2C
      ‖    ‖
      5C   3C
       \4⁄ \
        C   CL
        ‖ 8
      7C(CH3)3
```

FORMULA   C14H19O2CL   MOL WT   254.76
SOLVENT   CDCL3
ORIG ST   TMS   TEMP   AMB

178.10   174.80   129.30   147.40   135.90   155.10
 1/1   2/1   3/1   4/1   5/2   6/1
 35.50   28.60   37.50   29.00
 7/1   8/4   9/1   10/4

S.BERGER,A.RIEKER
TETRAHEDRON   28, 3123 (1972)

---

725   Q 003900   3-BROMO-4,6-DI-TERT-BUTYL-ORTHO-BENZOQUINONE

```
        O
10    9  ‖
(CH3)3C   C    O
      \ /1\ ⁄
      C6 2C
      ‖    ‖
      5C   3C
       \4⁄ \
        C   BR
        ‖ 8
      7C(CH3)3
```

FORMULA   C14H19O2BR   MOL WT   299.21
SOLVENT   CDCL3
ORIG ST   TMS   TEMP   AMB

178.20   175.00   122.00   147.50   136.30   158.40
 1/1   2/1   3/1   4/1   5/2   6/1
 35.50   28.80   38.30   29.00
 7/1   8/4   9/1   10/4

S.BERGER,A.RIEKER
TETRAHEDRON   28, 3123 (1972)

---

726   Q 003900   3,4,5,6-TETRACHLORO-ORTHO-BENZOQUINONE

```
       O
       ‖
CL     C    O
  \ /1\ ⁄
  C6 2C
  ‖    ‖
  C5 3C
 ⁄ \4⁄ \
CL   C   CL
     ‖
     CL
```

FORMULA   C6O2CL4   MOL WT   245.88
SOLVENT   CDCL3
ORIG ST   TMS   TEMP   AMB

168.80   143.80   131.90
 1/1   3/1   4/1

S.BERGER,A.RIEKER
TETRAHEDRON   28, 3123 (1972)

---

727   Q 003900   3-NITRO-4,6-DI-TERT-BUTYL-ORTHO-BENZOQUINONE

```
        O
10    9  ‖
(CH3)3C   C    O
      \ /1\ ⁄
      C6 2C
      ‖    ‖
      5C   3C
       \4⁄ \
        C   NO2
        ‖ 8
      7C(CH3)3
```

FORMULA   C14H19NO4   MOL WT   265.31
SOLVENT   CDCL3
ORIG ST   TMS   TEMP   AMB

175.30   171.80   143.30   149.60   133.10   150.90
 1/1   2/1   3/1   4/1   5/2   6/1
 35.90   27.20   37.60   28.80
 1/1   8/4   9/1   10/4

S.BERGER,A.RIEKER
TETRAHEDRON   28, 3123 (1972)

---

728   Q 005200   BENZONITRILE

```
    5 6
    C-C
   ⁄   ∖1 7
 4C      C-C≡N
   \   ⁄
    C=C
    3 2
```

FORMULA   C7H5N   MOL WT   103.12
SOLVENT   C7H5N
ORIG ST   CS2   TEMP   AMB

109.40   129.80   126.90   129.80   126.90   129.80
 1/1   2/2   3/2   4/2   5/2   6/2
115.90
 7/1

F.W.WEHRLI,J.W.DE HAAN,A.I.M.KEULEMANS,O.EXNER,
W.SIMON
HELV CHIM ACTA   52, 103 (1969)
```
```

729   Q 005200   PENTADEUTERIOBENZONITRILE

```
        D
       6C    C≡N
     D ⁄  ╲ ⁄
    5C    C1
     |    ||
    4C    C2
     D ╲ ⁄ D
       C3
        D
```

FORMULA	C7D5N			MOL WT	108.16
SOLVENT	C7D5N				
ORIG ST	TMS			TEMP	298

111.45	131.10	128.07	131.75	118.15
1/1	2/3	3/3	4/3	7/1

E.BREITMAIER,G.JUNG,W.VOELTER,L.POHL
UNPUBLISHED   (1972)

730   Q 005200   4-METHYLBENZONITRILE

```
      5 6
      C-C
     4⁄  ╲1 7
  H3C-C      C-C≡N
      ╲  ⁄
      C=C
      3 2
```

FORMULA	C8H7N			MOL WT	117.15
SOLVENT	C4H10O				
ORIG ST	CS2			TEMP	AMB

107.30	130.80	128.50	142.80	128.50	130.80
1/1	2/2	3/2	4/1	5/2	6/2
117.00					
7/1					

F.W.WEHRLI,J.W.DE HAAN,A.I.M.KEULEMANS,O.EXNER,
W.SIMON
HELV CHIM ACTA   52, 103 (1969)

731   Q 005200   4-FLUOROBENZONITRILE

```
      5 6
      C-C
     4⁄  ╲1 7
   F-C      C-C≡N
      ╲  ⁄
      C=C
      3 2
```

FORMULA	C7H4NF			MOL WT	121.12
SOLVENT	C3H6O				
ORIG ST	CS2			TEMP	AMB

104.50	131.30	112.70	162.90	112.70	131.30
1/1	2/2	3/2	4/1	5/2	6/2
113.70					
7/1					

F.W.WEHRLI,J.W.DE HAAN,A.I.M.KEULEMANS,O.EXNER,
W.SIMON
HELV CHIM ACTA   52, 103 (1969)

732   Q 005200   4-CHLOROBENZONITRILE

```
      5 6
      C-C
     4⁄  ╲1 7
  CL-C      C-C≡N
      ╲  ⁄
      C=C
      3 2
```

FORMULA	C7H4NCL			MOL WT	137.57
SOLVENT	C3H6O				
ORIG ST	CS2			TEMP	AMB

107.00	130.40	126.30	140.80	126.30	130.40
1/1	2/2	3/2	4/1	5/2	6/2
114.00					
7/1					

F.W.WEHRLI,J.W.DE HAAN,A.I.M.KEULEMANS,O.EXNER,
W.SIMON
HELV CHIM ACTA   52, 103 (1969)

733   Q 005200   4-BROMOBENZONITRILE

```
      5 6
      C-C
     4⁄  ╲1 7
  BR-C      C-C≡N
      ╲  ⁄
      C=C
      3 2
```

FORMULA	C7H4NBR			MOL WT	182.02
SOLVENT	C2H6OS				
ORIG ST	CS2			TEMP	AMB

109.50	133.40	132.00	160.40	132.00	133.40
1/1	2/2	3/2	4/1	5/2	6/2
119.20					
7/1					

F.W.WEHRLI,J.W.DE HAAN,A.I.M.KEULEMANS,O.EXNER,
W.SIMON
HELV CHIM ACTA   52, 103 (1969)

---

734 Q 005200 4-NITROBENZONITRILE

```
      5 6
      C-C
    4//   \\1 7
O2N-C      C-C≡N
     \   /
      C=C
      3 2
```

FORMULA	C7H4O2N2			MOL WT	148.12
SOLVENT	C2H6OS				
ORIG ST	CS2			TEMP	AMB

116.10	122.60	134.30	149.80	134.30	122.60
1/1	2/2	3/2	4/1	5/2	6/2
111.70					
7/1					

F.W.WEHRLI,J.W.DE HAAN,A.I.M.KEULEMANS,O.EXNER,
W.SIMON
HELV CHIM ACTA   52, 103 (1969)

---

735 Q 005200 4-AMINOBENZONITRILE

```
      5 6
      C-C
    4//   \\1 7
H2N-C      C-C≡N
     \   /
      C=C
      3 2
```

FORMULA	C7H6N2			MOL WT	118.14
SOLVENT	C3H6O				
ORIG ST	CS2			TEMP	AMB

90.80	127.30	107.10	146.40	107.10	127.30
1/1	2/2	3/2	4/1	5/2	6/2
114.20					
7/1					

F.W.WEHRLI,J.W.DE HAAN,A.I.M.KEULEMANS,O.EXNER,
W.SIMON
HELV CHIM ACTA   52, 103 (1969)

---

736 Q 005200 4-DIMETHYLAMINOBENZONITRILE

```
           5 6
    H3C     C-C
      \   4//   \\1 7
       N-C       C-C≡N
      /    \   /
    H3C     C=C
            3 2
```

FORMULA	C9H10N2			MOL WT	146.19
SOLVENT	C3H6O				
ORIG ST	CS2			TEMP	AMB

92.50	129.70	107.60	150.10	107.60	129.70
1/1	2/2	3/2	4/1	5/2	6/2
116.80					
7/1'					

F.W.WEHRLI,J.W.DE HAAN,A.I.M.KEULEMANS,O.EXNER,
W.SIMON
HELV CHIM ACTA   52, 103 (1969)

---

737 Q 005300 METHYL BENZOATE

```
    6   7  8
    C   C-OCH3
   //  \ / \
  5C   1C   O
  |    ||
  4C   C2
   \  /
    C
    3
```

FORMULA	C8H11O2			MOL WT	139.18
SOLVENT	C8H11O2				
ORIG ST	CS2			TEMP	AMB

129.70	127.90	127.90	131.90	165.60	51.00
1/1	2/2	3/2	4/2	7/1	8/4

K.S.DHAMI,J.B.STOTHERS
CAN J CHEM   45, 233 (1967)

---

738 Q 005300 METHYL 2-METHYLBENZOATE

```
    6   7  8
    C   C-OCH3
   //  \ / \
  5C   1C   O
  |    ||
  4C   2C
   \  / \
    C    CH3
    3    9
```

FORMULA	C9H10O2			MOL WT	150.18
SOLVENT	C9H10O2				
ORIG ST	CS2			TEMP	AMB

128.70	135.70	130.50	133.90	124.00	130.50
1/1	2/1	3/2	4/2	5/2	6/2
166.00	50.40				
7/1	9/4				

K.S.DHAMI,J.B.STOTHERS
CAN J CHEM   45, 233 (1967)

739   Q 005300   METHYL 3-METHYLBENZOATE

```
    6   7   8
    C   C-OCH3
   ⁄ \ ⁄ \
 5C  1C   O
  |   ||
 4C   C2
  \3⁄
    C
    |
   9CH3
```

FORMULA	C9H10O2			MOL WT	150.18
SOLVENT	C9H10O2				
ORIG ST	CS2			TEMP	AMB

129.80	126.90	136.90	130.50	126.90	125.30
1/1	2/2	3/1	4/2	5/2	6/2
165.30	50.40				
7/1	8/4				

K.S.DHAMI,J.B.STOTHERS
CAN J CHEM   45, 233 (1967)

740   Q 005300   METHYL 4-METHYLBENZOATE

```
    6   7   8
    C   C-OCH3
   ⁄ \ ⁄ \
 5C  1C   O
  |   ||
  C4  C2
 ⁄ \ ⁄
H3C   C
 9    3
```

FORMULA	C9H10O2			MOL WT	150.18
SOLVENT	C9H10O2				
ORIG ST	CS2			TEMP	AMB

126.40	128.10	128.10	141.90	165.00	50.20
1/1	2/2	3/2	4/1	7/1	8/4

K.S.DHAMI,J.B.STOTHERS
CAN J CHEM   45, 233 (1967)

741   Q 005300   METHYL 2,3-DIMETHYLBENZOATE

```
    6   7   8
    C   C-OCH3
   ⁄ \ ⁄ \
 5C  1C   O
  |   ||
 4C   2C
  \3⁄ \
    C   CH3
    |   9
   CH3
   10
```

FORMULA	C10H12O2			MOL WT	164.21
SOLVENT	C10H12O2				
ORIG ST	CS2			TEMP	AMB

129.60	136.70	136.70	132.10	126.80	133.90
1/1	2/1	3/1	4/2	5/2	6/2
166.80	50.30				
7/1	8/4				

K.S.DHAMI,J.B.STOTHERS
CAN J CHEM   45, 233 (1967)

742   Q 005300   METHYL 2,6-DIMETHYLBENZOATE

```
    6  10
    C-CH3
   ⁄ \  7  8
 5C  1C-C-OCH3
  |   ||  \
 4C   2C   O
  \ ⁄ \
   C   CH3
   3   9
```

FORMULA	C10H12O2			MOL WT	164.21
SOLVENT	C10H12O2				
ORIG ST	CS2			TEMP	AMB

133.30	133.30	126.50	128.20	168.90	50.40
1/1	2/1	3/2	4/2	7/1	8/4

K.S.DHAMI,J.B.STOTHERS
CAN J CHEM   45, 233 (1967)

743   Q 005300   METHYL 2,4,6-TRIMETHYLBENZOATE

```
   11CH3
    |   7   8
    C   C-OCH3
   ⁄6\ ⁄ \
 5C  1C   O
  |   ||
  C4  2C
 10⁄ \3⁄ \
H3C   C   9CH3
```

FORMULA	C11H14O2			MOL WT	178.23
SOLVENT	C11H14O2				
ORIG ST	CS2			TEMP	AMB

130.40	134.10	127.50	137.80	168.50	50.10
1/1	2/1	3/2	4/1	7/1	8/4

K.S.DHAMI,J.B.STOTHERS
CAN J CHEM   45, 233 (1967)

744   Q 005300   METHYL 2-CHLOROBENZOATE

```
    6   7   8
    C   C-OCH3
   ⁄ \ ⁄ ‖
 5C  1C   O
  |   ‖
 4C  2C
   \ ⁄ \
    C   CL
    3
```

FORMULA	C8H7O2CL			MOL WT	170.60
SOLVENT	C8H7O2CL				
ORIG ST	CS2			TEMP	AMB

129.50	136.10	126.10	130.70	126.10	126.10
1/1	2/1	3/2	4/2	5/2	6/2
164.60	51.50				
7/1	8/4				

K.S.DHAMI,J.B.STOTHERS
CAN J CHEM   45, 233 (1967)

---

745   Q 005300   METHYL 2-BROMOBENZOATE

```
    6   7   8
    C   C-OCH3
   ⁄ \ ⁄ ‖
 5C  1C   O
  |   ‖
 4C  2C
   \ ⁄ \
    C   BR
    3
```

FORMULA	C8H7O2BR			MOL WT	215.05
SOLVENT	C8H7O2BR				
ORIG ST	CS2			TEMP	AMB

131.70	121.00	131.40	133.30	126.30	126.30
1/1	2/1	3/2	4/2	5/2	6/2
165.10	51.90				
7/1	8/4				

K.S.DHAMI,J.B.STOTHERS
CAN J CHEM   45, 233 (1967)

---

746   Q 005300   METHYL 2-IODOBENZOATE

```
    6   7   8
    C   C-OCH3
   ⁄ \ ⁄ ‖
 5C  1C   O
  |   ‖
 4C  2C
   \ ⁄ \
    C   J
    3
```

FORMULA	C8H7O2I			MOL WT	262.05
SOLVENT	C8H7O2I				
ORIG ST	CS2			TEMP	AMB

134.50	94.10	141.30	132.10	127.50	130.50
1/1	2/1	3/2	4/2	5/2	6/2
165.60	52.40				
7/1	8/4				

K.S.DHAMI,J.B.STOTHERS
CAN J CHEM   45, 233 (1967)

---

747   Q 005300   METHYL 2,6-DICHLOROBENZOATE

```
    CL
    |   7   8
    C   C-OCH3
   ⁄6\ ⁄ ‖
 5C  1C   O
  |   ‖
 4C  2C
   \3⁄ \
    C   CL
```

FORMULA	C8H6O2CL2			MOL WT	205.04
SOLVENT	C8H6O2CL2				
ORIG ST	CS2			TEMP	AMB

| 130.80 | 132.60 | 126.60 | 130.20 | 163.70 | 52.00 |
| 1/1 | 2/1 | 3/2 | 4/2 | 7/1 | 8/4 |

K.S.DHAMI,J.B.STOTHERS
CAN J CHEM   45, 233 (1967)

---

748   Q 005300   METHYL 2,4,6-TRIBROMOBENZOATE

```
    BR
    |   7   8
    C   C-OCH3
   ⁄6\ ⁄ ‖
 5C  1C   O
  |   ‖
  C4 2C
  ⁄ \3⁄ \
 BR  C   BR
```

FORMULA	C8H5O2BR3			MOL WT	372.84
SOLVENT	CHCL3				
ORIG ST	CS2			TEMP	AMB

| 136.60 | 120.00 | 133.40 | 123.70 | 165.30 | 53.30 |
| 1/1 | 2/1 | 3/2 | 4/1 | 7/1 | 8/4 |

K.S.DHAMI,J.B.STOTHERS
CAN J CHEM   45, 233 (1967)

749 Q 005300 METHYL 2—NITROBENZOATE

```
      6   7   8
      C   C—OCH3
     ⫽ ⟍ ⟋ ⟍
    5C  1C   O
    |   ‖
   4C  2C
     ⟍ ⟋
      C   NO2
      3
```

FORMULA	C8H7N O4			MOL WT	181.15
SOLVENT	C8H7O4N				
ORIG ST	CS2			TEMP	AMB

125.90	146.80	122.60	131.40	131.40	128.70
1/1	2/1	3/2	4/2	5/2	6/2
164.10	52.00				
7/1	8/4				

K.S.DHAMI,J.B.STOTHERS
CAN J CHEM   45, 233 (1967)

---

750 Q 005300 METHYL 4—NITROBENZOATE

```
      6   7   8
      C   C—OCH3
     ⫽ ⟍ ⟋ ⟍
    5C  1C   O
    |   ‖
   C4  C2
   ⟋ ⟍ ⟋
 O2N   C
       3
```

FORMULA	C8H7N O4			MOL WT	181.15
SOLVENT	CHCL3				
ORIG ST	CS2			TEMP	AMB

135.80	130.40	123.30	149.90	164.90	53.00
1/1	2/2	3/2	4/1	7/1	8/4

K.S.DHAMI,J.B.STOTHERS
CAN J CHEM   45, 233 (1967)

---

751 Q 005300 METHYL 4—METHOXYBENZOATE

```
      6   7   8
      C   C—OCH3
     ⫽ ⟍ ⟋ ⟍
    5C  1C   O
    |   ‖
   C4  C2
   ⟋ ⟍ ⟋
 H3CO   C
        3
```

FORMULA	C9H10O3			MOL WT	166.18
SOLVENT	C9H10O3				
ORIG ST	CS2			TEMP	AMB

122.00	130.60	113.10	162.50	165.30	50.90
1/1	2/2	3/2	4/1	7/1	8/4

K.S.DHAMI,J.B.STOTHERS
CAN J CHEM   45, 233 (1967)

---

752 Q 007800 NAPHTHALENE

```
    8    1
    C    C
   ⫽ ⟍ ⟋ ⟍
  7C  C9  C2
  |   ‖   |
  6C  C10 C3
   ⟍ ⟋ ⟍ ⫽
    C    C
    5    4
```

FORMULA	C10H8		MOL WT	128.18
SOLVENT	CS2			
ORIG ST	C6H6		TEMP	AMB

128.05	125.95	133.70
1/2	2/2	9/1

T.D.ALGER,D.M.GRANT,E.G.PAUL
J AM CHEM SOC   88, 5397 (1970)

---

753 Q 007800 1,8—DIMETHYLNAPHTHALENE

```
   H3C  12CH3
   11|    |
    C8    C
   ⫽ ⟍  ⟋1⟍
  7C  C9  C2
  |   ‖   |
  6C  C10 C3
   ⟍ ⟋ ⟍ ⫽
    C    C
    5    4
```

FORMULA	C12H12			MOL WT	156.23
SOLVENT	CS2				
ORIG ST	C6H6			TEMP	AMB

135.60	128.40	129.80	125.35	133.55	136.35
1/1	2/2	3/2	4/2	9/1	10/1
25.95					
11/4					

A.J.JONES,T.D.ALGER,D.M.GRANT,W.M.LITCHMAN
J AM CHEM SOC   92, 2386 (1970)

754   Q 007800 AZULENE

```
    3    4 5
    C   C-C
   // \ // \ \
      C10
  2C   |    C6
   \   C9   /
    \ // \ /
    C   C=C
    1   8 7
```

FORMULA	C10H8			MOL WT	128.18
SOLVENT	C S2				
ORIG ST	C6H6			TEMP	AMB
118.95	137.65	136.75	123.05	137.25	140.65
1/2	2/2	4/2	5/2	6/2	9/1

A.J.JONES,T.D.ALGER,D.M.GRANT,W.M.LITCHMAN
J AM CHEM SOC   92, 2386 (1970)

---

755   Q 010700 ACENAPHTHYLENE

```
  1C===C2
  |      |
  9C    C10
 // \  / //
 8C   C11 C3
 |    ||   |
 7C   C12 C4
 \\  / \ //
   C    C
   6    5
```

FORMULA	C12H8			MOL WT	152.20
SOLVENT	C S2				
ORIG ST	C6H6			TEMP	AMB
129.65	124.30	127.85	127.35	140.00	128.65
1/2	3/2	4/2	5/2	9/1	11/1
128.40					
12/1					

A.J.JONES,T.D.ALGER,D.M.GRANT,W.M.LITCHMAN
J AM CHEM SOC   92, 2386 (1970)

---

756   Q 010700 FLUORANTHENE

```
  8C---C9
 //     \\
 7C      C10
  \      /
  12C===C11
   |      |
  14C    C13
 // \  / \\
 6C   C15 C1
 |    ||   |
 5C   C16 C2
 \\  / \ //
   C4   C3
```

FORMULA	C16H10			MOL WT	202.26
SOLVENT	C S2				
ORIG ST	C6H6			TEMP	AMB
122.90	128.50	127.25	120.65	128.20	140.15
1/2	2/2	3/2	7/2	8/2	11/1
137.65	132.90	130.70			
13/1	15/1	16/1			

A.J.JONES,T.D.ALGER,D.M.GRANT,W.M.LITCHMAN
J AM CHEM SOC   92, 2386 (1970)

---

757   Q 010700 BENZO(GHI)FLUCRANTHENE

```
  5C          C6
 / \        / \
 4C 15C---C16 C7
 ||  |    ||   |
 3C 13C   C14 C8
  \ // \ / \ //
  17C   C12 C18
   |    ||   |
  2C   C11  C9
  \\  / \ //
   1C    C10
```

FORMULA	C18H10			MOL WT	226.28
SOLVENT	C S2				
ORIG ST	C6H6			TEMP	AMB
125.45	127.05	126.70	128.75	123.65	133.40
1/2	2/2	3/2	4/2	5/2	11/1
126.85	128.05	137.75	133.65		
12/1	13/1	15/1	17/1		

A.J.JONES,T.D.ALGER,D.M.GRANT,W.M.LITCHMAN
J AM CHEM SOC   92, 2386 (1970)

---

758   Q 010700 ACENAPHTHENE

```
   1    2
   C---C
   |    |
   9C   C10
  // \ / /
  8C   C11 C3
  |    ||  |
  7C   C12 C4
  \\  / \ //
    C    C
    6    5
```

FORMULA	C12H10			MOL WT	154.21
SOLVENT	C S2				
ORIG ST	C6H6			TEMP	AMB
30.25	119.45	128.15	122.65	145.85	139.65
1/3	3/2	4/2	5/2	9/1	11/1
132.05					
12/1					

A.J.JONES,T.D.ALGER,D.M.GRANT,W.M.LITCHMAN
J AM CHEM SOC   92, 2386 (1970)

759   Q 010700   ACEPLEIADIENE

```
  1C---C2
  |     |
 11C    C12
  / \ / \
10C  C16 C3
 ||   |   |
 9C  C15 C4
  \ / \ /
 13C    C14
  /       \
 8C        C5
  \\      //
   7C---C6
```

FORMULA	C16H12			MOL WT	204.27
SOLVENT	CS2				
ORIG ST	C6H6			TEMP	AMB

29.60	120.05	127.95	125.90	138.40	143.85
1/3	3/2	4/2	5/2	6/2	11/1
135.85	136.50	142.85			
13/1	15/1	16/1			

A.J.JONES,P.D.GARDNER,D.M.GRANT,W.M.LITCHMAN,
V.BOEKELHEIDE
J AM CHEM SOC   92, 2395 (1970)

---

760   Q 010700   ACEPLEIDYLENE

```
  1C===C2
  |     |
 11C    C12
  / \ / \
10C  C16 C3
 ||   |   |
 9C  C15 C4
  \ / \ /
 13C    C14
  /       \
 8C        C5
  \\      //
   7C---C6
```

FORMULA	C16H10			MOL WT	202.26
SOLVENT	CS2				
ORIG ST	C6H6			TEMP	AMB

126.15	125.80	127.40	126.85	137.00	138.15
1/2	3/2	4/2	5/2	6/2	11/1
134.85	127.20	126.60			
13/1	15/1	16/1			

A.J.JONES,P.D.GARDNER,D.M.GRANT,W.M.LITCHMAN,
V.BOEKELHEIDE
J AM CHEM SOC   92, 2395 (1970)

---

761   Q 010900   PHENANTHRENE

```
  10    1
   C    C
  / \  / \
 9C   C11 C2
  |    ||  |
14C   C12 C3
 / \ / \ /
8C 13C   C
 ||  |    4
7C   C5
 \  /
  6C
```

FORMULA	C14H10			MOL WT	178.24
SOLVENT	CS2				
ORIG ST	C6H6			TEMP	AMB

128.90	126.75	126.75	123.05	127.30	132.30
1/2	2/2	3/2	4/2	9/2	11/1
130.50					
12/1					

T.D.ALGER,D.M.GRANT,E.G.PAUL
J AM CHEM SOC   88, 5397 (1966)

---

762   Q 011200   PYRENE

```
        C2
       / \
  1C     C3
   ||    |
 11C    C12
  / \  / \
10C  C15 C4
 ||   |   ||
 9C  C16 C5
  \ / \ /
 14C    C13
  |      ||
 8C      C6
  \\    /
    C7
```

FORMULA	C16H10			MOL WT	202.26
SOLVENT	CS2				
ORIG ST	C6H6			TEMP	AMB

125.25	126.10	127.65	131.30	124.90
1/2	2/2	4/2	11/1	15/1

T.D.ALGER,D.M.GRANT,E.G.PAUL
J AM CHEM SOC   88, 5397 (1966)

---

763   R 000600   TETRAHYDROFURAN

```
  4    3
H2C---CH2
 |     |
H2C   CH2
 5 \  / 2
    O
```

FORMULA	C4H8O	MOL WT	72.11
SOLVENT	C4H8O		
ORIG ST	TMS	TEMP	298

66.90	25.05
2/3	3/3

E.BREITMAIER,G.JUNG,W.VOELTER,L.POHL
UNPUBLISHED   (1972)

764   R 000600   OCTADEUTERIOTETRAHYDROFURAN

```
   4    3
D2C----CD2          FORMULA   C4D8O              MOL WT   80.16
  |    |             SOLVENT   C4D8O
D2C    CD2           ORIG ST   TMS                TEMP      298
  5\  /2
    O                    66.05    24.05
                          2/5      3/5

                    E.BREITMAIER,G.JUNG,W.VOELTER,L.POHL
                    UNPUBLISHED                        (1972)
```

---

765   R 000900   SULFOLANE

```
   4    3
H2C----CH2          FORMULA   C4H8O2S             MOL WT   120.17
  |    |             SOLVENT   C4H8O2S
H2C    CH2           ORIG ST   TMS                 TEMP      298
  5\  /2
    S                    50.95    22.65
   // \\                  2/3      3/3
  O    O
                    E.BREITMAIER,G.JUNG,W.VOELTER,L.POHL
                    UNPUBLISHED                        (1972)
```

---

766   R 000900   OCTADEUTERIOSULFOLANE

```
   4    3
D2C----CD2          FORMULA   C4D8O2S             MOL WT   128.22
  |    |             SOLVENT   C4D8O2S
D2C    CD2           ORIG ST   TMS                 TEMP      298
  5\  /2
    S                    50.05    21.35
   // \\                  2/5      3/5
  O    O
                    E.BREITMAIER,G.JUNG,W.VOELTER,L.POHL
                    UNPUBLISHED                        (1972)
```

---

767   R 001200   PYRROLE ANION

```
    4 3
    C-C             FORMULA   C4H4N               MOL WT   66.08
   //  \\           SOLVENT   C4H8O
 5C  -  C2          ORIG ST   C6H6                 TEMP      AMB
   \   /
    \ /          127.05   106.38   106.38   127.05
     N             2/2      3/2      4/2      5/2
     1
                    R.J.PUGMIRE,D.M.GRANT
                    J AM CHEM SOC                 90, 4232 (1968)
```

---

768   R 001200   PYRROLE

```
    4 3
    C-C             FORMULA   C4H5N               MOL WT   67.09
   //  \\           SOLVENT   C4H5N
 5C     C2          ORIG ST   C6H6                 TEMP      AMB
   \   /
    \1/          118.41   108.02   108.02   118.41
     N             2/2      3/2      4/2      5/2
     H
                    R.J.PUGMIRE,D.M.GRANT
                    J AM CHEM SOC                 90, 4232 (1968)
```

769   R 001400 INDOLE

```
      4
      C
  5 // \8     3
  C   C---C
  |   ||    ||
  C   C    C
  6 \ /9\ / 2
    C   N
    7   H
```

FORMULA	C8H7N			MOL WT	117.15
SOLVENT	C4H8O2				
ORIG ST	CS2			TEMP	AMB

124.85	102.35	120.95	122.00	119.95	111.55
2/2	3/2	4/2	5/2	6/2	7/2
128.45	135.85				
8/1	9/1				

R.G.PARKER,J.D.ROBERTS
J ORG CHEM   35, 996 (1970)

---

770   R 001400 1-METHYLINDOLE

```
      4
      C
  5 // \8     3
  C   C---C
  |   ||    ||
  C   C    C
  6 \ /9\ / 2
    C   N
    7   |
      10CH3
```

FORMULA	C9H9N			MOL WT	131.18
SOLVENT	C4H8O2				
ORIG ST	CS2			TEMP	AMB

129.00	101.00	121.00	121.60	119.45	109.50
2/2	3/2	4/2	5/2	6/2	7/2
129.10	137.25	31.80			
8/1	9/1	10/4			

R.G.PARKER,J.D.ROBERTS
J ORG CHEM   35, 996 (1970)

---

771   R 001400 2-METHYLINDOLE

```
      4
      C
  5 // \8     3
  C   C---C
  |   ||    ||
  C   C    C2
  6 \ /9\ /  \
    C   N   CH3
    7   H   10
```

FORMULA	C9H9N			MOL WT	131.18
SOLVENT	C4H8O2				
ORIG ST	CS2			TEMP	AMB

135.40	100.10	119.75	120.80	119.55	110.60
2/1	3/2	4/2	5/2	6/2	7/2
129.60	136.80	13.10			
8/1	9/1	10/4			

R.G.PARKER,J.D.ROBERTS
J ORG CHEM   35, 996 (1970)

---

772   R 001400 3-METHYLINDOLE

```
      4        10
      C        CH3
  5 // \8      /
  C   C---C3
  |   ||    ||
  C   C    C
  6 \ /9\ / 2
    C   N
    7   H
```

FORMULA	C9H9N			MOL WT	131.18
SOLVENT	C4H8O2				
ORIG ST	CS2			TEMP	AMB

122.45	111.15	119.10	121.95	119.30	111.45
2/2	3/1	4/2	5/2	6/2	7/2
128.90	137.00	9.55			
8/1	9/1	10/4			

R.G.PARKER,J.D.ROBERTS
J ORG CHEM   35, 996 (1970)

---

773   R 001400 4-METHYLINDOLE

```
  10CH3
   |
   4C
  5 // \8     3
  C   C---C
  |   ||    ||
  C   C    C
  6 \ /9\ / 2
    C   N
    7   H
```

FORMULA	C9H9N			MOL WT	131.18
SOLVENT	C4H8O2				
ORIG ST	CS2			TEMP	AMB

123.90	100.75	129.90	121.90	119.85	109.00
2/2	3/2	4/1	5/2	6/2	7/2
128.40	136.25	21.30			
8/1	9/1	10/4			

R.G.PARKER,J.D.ROBERTS
J ORG CHEM   35, 996 (1970)

774　　　　R 001400　5-METHYLINDOLE

```
 10    4
H3C    C
  \ ⁄ \8   3
  5C   C---C
  |    ‖   ‖
  C    C   C
 6 \ ⁄9\ ⁄ 2
     C   N
     7   H
```

FORMULA　C9H9N　　　　　　MOL WT　131.18
SOLVENT　C4H8O2
ORIG ST　CS2　　　　　　　TEMP　　　AMB

124.70	101.80	123.45	128.50	120.50	111.45
2/2	3/2	4/2	5/1	6/2	7/2
128.85	134.95	21.20			
8/1	9/1	10/4			

R.G.PARKER,J.D.ROBERTS
J ORG CHEM　　　　　　　　35,　996 (1970)

775　　　　R 001400　6-METHYLINDOLE

```
    4
    C
 5 ⁄ \8   3
  C   C---C
  |   ‖   ‖
 6C   C   C
 ⁄ \ ⁄9\ ⁄ 2
H3C   C   N
 10   7   H
```

FORMULA　C9H9N　　　　　　MOL WT　131.18
SOLVENT　C4H8O2
ORIG ST　CS2　　　　　　　TEMP　　　AMB

124.00	102.00	120.45	121.55	131.20	111.30
2/2	3/2	4/2	5/2	6/1	7/2
126.35	137.00	21.40			
8/1	9/1	10/4			

R.G.PARKER,J.D.ROBERTS
J ORG CHEM　　　　　　　　35,　996 (1970)

776　　　　R 001400　7-METHYLINDOLE

```
    4
    C
 5 ⁄ \8   3
  C   C---C
  |   ‖   ‖
  C   C   C
 6 \ ⁄9\ ⁄ 2
 7C   N
  |   H
  CH3
  10
```

FORMULA　C9H9N　　　　　　MOL WT　131.18
SOLVENT　C4H8O2
ORIG ST　CS2　　　　　　　TEMP　　　AMB

124.45	102.70	118.60	122.40	120.00	120.55
2/2	3/2	4/2	5/2	6/2	7/1
128.10	136.10	16.35			
8/1	9/1	10/2			

R.G.PARKER,J.D.ROBERTS
J ORG CHEM　　　　　　　　35,　996 (1970)

777　　　　R 001400　1,2-DIMETHYLINDOLE

```
    4
    C
 5 ⁄ \8   3
  C   C---C
  |   ‖   ‖
  C   C   C2
 6 \ ⁄9\ ⁄ \
  C   N   CH3
  7   |   11
     CH3
     10
```

FORMULA　C10H11N　　　　　MOL WT　145.21
SOLVENT　C4H8O2
ORIG ST　CS2　　　　　　　TEMP　　　AMB

137.75	99.70	119.70	120.40	119.30	108.90
2/1	3/2	4/2	5/2	6/2	7/2
128.55	136.75	28.35	11.95		
8/1	9/1	10/4	11/4		

R.G.PARKER,J.D.ROBERTS
J ORG CHEM　　　　　　　　35,　996 (1970)

778　　　　R 001400　2,3-DIMETHYLINDOLE

```
    4       11
    C       CH3
 5 ⁄ \8   ⁄
  C   C---C3
  |   ‖   ‖
  C   C   C2
 6 \ ⁄9\ ⁄ \
  C   N   CH3
  7   H   10
```

FORMULA　C10H11N　　　　　MOL WT　145.21
SOLVENT　C4H8O2
ORIG ST　CS2　　　　　　　TEMP　　　AMB

131.05	106.55	118.10	120.85	119.00	110.45
2/1	3/1	4/2	5/2	6/2	7/2
129.95	135.95	10.85	8.20		
8/1	9/1	10/4	11/4		

R.G.PARKER,J.D.ROBERTS
J ORG CHEM　　　　　　　　35,　996 (1970)

779   R 001400   2,7-DIMETHYLINDOLE

```
        4
        C
   5 ⁄ \8      3
   C    C---C
   ‖    ‖    ‖
   C    C    C2
   6 ⦇ ⁄9\ ⁄ \
    7C   N   CH3
     ‖   H   10
     CH3
     11
```

FORMULA	C10H11N			MOL WT	145.21
SOLVENT	C4H8O2				
ORIG ST	CS2			TEMP	AMB

134.85	100.65	117.35	121.35	119.55	119.65
2/1	3/2	4/2	5/2	6/2	7/1
129.15	136.20	13.10	16.35		
8/1	9/1	10/4	11/4		

R.G.PARKER,J.D.ROBERTS
J ORG CHEM   35, 996 (1970)

780   R 001400   2,3,5-TRIMETHYLINDOLE

```
  12    4        11
  H3C   C        CH3
    \ ⁄ \8    ⁄
    5C    C---C3
     ‖    ‖    ‖
     C    C    C2
    6 ⦇ ⁄9\ ⁄ \
       C   N   CH3
       7   H   10
```

FORMULA	C11H13N			MOL WT	159.23
SOLVENT	C4H8O2				
ORIG ST	CS2			TEMP	AMB

130.90	106.00	122.20	127.50	117.85	109.90
2/1	3/1	4/2	5/1	6/2	7/2
130.15	134.30	10.85	8.10	21.25	
8/1	9/1	10/4	11/4	12/4	

R.G.PARKER,J.D.ROBERTS
J ORG CHEM   35, 996 (1970)

781   R 001600   4-AZAINDENE

```
     8
     C
  7 ⁄ \9      1
  C    C===C
  ‖    ‖    ‖
  C    N    C
  6 ⦇ ⁄ \ ⁄ 2
     C    C
     5    3
```

FORMULA	C8H7N			MOL WT	117.15
SOLVENT	CHCL3				
ORIG ST	TMS			TEMP	AMB

99.45	114.05	113.00	125.60	110.45	117.15
1/2	2/2	3/2	5/2	6/2	7/2
119.55	133.35				
8/2	9/1				

R.J.PUGMIRE,M.J.ROBINS,D.M.GRANT,R.K.ROBINS
J AM CHEM SOC   93, 1887 (1971)

782   R 001800   PYRAZOLE ANION

```
     5 4
     C=C
    ⁄    \
  1N   -   C3
    \    ⁄
     \ ⁄
      N
      2
```

FORMULA	C3H3N2		MOL WT	67.07
SOLVENT	H2O			
ORIG ST	C6H6		TEMP	AMB

138.52	103.40	138.52
3/2	4/2	5/2

R.J.PUGMIRE,D.M.GRANT
J AM CHEM SOC   90, 4232 (1968)

783   R 001800   PYRAZOLE

```
     5 4
     C=C
    ⁄    \
  H-N1   C3
    \    ⁄
     \ ⁄
      N
      2
```

FORMULA	C3H4N2		MOL WT	68.08
SOLVENT	H2O			
ORIG ST	C6H6		TEMP	AMB

134.56	104.37	134.56
3/2	4/2	5/2

R.J.PUGMIRE,D.M.GRANT
J AM CHEM SOC   90, 4232 (1968)

784   R 001800   PYRAZOLE CATION

```
      5 4
      C=C
     /    \
  H—N1 +  C3
     \    //
      \2//
       N
       |
       H
```

FORMULA   C3H5N2   MOL WT   69.09
SOLVENT   H2O
ORIG ST   C6H6   TEMP   AMB

135.02   108.93   135.02
3/2   4/2   5/2

R.J.PUGMIRE,D.M.GRANT
J AM CHEM SOC   90, 4232 (1968)

---

785   R 001800   3,4—DIAZAINDENE

```
        8
        C
    7 // \9   1
    C    C===C
    |    |   |
    C    N   C
   6 \  / \ // 2
      C    N
      5
```

FORMULA   C7H6N2   MOL WT   118.14
SOLVENT   C7H6N2
ORIG ST   TMS   TEMP   AMB

96.25   141.30   128.30   110.85   112.35   117.35
1/2   2/2   5/2   6/2   7/2   8/2
139.50
9/1

R.J.PUGMIRE,M.J.ROBINS,D.M.GRANT,R.K.ROBINS
J AM CHEM SOC   93, 1887 (1971)

---

786   R 001900   IMIDAZOLE ANION

```
      5 4
      C=C
     /    \
   1N  —  N3
     \    //
      \  //
       C
       2
```

FORMULA   C3H3N2   MOL WT   67.07
SOLVENT   H2O
ORIG ST   C6H6   TEMP   AMB

111.95   126.72   126.72
2/2   4/2   5/2

R.J.PUGMIRE,D.M.GRANT
J AM CHEM SOC   90, 4232 (1968)

---

787   R 001900   IMIDAZOLE

```
      5 4
      C=C
     /    \
  H—N1    N3
     \    //
      \  //
       C
       2
```

FORMULA   C3H4N2   MOL WT   68.08
SOLVENT   H2O
ORIG ST   C6H6   TEMP   AMB

136.19   122.29   122.29
2/2   4/2   5/2

R.J.PUGMIRE,D.M.GRANT
J AM CHEM SOC   90, 4232 (1968)

---

788   R 001900   IMIDAZOLE CATION

```
       5 4
       C=C
      /    \
  H—N1 + 3N—H
      \    //
       \  //
        C
        2
```

FORMULA   C3H5N2   MOL WT   69.09
SOLVENT   H2O
ORIG ST   C6H6   TEMP   AMB

134.55   120.06   120.06
2/2   4/2   5/2

R.J.PUGMIRE,D.M.GRANT
J AM CHEM SOC   90, 4232 (1968)

789 R 001900 1,4-DIAZAINDENE

```
      8
      C
    7 ⁄ \9
    C   C===N
    |   |   |
    C   N   C
  6 \ ⁄ \ ⁄ 2
    C   C
    5   3
```

FORMULA	C7H6N2			MOL WT	118.14
SOLVENT	C7H6N2				
ORIG ST	TMS			TEMP	AMB

134.05	113.40	126.95	112.20	124.60	117.60
2/2	3/2	5/2	6/2	7/2	8/2
145.60					
9/1					

R.J.PUGMIRE,M.J.ROBINS,D.M.GRANT,R.K.ROBINS
J AM CHEM SOC   93, 1887 (1971)

790 R 001900 2,4-DIAZAINDENE

```
      8
      C
    7 ⁄ \9   1
    C   C===C
    |   |   |
    C   N   N
  6 \ ⁄ \ ⁄
    C   C
    5   3
```

FORMULA	C7H6N2			MOL WT	118.14
SOLVENT	CHCL3				
ORIG ST	TMS			TEMP	AMB

119.95	128.35	122.80	112.65	119.35	118.15
1/2	3/2	5/2	6/2	7/2	8/2
130.65					
9/1					

R.J.PUGMIRE,M.J.ROBINS,D.M.GRANT,R.K.ROBINS
J AM CHEM SOC   93, 1887 (1971)

791 R 003800 PYRIDINE

```
      4
      C
    ⁄⁄ \
   5C   C3
    |   ||
   6C   C2
    \\ ⁄
      N
```

FORMULA	C5H5N		MOL WT	79.10
SOLVENT	C5H5N			
ORIG ST	C6H6		TEMP	AMB

| 150.20 | 123.90 | 135.95 |
| 2/2 | 3/2 | 4/2 |

R.J.PUGMIRE,D.M.GRANT
J AM CHEM SOC   90, 697 (1968)

792 R 003800 PYRIDINE CATION

```
      C4
    ⁄⁄ \
   5C   C3
    | + ||
   6C   C2
    \\ ⁄
      N
      |
      H
```

FORMULA	C5H6N		MOL WT	80.11
SOLVENT	H2O			
ORIG ST	C6H6		TEMP	AMB

| 142.45 | 128.95 | 148.35 |
| 2/2 | 3/2 | 4/2 |

R.J.PUGMIRE,D.M.GRANT
J AM CHEM SOC   90 697 (1968)

793 R 003800 PYRIDINE

```
      4
      C
    ⁄⁄ \
   5C   C3
    |   ||
   6C   C2
    \\ ⁄
      N
```

FORMULA	C5H5N		MOL WT	79.10
SOLVENT	C5H5N			
ORIG ST	TMS		TEMP	298

| 149.10 | 122.85 | 134.80 |
| 2/2 | 3/2 | 4/2 |

E.BREITMAIER,G.JUNG,W.VOELTER,L.POHL
UNPUBLISHED   (1972)

794   R 003800   PENTADEUTERIOPYRIDINE

```
        D
        C4
    D ⫽   ⟍ D
    5C      C3
    |       ‖
    6C      C2
    D ⟍   ⫽ D
        N
```

FORMULA   C5D5N   MOL WT   84.13
SOLVENT   C5D5N
ORIG ST   TMS   TEMP   298

148.70	122.35	134.35
2/3	3/3	4/3

E.BREITMAIER,G.JUNG,W.VOELTER,L.POHL
UNPUBLISHED   (1972)

795   R 003800   2,5-DIMETHYL-3-ETHOXYCARBONYLPYRIDINE

```
    8    4    9 10 11
   H3C   C    COOCH2CH3
     ⟍ ⫽ ⟋
     5C    C3
     |     ‖
     6C    C2
     ⟍ ⫽ ⟍
      N     CH3
            7
```

FORMULA   C10H13O2N   MOL WT   179.22
SOLVENT   CDCL3
ORIG ST   TMS   TEMP   303

156.75	130.25	138.55	124.95	152.15	24.30
2/1	3/1	4/2	5/1	6/2	7/4
17.70	166.35	57.20	14.35		
8/4	9/1	10/3	11/4		

E.BREITMAIER
UNPUBLISHED   (1973)

796   R 003800   1,3,5-TRIMETHYL-1-H-PYRAZOLO(3,4-B)PYRIDINE

```
   12    4      11
  H3C    C      CH3
    ⟍ ⫽ ⟍8  ⟋
    5C    C----C3
    |     ‖    ‖
    6C    C    N
    ⟍ ⫽9⟍ ⟋
     N    N
          |
         CH3
         10
```

FORMULA   C9H11N3   MOL WT   161.21
SOLVENT   CDCL3
ORIG ST   TMS   TEMP   301

139.05	128.05	114.70	149.75	124.40	149.75
3/1	4/2	5/1	6/2	8/1	9/1
33.35	12.30	18.25			
10/4	11/4	12/4			

E.BREITMAIER,J.HAEUFEL
UNPUBLISHED   (1973)

797   R 003800   1-ETHYL-5-N-PROPYL-1-H-PYRAZOLO(3,4-B)PYRIDINE

```
14   12    4
CH3 CH2    C
  ⟍ ⟋ ⟍ ⫽ ⟍8
  CH2 C5    C----C3
  13 |      ‖    ‖
     C6     C    N
     ⟍ ⫽9⟍ ⟋
      N    N
           |
         10CH2
           ⟍
         11CH3
```

FORMULA   C11H15N3   MOL WT   189.26
SOLVENT   CDCL3
ORIG ST   TMS   TEMP   303

131.00	128.20	115.65	149.75	130.45	149.20
3/2	4/2	5/1	6/2	8/1	9/1
41.95	15.00	25.05	35.05	13.60	
10/3	11/4	12/3	13/3	14/3	

E.BREITMAIER,J.HAEUFEL
UNPUBLISHED   (1973)

798   R 004100   QUINOLINE

```
     5    4
     C    C
  6 ⫽ ⟍ ⟋ ⟍ 3
  C    C10 C
  |     ‖   |
  C    9C   C
  7 ⟍ ⟋ ⟍ ⫽ 2
     C    N
     8
```

FORMULA   C9H7N   MOL WT   129.16
SOLVENT   C9H7N
ORIG ST   C6H6   TEMP   AMB

150.85	121.55	136.05	128.35	126.80	129.75
2/2	3/2	4/2	5/2	6/2	7/2
130.10	149.00	128.70			
8/2	9/1	10/1			

R.J.PUGMIRE,D.M.GRANT,M.J.ROBINS,R.K.ROBINS
J AM CHEM SOC   91, 6381 (1969)

799   R 004200   **ISOQUINOLINE**

```
    5    4
    C    C
6 ∥ \  / ∖ 3
  C   C10  C
  |   ∥    |
  C   9C   N
7 ∖ /  \ ∥
    C    C
    8    1
```

FORMULA	C9H7N			MOL WT	129.16
SOLVENT	C9H7N				
ORIG ST	C6H6			TEMP	AMB

153.10	143.80	120.85	126.80	130.50	127.55
1/2	3/2	4/2	5/2	6/2	7/2
127.85	129.10	136.00			
8/2	9/1	10/1			

R.J.PUGMIRE,D.M.GRANT,M.J.ROBINS,R.K.ROBINS
J AM CHEM SOC   91, 6381 (1969)

---

800   R 004300   **ACRIDINE**

```
    5   10    4
    C    C    C
6 ∥ \ / ∖ / ∖ 3
  C  14C   C11  C
  |   ∥    |    |
  C  13C   C12  C
7 ∖ / ∖ ∥ ∖ ∥ 2
    C    N    C
    8         1
```

FORMULA	C13H9N			MOL WT	179.22
SOLVENT	CHCL3				
ORIG ST	C6H6			TEMP	AMB

129.55	128.35	125.45	130.30	135.90	126.55
1/2	2/2	3/2	4/2	10/2	11/1
149.15					
12/1					

R.J.PUGMIRE,D.M.GRANT,M.J.ROBINS,R.K.ROBINS
J AM CHEM SOC   91, 6381 (1969)

---

801   R 004700   **1,3-DIOXANE**

```
    6
   C--O
  /    \
5C      C2
  \    /
   C--O
    4
```

FORMULA	C4H8C2		MOL WT	88.11
SOLVENT	C4H8O2			
ORIG ST	TMS		TEMP	AMB

96.75	68.70	27.95
2/3	4/3	5/3

A.J.JONES,E.L.ELIEL,D.M.GRANT,M.C.KNOEBER,
W.F.BAILEY
J AM CHEM SOC   93, 4772 (1971)

---

802   R 004700   **2-METHYL-1,3-DIOXANE**

```
    6
   C--O
  /    \  7
5C      2C-CH3
  \    /
   C--O
    4
```

FORMULA	C5H10O2			MOL WT	102.13
SOLVENT	C5H10O2				
ORIG ST	TMS			TEMP	AMB

101.85	68.40	26.95	22.00
2/2	4/3	5/3	7/4

A.J.JONES,E.L.ELIEL,D.M.GRANT,M.C.KNOEBER,
W.F.BAILEY
J AM CHEM SOC   93, 4772 (1971)

---

803   R 004700   **2,2-DIMETHYL-1,3-DIOXANE**

```
    6      7
   C--O   CH3
  /    \ /
5C      C2
  \    / \
   C--O   CH3
    4      8
```

FORMULA	C6H12O2			MOL WT	116.16
SOLVENT	C6H12O2				
ORIG ST	TMS			TEMP	AMB

100.00	61.20	26.95	24.95
2/1	4/3	5/3	7/4

A.J.JONES,E.L.ELIEL,D.M.GRANT,M.C.KNOEBER,
W.F.BAILEY
J AM CHEM SOC   93, 4772 (1971)

804   R 004700   5,5-DIMETHYL-1,3-DIOXANE

```
   7     6
 H3C    C--O
    \  /   \
    5C      C2
    /  \   /
 H3C    C--O
   8     4
```

FORMULA	C6H12O2		MOL WT	116.16
SOLVENT	C6H12O2			
ORIG ST	TMS		TEMP	AMB

96.20	79.10	31.70	23.20
2/3	4/3	5/1	7/4

A.J.JONES,E.L.ELIEL,D.M.GRANT,M.C.KNOEBER,
W.F.BAILEY
J AM CHEM SOC   93, 4772 (1971)

805   R 004700   CIS-2,4-DIMETHYL-1,3-DIOXANE

```
    6
    C--O
   /    \
 5C      C2
   \    /|
  4C--O CH3
    |    7
   H3C
    8
```

FORMULA	C6H12O2		MOL WT	116.16
SOLVENT	C6H12O2			
ORIG ST	TMS		TEMP	AMB

98.85	72.45	33.40	66.35	21.40	21.95
2/2	4/2	5/3	6/3	7/4	8/4

A.J.JONES,E.L.ELIEL,D.M.GRANT,M.C.KNOEBER,
W.F.BAILEY
J AM CHEM SOC   93, 4772 (1971)

806   R 004700   2-TERT-BUTYL-1,3-DIOXANE

```
    6
    C--O
   /    \  7 8
 5C      2C-C(CH3)3
   \    /
    C--O
    4
```

FORMULA	C8H16O2		MOL WT	144.22
SOLVENT	C8H16O2			
ORIG ST	TMS		TEMP	AMB

107.85	66.90	26.35	35.30	25.00
2/2	4/3	5/3	7/1	8/4

A.J.JONES,E.L.ELIEL,D.M.GRANT,M.C.KNOEBER,
W.F.BAILEY
J AM CHEM SOC   93, 4772 (1971)

807   R 004700   5-TERT-BUTYL-1,3-DIOXANE

```
          6
          C--O
   8   7 /    \
(CH3)3C-C5     C2
          \    /
          C--O
          4
```

FORMULA	C8H16O2		MOL WT	144.22
SOLVENT	C8H16O2			
ORIG ST	TMS		TEMP	AMB

93.65	68.55	44.40	30.65	27.60
2/3	4/3	5/2	7/1	8/4

A.J.JONES,E.L.ELIEL,D.M.GRANT,M.C.KNOEBER,
W.F.BAILEY
J AM CHEM SOC   93, 4772 (1971)

808   R 004700   CIS-2-METHYL-5-TERT-BUTYL-1,3-DIOXANE

```
       6
       C--O
      /    \
    5C      C2
    |\     /|
 (CH3)3C C--O CH3
    9   8 4   7
```

FORMULA	C9H18O2		MOL WT	158.24
SOLVENT	C9H18O2			
ORIG ST	TMS		TEMP	AMB

99.35	67.30	43.60	21.35	32.65	29.70
2/2	4/3	5/2	7/4	8/1	9/4

A.J.JONES,E.L.ELIEL,D.M.GRANT,M.C.KNOEBER,
W.F.BAILEY
J AM CHEM SOC   93, 4772 (1971)

809   R 004700   TRANS-2-METHYL-5-TERT-BUTYL-1,3-DIOXANE

```
  9    8 6
(CH3)3C C--O
     I/    \
     5C      C2
      \    /I
       C--O CH3
       4    7
```

FORMULA	C9H1802			MOL WT	158.24
SOLVENT	C9H1802				
ORIG ST	TMS			TEMP	AMB

| 99.05 | 68.60 | 44.60 | 21.25 | 30.55 | 27.70 |
| 2/2 | 4/3 | 5/2 | 7/4 | 8/1 | 9/4 |

A.J.JONES,E.L.ELIEL,D.M.GRANT,M.C.KNOEBER,
W.F.BAILEY
J AM CHEM SOC   93, 4772 (1971)

---

810   R 004700   CIS-2-TERT-BUTYL-5-METHYL-1,3-DIOXANE

```
      6
      C--O
    /    \
  5C      C2
  I\    /I
 H3C C--O C(CH3)3
  9  4   7 8
```

FORMULA	C9H1802			MOL WT	158.24
SOLVENT	C9H1802				
ORIG ST	TMS			TEMP	AMB

| 108.10 | 72.00 | 29.70 | 35.30 | 24.70 | 15.95 |
| 2/2 | 4/3 | 5/2 | 7/1 | 8/4 | 9/4 |

A.J.JONES,E.L.ELIEL,D.M.GRANT,M.C.KNOEBER,
W.F.BAILEY
J AM CHEM SOC   93, 4772 (1971)

---

811   R 004700   TRANS-2-TERT-BUTYL-5-METHYL-1,3-DIOXANE

```
  9 6
 H3C C--O
  I/    \
  5C      C2
   \    /I
    C--O C(CH3)3
    4    7 8
```

FORMULA	C9H1802			MOL WT	158.24
SOLVENT	C9H1802				
ORIG ST	TMS			TEMP	AMB

| 107.70 | 73.60 | 29.70 | 35.25 | 24.85 | 12.40 |
| 2/2 | 4/3 | 5/2 | 7/1 | 8/4 | 9/4 |

A.J.JONES,E.L.ELIEL,D.M.GRANT,M.C.KNOEBER,
W.F.BAILEY
J AM CHEM SOC   93, 4772 (1971)

---

812   R 004700   CIS-2-TERT-BUTYL-4-METHYL-1,3-DIOXANE

```
      6
      C--O
    /    \
  5C      C2
   \    /I
  4C--O C(CH3)3
   I    7 8
   CH3
   9
```

FORMULA	C9H1802			MOL WT	158.24
SOLVENT	C9H1802				
ORIG ST	TMS			TEMP	AMB

107.25	72.45	33.70	66.40	35.05	24.95
2/2	4/2	5/3	6/3	7/1	8/4
21.90					
9/4					

A.J.JONES,E.L.ELIEL,D.M.GRANT,M.C.KNOEBER,
W.F.BAILEY
J AM CHEM SOC   93, 4772 (1971)

---

813   R 004700   2,2-DIMETHYL-5-TERT-BUTYL-1,3-DIOXANE

```
      6    7
      C--O CH3
 10    9 /   \I
(CH3)3C-C5    C2
      \    /I
       C--O CH3
       4    8
```

FORMULA	C10H2002			MOL WT	172.27
SOLVENT	C10H2002				
ORIG ST	TMS			TEMP	AMB

97.45	60.85	44.25	28.00	20.30	30.95
2/1	4/3	5/2	7/4	8/4	9/1
27.55					
10/4					

A.J.JONES,E.L.ELIEL,D.M.GRANT,M.C.KNOEBER,
W.F.BAILEY
J AM CHEM SOC   93, 4772 (1971)

---

814   R 004700   2-TERT-BUTYL-5,5-DIMETHYL-1,3-DIOXANE

```
        9  6
      H3C C--O
        I/    \
       5C      C2
        I\    /I
      H3C C--O C(CH3)3
      10 4    7 8
```

FORMULA	C10H20O2			MOL WT	172.27
SOLVENT	CS2				
ORIG ST	TMS			TEMP	AMB
108.40	77.30	30.15	35.00	25.15	22.20
2/2	4/3	5/1	7/1	8/4	9/4
23.35					
10/4					

A.J.JONES,E.L.ELIEL,D.M.GRANT,M.C.KNOEBER,
W.F.BAILEY
J AM CHEM SOC   93, 4772 (1971)

---

815   R 004700   CIS-2,5-DI-TERT-BUTYL-1,3-DIOXANE

```
          6
        C--O
       /     \
      5C      C2
       I\    /I
 (CH3)3C C--O C(CH3)3
 10     9 4    7 8
```

FORMULA	C12H24O2			MOL WT	200.32
SOLVENT	CS2				
ORIG ST	TMS			TEMP	AMB
108.60	68.00	43.55	35.20	25.05	32.75
2/2	4/3	5/2	7/1	8/4	9/1
29.80					
10/4					

A.J.JONES,E.L.ELIEL,D.M.GRANT,M.C.KNOEBER,
W.F.BAILEY
J AM CHEM SOC   93, 4772 (1971)

---

816   R 004700   TRANS-2,5-DI-TERT-BUTYL-1,3-DIOXANE

```
 10    9  6
 (CH3)3C C--O
       I/    \
      5C      C2
       \    /I
        C--O C(CH3)3
        4    7 8
```

FORMULA	C12H24O2			MOL WT	200.32
SOLVENT	CS2				
ORIG ST	TMS			TEMP	AMB
107.20	68.60	43.70	34.70	24.90	30.00
2/2	4/3	5/2	7/1	8/4	9/1
27.45					
10/4					

A.J.JONES,E.L.ELIEL,D.M.GRANT,M.C.KNOEBER,
W.F.BAILEY
J AM CHEM SOC   93, 4772 (1971)

---

817   R 004700   CIS-2-PHENYL-4,6-DIMETHYL-1,3-DIOXANE

```
          6
        C--O
       /I    \
      5C CH3  C2
       \14   /I
       4C--O C7
        I    /  \
      H3C12C   C8
       13 I    II
         11C   C9
           \   /
           10C
```

FORMULA	C12H16O2			MOL WT	192.26
SOLVENT	CS2				
ORIG ST	TMS			TEMP	AMB
100.85	72.85	40.90	139.95	126.70	127.95
2/2	4/2	5/3	7/1	8/2	9/2
128.40	21.85				
10/2	13/4				

A.J.JONES,E.L.ELIEL,D.M.GRANT,M.C.KNOEBER,
W.F.BAILEY
J AM CHEM SOC   93, 4772 (1971)

---

818   R 004700   TRANS-2-PHENYL-5-TERT-BUTYL-1,3-DIOXANE

```
 14   13 6
 (CH3)3C C--O
       I/    \
      5C      C2
       \    /I
        C--O C7
        4   /  \
       12C   C8
        I    II
       11C   C9
         \   /
         10C
```

FORMULA	C14H20O2			MOL WT	220.31
SOLVENT	CS2				
ORIG ST	TMS			TEMP	AMB
101.40	69.25	44.00	139.90	126.95	128.25
2/2	4/3	5/2	7/1	8/2	9/2
128.85	30.55	27.90			
10/2	13/1	14/4			

A.J.JONES,E.L.ELIEL,D.M.GRANT,M.C.KNOEBER,
W.F.BAILEY
J AM CHEM SOC   93, 4772 (1971)

819   R 004700   1,4-DIOXANE

```
      O
    5/ \3
    C   C
    |   |
    C   C
    6\ /2
      O
```

FORMULA	C4H8O2	MOL WT	88.11
SOLVENT	C4H8O2		
ORIG ST	TMS	TEMP	298

66.60
2/3

E.BREITMAIER,G.JUNG,W.VOELTER,L.POHL
UNPUBLISHED   (1972)

---

820   R 004700   OCTADEUTERIO-1,4-DIOXANE

```
       O
     5/ \3
   D2C   CD2
    |     |
   D2C   CD2
     6\ /2
       O
```

FORMULA	C4D8O2	MOL WT	96.16
SOLVENT	C4D8O2		
ORIG ST	TMS	TEMP	298

65.50
2/5

E.BREITMAIER,G.JUNG,W.VOELTER,L.POHL
UNPUBLISHED   (1972)

---

821   R 005000   PYRIDAZINE

```
      C4
     ⁄ \
   5C   C3
    |   ||
   6C   N2
     \ /
      N
      1
```

FORMULA	C4H4N2	MOL WT	80.09
SOLVENT	C4H4N2		
ORIG ST	C6H6	TEMP	AMB

152.80   127.65
3/2   4/2

R.J.PUGMIRE,D.M.GRANT
J AM CHEM SOC   90, 697 (1968)

---

822   R 005000   PYRIDAZINE CATION

```
      C4
     ⁄ \
   5C   C3
    | + ||
   6C   N2
     \ /
      N1
      |
      H
```

FORMULA	C4H5N2	MOL WT	81.10
SOLVENT	H2O		
ORIG ST	C6H6	TEMP	AMB

151.70   137.75
3/2   4/2

R.J.PUGMIRE,D.M.GRANT
J AM CHEM SOC   90, 697 (1968)

---

823   R 005000   PHTHALAZINE

```
    5   4
    C   C
  6 ⁄ \ / \
  C   C10  N
  |   ||   |
  C   9C   N
  7 \ / \ ⁄
    C   C
    8   1
```

FORMULA	C8H6N2	MOL WT	130.15
SOLVENT	CHCL3		
ORIG ST	C6H6	TEMP	AMB

152.00   126.65   133.20   126.65
1/2   5/2   6/2   9/1

R.J.PUGMIRE,D.M.GRANT,M.J.ROBINS,R.K.ROBINS
J AM CHEM SOC   91, 6381 (1969)

824　　　R 005000　**CINNOLINE**

```
    5    4
    C    C
6 ╱ ╲ ╱ ╲ 3
  C   C10  C
  │    ║   │
  C   9C   N
7 ╲ ╱ ╲ ╱
    C    N
    8
```

FORMULA	C8H6N2			MOL WT	130.15
SOLVENT	CHCL3				
ORIG ST	C6H6			TEMP	AMB

146.10	124.65	127.90	132.30	132.10	129.50
3/2	4/2	5/2	6/2	7/2	8/2
151.00	126.80				
9/1	10/1				

R.J.PUGMIRE,D.M.GRANT,M.J.ROBINS,R.K.ROBINS
J AM CHEM SOC　　　　　　　　　　91, 6381 (1969)

825　　　R 005100　**PYRIMIDINE**

```
    C4
   ╱ ╲
 5C    N
  │    ║
 6C    C2
   ╲ ╱
    N
```

FORMULA	C4H4N2	MOL WT	80.09
SOLVENT	C4H4N2		
ORIG ST	C6H6	TEMP	AMB

159.50	157.45	122.10
2/2	4/2	5/2

R.J.PUGMIRE,D.M.GRANT
J AM CHEM SOC　　　　90　　697 (1968)

826　　　R 005100　**PYRIMIDINE CATION**

```
    C4
   ╱ ╲
 5C    N
  │ +  ║
 6C    C2
   ╲ ╱
    N
    │
    H
```

FORMULA	C4H5N2	MOL WT	81.10
SOLVENT	H2O		
ORIG ST	C6H6	TEMP	AMB

152.20	158.80	125.10
2/2	4/2	5/2

R.J.PUGMIRE,D.M.GRANT
J AM CHEM SOC　　　　90　　697 (1968)

827　　　R 005100　**PYRIMIDINE DICATION**

```
    C4
   ╱ ╲
 5C +  N—H
  │ +  ║
 6C    C2
   ╲ ╱
    N
    │
    H
```

FORMULA	C4H6N2	MOL WT	82.11
SOLVENT	H2O		
ORIG ST	C6H6	TEMP	AMB

151.00	159.05	128.15
2/2	4/2	5/2

R.J.PUGMIRE,D.M.GRANT
J AM CHEM SOC　　　　90　　697 (1968)

828　　　R 005150　**QUINAZOLINE**

```
    5    4
    C    C
6 ╱ ╲ ╱ ╲
  C   C10  N
  │    ║   │
  C   9C   C
7 ╲ ╱ ╲ ╱ 2
    C    N
    8
```

FORMULA	C8H6N2			MOL WT	130.15
SOLVENT	CHCL3				
ORIG ST	C6H6			TEMP	AMB

160.50	155.70	127.40	127.95	134.15	128.55
2/2	4/2	5/2	6/2	7/2	8/2
150.15	125.20				
9/1	10/1				

R.J.PUGMIRE,D.M.GRANT,M.J.ROBINS,R.K.ROBINS
J AM CHEM SOC　　　　　　　　　　91, 6381 (1969)

829 R 005150 1,4,8-TRIAZAINDENE

```
      N
   7 ⁄ \9
   C   C≡≡≡N
   |   |   |
   C   N   C
  6 \ ⁄ \ ⁄ 2
     C   C
     5   3
```

FORMULA	C6H5N3			MOL WT	119.13
SOLVENT	C2H6S O				
ORIG ST	TMS			TEMP	AMB

| 135.15 | 112.65 | 136.05 | 109.40 | 150.95 | 148.85 |
| 2/2 | 3/2 | 5/2 | 6/2 | 7/2 | 9/1 |

R.J.PUGMIRE,M.J.ROBINS,D.M.GRANT,R.K.ROBINS
J AM CHEM SOC   93, 1887 (1971)

---

830 R 005150 6-METHYL-PYRIDO(2,3-D)1,2,3,4-TETRAHYDRO-
PYRIMIDINE-2,4-DIONE

```
        O
  11   5  ||
 H3C   C   C4
   \ ⁄ \ ⁄ \
   6C  9C   NH
   |   ||   |
   7C  C10  C2
   \ ⁄ \ ⁄ \
    N   N   O
        H
```

FORMULA	(CD3)2SO			MOL WT	177.16
SOLVENT	C8H7O2N3				
ORIG ST	TMS			TEMP	303

150.40	162.50	135.95	109.30	154.85	128.20
2/1	4/1	5/2	6/1	7/2	9/1
150.40	17.15				
10/1	11/4				

E.STARK,E.BREITMAIER
TETRAHEDRON   29, 2209 (1973)

---

831 R 005500 PYRAZINE

```
      N
   ⁄ \
  5C   C3
  |    ||
  6C   C2
   \ ⁄
    N
```

FORMULA	C4H4N2	MOL WT	80.09
SOLVENT	H2O		
ORIG ST	C6H6	TEMP	AMB

| 145.65 |
| 2/2 |

R.J.PUGMIRE,D.M.GRANT
J AM CHEM SOC   90   697 (1968)

---

832 R 005500 PYRAZINE CATION

```
      N
   ⁄ \
  5C   C3
  | + ||
  6C   C2
   \ ⁄
    N
    |
    H
```

FORMULA	C4H5N2	MOL WT	81.10
SOLVENT	H2O		
ORIG ST	C6H6	TEMP	AMB

| 142.95 |
| 2/2 |

R.J.PUGMIRE,D.M.GRANT
J AM CHEM SOC   90   697 (1968)

---

833 R 005500 PYRAZINE DICATION

```
    H
    |
    N
   ⁄ \
  5C + C3
  | + ||
  6C   C2
   \ ⁄
    N
    |
    H
```

FORMULA	C4H6N2	MOL WT	82.11
SOLVENT	H2O		
ORIG ST	C6H6	TEMP	AMB

| 144.00 |
| 2/2 |

R.J.PUGMIRE,D.M.GRANT
J AM CHEM SOC   90   697 (1968)

834   R 005500 QUINOXALINE

```
    5
    C   N
 6 ⁄ \ ⁄ ⬊ 3
    C   C10 C
    |   ||   |
    C   9C  C
 7 ⬊ ⁄ \ ⁄ 2
    C   N
    8
```

FORMULA   C8H6N2   MOL WT   130.15
SOLVENT   CHCL3
ORIG ST   C6H6   TEMP   AMB

145.50   129.80   129.90   143.20
 2/2   5/2   6/2   9/1

R.J.PUGMIRE,D.M.GRANT,M.J.ROBINS,R.K.ROBINS
J AM CHEM SOC   91, 6381 (1969)

---

835   R 005700 PHENAZINE

```
    5        4
    C   N    C
 6 ⁄ \ ⁄ \ ⁄ ⬊ 3
  C 14C   C11 C
  |   ||   |   |
  C 13C   C12 C
 7 ⬊ ⁄ \ ⁄ \ ⁄ 2
    C   N    C
    8        1
```

FORMULA   C12H8N2   MOL WT   180.21
SOLVENT   CHCL3
ORIG ST   C6H6   TEMP   AMB

133.90   130.30   144.00
 1/2   2/2   11/1

R.J.PUGMIRE,D.M.GRANT,M.J.ROBINS,R.K.ROBINS
J AM CHEM SOC   91, 6381 (1969)

---

836   R 006500 S-TRIAZINE

```
      C4
     ⁄ \
  5N     N3
   |     ||
  6C     C2
     \ ⁄
      N
      1
```

FORMULA   C3H3N3   MOL WT   81.08
SOLVENT   CHCL3
ORIG ST   C6H6   TEMP   AMB

167.50
 2/2

T.TOKUHIRO,G.FRAENKEL
J AM CHEM SOC   91, 5005 (1969)

---

837   R 006700 S-TETRAZINE

```
      N4
     ⁄ \
  5N     C3
   |     ||
  6C     N2
     \ ⁄
      N
      1
```

FORMULA   C2H2N4   MOL WT   82.07
SOLVENT   CHCL3
ORIG ST   C6H6   TEMP   AMB

161.90
 3/2

T.TOKUHIRO,G.FRAENKEL
J AM CHEM SOC   91, 5005 (1969)

---

838   S 000600 1,1,3,3,5,5-HEXAKIS-(TRIDEUTERIOMETHYL)-
                     1,3,5-TRISILACYCLOHEXANE

```
  (CD3)2SI---CH2
      ⁄5   6\   7
   H2C4      1SI(CD3)2
      \3    2⁄
  (CD3)2SI---CH2
```

FORMULA   C9H6D18SI3   MOL WT   234.66
SOLVENT   C9H6D18SI3
ORIG ST   TMS   TEMP   298

2.25   1.10
 2/3   7/5

E.BREITMAIER,G.JUNG,W.VOELTER,L.POHL
UNPUBLISHED   (1972)

839   S 000800   HEXAMETHYLPHOSPHORAMIDE

```
                            FORMULA   C6H18N3OP            MOL WT   179.20
        N(CH3)2             SOLVENT   C6H18N3O P
          /                 ORIG ST   TMS                 TEMP        298
   O=P-N(CH3)2
          \                    35.65
        N(CH3)2                1/4
```

E.BREITMAIER,G.JUNG,W.VOELTER,L.POHL
UNPUBLISHED   (1972)

840   S 000800   OCTADECADEUTERIOHEXAMETHYLPHOSPHORAMIDE

```
           1                FORMULA   C6D18N3OP            MOL WT   197.31
        N(CD3)2             SOLVENT   C6D18N3O P
          /                 ORIG ST   TMS                 TEMP        298
   O=P-N(CD3)2
          \                    35.40
        N(CD3)2                1/7
```

E.BREITMAIER,G.JUNG,W.VOELTER,L.POHL
UNPUBLISHED   (1972)

841   U 002000   **LINALOOL**

```
      10CH3                 FORMULA   C10H18O              MOL WT   154.25
        |                   SOLVENT   C10H18O
      6C-OH                 ORIG ST   TMS                 TEMP        300
     5/ \7
   H2C    CH                 25.25  130.25  124.60   22.55   42.20   72.70
    |     ||                 1/4     2/1     3/2     4/3     5/3     6/1
   H2C    CH2               145.00  111.25   17.15   27.20
    4\   8                   7/2     8/3     9/4    10/4
     3CH
      ||
      2C                    F.J.WEIGERT,M.JAUTELAT,J,D,ROBERTS
     9/ \1                  PROC NAT ACAD SCI US          60, 1152 (1968)
   H3C    CH3               W.VOELTER,G.HAAS,J.LUECKE,E.BREITMAIER
                            UNPUBLISHED                           (1972)
```

842   U 002000   2,3-DIHYDROLINALOOL

```
      10CH3                 FORMULA   C10H20O              MOL WT   156.27
        |                   SOLVENT   C10H20O
      6C-OH                 ORIG ST   TMS                 TEMP        300
     5/ \7
   H2C    CH                 22.25   27.50   39.15   21.35   42.40   72.60
    |     ||                 1/4     2/2     3/3     4/3     5/3     6/1
   H2C    CH2               145.00  110.90   26.95
    4\   8                   7/2     8/3    10/4
     3CH2
      |
     2CH
     9/ \1                  W.VOELTER,G.HAAS,J.LUECKE,E.BREITMAIER
   H3C    CH3               UNPUBLISHED                           (1972)
```

843   U 002000   7,8-DEHYDROLINALOOL

```
      10CH3                 FORMULA   C10H16O              MOL WT   152.24
        |                   SOLVENT   C10H16O
      6C-OH                 ORIG ST   TMS                 TEMP        300
     5/ \7
   H2C    C                  25.25  130.85  123.85   23.20   43.05   67.35
    |    12                  1/4     2/1     3/2     4/3     5/3     6/1
   H2C    CH                 87.60   71.45   17.25   29.35
    4\   8                   7/1     8/2     9/4    10/4
     3CH
      ||
      2C
     9/ \1                  W.VOELTER,G.HAAS,J.LUECKE,E.BREITMAIER
   H3C    CH3               UNPUBLISHED                           (1972)
```

844   U 002000   GERANIOL

```
   10CH3
     |
    6C
   5/ //7
  H2C   CH
   |    |
  H2C   CH2
   4\  8\
    3CH  OH
     ‖
    2C
   9/ \1
  H3C   CH3
```

FORMULA	C10H18O			MOL WT	154.25
SOLVENT	C10H18O				
ORIG ST	C S2			TEMP	AMB

25.50	131.20	124.90	26.60	39.70	137.30
1/4	2/1	3/2	4/3	5/3	6/1
124.50	58.70	17.40	16.00		
7/2	8/3	9/4	10/4		

M.JAUTELAT,J.B.GRUTZNER,J.D.ROBERTS
PROC NAT ACAD SCI US   65, 288 (1970)

845   U 002000   CIS—CITRAL

```
   10CH3
     |
    6C
   5/ //7
  H2C   CH
   |    |
  H2C  H-C
   4\  //8//
    3CH  O
     ‖
    2C
   9/ \1
  H3C   CH3
```

FORMULA	C10H16O			MOL WT	152.24
SOLVENT	C10H16O				
ORIG ST	C S2			TEMP	AMB

25.30	132.90	123.10	27.20	32.50	162.10
1/4	2/1	3/2	4/3	5/3	6/1
128.70	189.40	17.40	24.40		
7/2	8/2	9/4	10/4		

M.JAUTELAT,J.B.GRUTZNER,J.D.ROBERTS
PROC NAT ACAD SCI US   65, 288 (1970)

846   U 002000   TRANS—CITRAL

```
   10CH3 H
     |   |
    6C   C8
   5/ // // //
  H2C  CH  O
   |   7
  H2C
   4\
    3CH
     ‖
    2C
   9/ \1
  H3C   CH3
```

FORMULA	C10H16O			MOL WT	152.24
SOLVENT	C10H16O				
ORIG ST	C S2			TEMP	AMB

25.30	132.30	123.50	26.00	40.50	162.10
1/4	2/1	3/2	4/3	5/3	6/1
127.50	190.00	17.40	17.00		
7/2	8/2	9/4	10/4		

M.JAUTELAT,J.B.GRUTZNER,J.D.ROBERTS
PROC NAT ACAD SCI US   65, 288 (1970)

847   U 002000   FARNESOL

```
   14CH3
     |      12
    6C      CH2
   5/ //7  / \
  H2C   CH HC11 OH
   |    |   ‖
  H2C H2C  C10
   4\  8\ / \
    3CH  CH2 CH3
     ‖   9   15
    2C
   13/ \1
  H3C   CH3
```

FORMULA	C15H26O			MOL WT	222.37
SOLVENT	C10H16O				
ORIG ST	C S2			TEMP	AMB

25.40	130.80	125.00	26.90	39.70	134.90
1/4	2/1	3/2	4/3	5/3	6/1
124.30	25.60	39.80	137.10	124.70	58.60
7/2	8/3	9/3	10/1	11/2	12/3
17.40	13.70	15.90			
13/4	14/4	15/4			

M.JAUTELAT,J.B.GRUTZNER,J.D.ROBERTS
PROC NAT ACAD SCI US   65, 288 (1970)

848   U 002000   SQUALENE

```
   14CH3
     |
    6C     12CH2-)2
   5/ //7    /
  H2C   CH HC11
   |    |   ‖
  H2C H2C 10C
   4\  8\ / \
    3CH  CH2 CH3
     ‖   9   15
    2C
   13/ \1
  H3C   CH3)
```

FORMULA	C30H50			MOL WT	410.73
SOLVENT	C30H50				
ORIG ST	C S2			TEMP	AMB

25.50	130.60	124.80	27.00	39.90	134.80
1/4	2/1	3/2	4/3	5/3	6/1
124.60	26.90	39.90	134.60	124.60	28.40
7/2	8/3	9/3	10/1	11/2	12/3
17.50	15.90	15.90			
13/4	14/4	15/4			

M.JAUTELAT,J.B.GRUTZNER,J.D.ROBERTS
PROC NAT ACAD SCI US   65, 288 (1970)

849   U 002000   MENTHANE

```
      7CH3
       |
       C
      /1\
   6C    C2
    |    |
   5C    C3
      \4/
       C
       |
       CH
   10/8\9
   H3C   CH3
```

FORMULA	C10H20			MOL WT	140.27
SOLVENT	C10H20				
ORIG ST	CS2			TEMP	AMB

35.70	33.10	29.90	44.10	22.50	35.70
1/2	2/3	3/3	4/2	7/4	8/2
19.00					
9/4					

M.JAUTELAT,J.B.GRUTZNER,J.D.ROBERTS
PROC NAT ACAD SCI US   65, 288 (1970)

---

850   U 002000   MENTHOL

```
      7CH3
       |
       C
      /1\
   6C    C2
    |    |
   5C    C3
      \4/ \
       C  OH
       |
       CH
   10/8\9
   H3C   CH3
```

FORMULA	C10H20O			MOL WT	156.27
SOLVENT	CS2				
ORIG ST	CS2			TEMP	AMB

31.90	45.60	70.90	50.40	23.50	35.00
1/2	2/3	3/2	4/2	5/3	6/3
22.30	25.80	16.00	21.00		
7/4	8/2	9/4	10/4		

M.JAUTELAT,J.B.GRUTZNER,J.D.ROBERTS
PROC NAT ACAD SCI US   65, 288 (1970)

---

851   U 002000   CINEOL

```
      7CH3
       |
       C-------O
      /1\    /
   6C    C2 /
    | |    /
   5C   C3/
      \4/ /
       C /
       |/
       C
   10/8\9
   H3C   CH3
```

FORMULA	C10H18O			MOL WT	154.25
SOLVENT	C10H18O				
ORIG ST	CS2			TEMP	AMB

69.10	31.70	23.00	33.10	27.40	73.00
1/4	2/3	3/3	4/2	7/4	8/1
28.80					
9/4					

M.JAUTELAT,J.B.GRUTZNER,J.D.ROBERTS
PROC NAT ACAD SCI US   65, 288 (1970)

---

852   U 002000   LIMONENE

```
      7CH3
       |
       C
      /1\
   6C    C2
    |    |
   5C    C3
      \4/
       C
       |
       C
   10/8\9
   H2C   CH3
```

FORMULA	C10H16			MOL WT	136.24
SOLVENT	C10H16				
ORIG ST	CS2			TEMP	AMB

133.20	120.80	30.60	41.20	28.00	30.90
1/1	2/2	3/3	4/2	5/3	6/3
23.80	149.70	108.40	20.50		
7/4	8/1	9/3	10/4		

M.JAUTELAT,J.B.GRUTZNER,J.D.ROBERTS
PROC NAT ACAD SCI US   65, 288 (1970)

---

853   U 002000   CARVONE

```
      7CH3
       |
    O  C
     \\/1\
   6C    C2
    |    |
   5C    C3
      \4/
       C
       |
       C
   10/8\9
   H3C   CH2
```

FORMULA	C10H14O			MOL WT	150.22
SOLVENT	C10H14O				
ORIG ST	CS2			TEMP	AMB

135.20	143.80	31.30	42.70	43.10	197.70
1/1	2/2	3/3	4/3	5/3	6/1
15.40	147.20	110.30	20.20		
7/4	8/1	9/3	10/4		

M.JAUTELAT,J.B.GRUTZNER,J.D.ROBERTS
PROC NAT ACAD SCI US   65, 288 (1970)

854 — U 002000 PULEGONE

```
        7CH3
         |
         C
        /1\
      6C   C2
      |    |
      5C   C3
       \4/ ‖
        C   O
        ‖
        C
    10/8\9
     H3C  CH3
```

FORMULA C10H16O
SOLVENT C10H16O
ORIG ST CS2

MOL WT 152.24

TEMP AMB

31.40	50.70	201.10	131.70	28.50	32.90
1/2	2/3	3/1	4/1	5/3	6/3
21.70	140.80	21.80	22.70		
7/4	8/1	9/4	10/4		

M.JAUTELAT,J.B.GRUTZNER,J.D.ROBERTS
PROC NAT ACAD SCI US   65, 288 (1970)

855 — U 002000 ALPHA-PINENE

```
      3    4
      C----C
    2/10CH3\
   H3C-C  8C----C5
    1  \ /CH3/
       C----C
       7    6
```

FORMULA C10H16
SOLVENT C10H16
ORIG ST CS2

MOL WT 136.24

TEMP AMB

20.80	144.10	116.20	31.50	41.50	31.40
1/4	2/1	3/2	4/3	5/2	6/3
47.20	38.00	26.50	22.80		
7/2	8/1	9/4	10/4		

M.JAUTELAT,J.B.GRUTZNER,J.D.ROBERTS
PROC NAT ACAD SCI US   65, 288 (1970)

856 — U 002000 BETA-PINENE

```
      3    4
      C----C
    2/10CH3\
   H2C=C  8C----C5
    1  \ /CH3/
       C----C
       7    6
```

FORMULA C10H16
SOLVENT C10H16
ORIG ST CS2

MOL WT 136.24

TEMP AMB

106.30	151.30	23.80	23.60	40.80	27.00
1/3	2/1	3/3	4/3	5/2	6/3
52.10	40.80	25.80	21.70		
7/2	8/1	9/4	10/4		

M.JAUTELAT,J.B.GRUTZNER,J.D.ROBERTS
PROC NAT ACAD SCI US   65, 288 (1970)

857 — U 002000 CAMPHOR

```
      6    5
      C----C
    1/ 9CH3\
  H3C-C---C---C4
  10  \ 8CH3/
      C----C
     /2    3
    O
```

FORMULA C10H16O
SOLVENT CCL4
ORIG ST CS2

MOL WT 152.24

TEMP AMB

57.00	214.70	43.20	43.60	27.40	30.10
1/1	2/1	3/3	4/2	5/3	6/3
46.60	20.00	19.50	9.70		
7/1	8/4	9/4	10/4		

E.WENKERT,A.O.CLOUSE,D.W.COCHRAN,D.DODRELL
CHEM COMMUN   1969, 1433 (1969)

858 — U 002000 3-BROMOCAMPHOR,ENDO

```
      6    5
      C----C
    1/ 9CH3\
  H3C-C---C---C4
  10  \ 8CH3/
      C----C3
     /2    |
    O      BR
```

FORMULA C10H15O BR
SOLVENT CCL4
ORIG ST CS2

MOL WT 231.13

TEMP AMB

57.10	209.30	53.90	49.80	22.90	30.70
1/1	2/1	3/2	4/2	5/3	6/3
45.80	20.20	20.20	10.00		
7/1	8/4	9/4	10/4		

E.WENKERT,A.O.CLOUSE,D.W.COCHRAN,D.DODRELL
CHEM COMMUN   1969, 1433 (1969)

859   U 002000   3,9-DIBROMOCAMPHOR

```
      6    5
      C---C
   1/H2CBR\
H3C-C---C---C4
  10 \  8CH3/
      C---C3
     //2   |
      O      BR
```

FORMULA	C10H14O BR2			MOL WT	310.03
SOLVENT	CHCL3				
ORIG ST	CS2			TEMP	AMB
58.30	209.90	52.40	47.80	22.10	30.40
1/1	2/1	3/2	4/2	5/3	6/3
50.10	17.20	39.20	10.20		
7/1	8/4	9/3	10/4		

E.WENKERT,A.O.CLOUSE,D.N.COCHRAN,D.DODRELL
CHEM COMMUN   1969, 1433 (1969)

860   U 002000   FENCHONE

```
      6    5
      C---C
   1/  7  \
H3C-C---C---C4
  10 \   3/
      C---C-CH3
     //2   | 8
      O     CH3
             9
```

FORMULA	C10H16O			MOL WT	152.24
SOLVENT	CCL4				
ORIG ST	CS2			TEMP	AMB
53.80	219.10	47.10	45.50	25.30	32.00
1/1	2/1	3/1	4/2	5/3	6/3
41.80	21.90	23.60	15.00		
7/3	8/4	9/4	10/4		

E.WENKERT,A.O.CLOUSE,D.W.COCHRAN,D.DODRELL
CHEM COMMUN   1969, 1433 (1969)

861   U 002000   PIMARADIENE

```
        16CH2
        15/
       12C  CH
       11/ \|
    20  C  13C.CH3
   H3C |   |17
   1C |  C9  C14
   / \|/.\ /
  2C 10C H C8
   |   |   |
  3C  5C   C7
   \ /.\  /
    4C H C6
 19/ .
H3C 18CH3
```

FORMULA	C20H32			MOL WT	272.48
SOLVENT	CHCL3				
ORIG ST	TMS			TEMP	AMB
39.70	19.40	42.50	33.50	55.20	22.90
1/3	2/3	3/3	4/1	5/2	6/3
36.30	138.80	51.80	38.80	19.10	36.30
7/3	8/1	9/2	10/1	11/3	12/3
38.80	128.10	147.70	112.90	29.80	34.50
13/1	14/2	15/2	16/3	17/4	18/4
22.50	14.90				
19/4	20/4				

E.WENKERT,B.L.BUCKWALTER
J AM CHEM SOC   94, 4367 (1972)

862   U 002000   PIMAROL

```
        16CH2
        15/
       12C  CH
       11/ \|
    20  C  13C.CH3
   H3C |   |17
   1C |  C9  C14
   / \|/.\ /
  2C 10C H C8
   |   |   |
  3C  5C   C7
   \ /.\  /
    4C H C6
 19/ .
H3C 18CH2OH
```

FORMULA	C20H32O			MOL WT	288.48
SOLVENT	CCL4				
ORIG ST	TMS			TEMP	AMB
38.30	18.50	35.50	37.90	47.50	22.50
1/3	2/3	3/3	4/1	5/2	6/3
35.50	138.10	51.50	38.80	19.30	36.00
7/3	8/1	9/2	10/1	11/3	12/3
39.00	128.10	147.00	113.10	29.80	71.70
13/1	14/2	15/2	16/3	17/4	18/3
18.30	15.60				
19/4	20/4				

E.WENKERT,B.L.BUCKWALTER
J AM CHEM SOC   94, 4367 (1972)

863   U 002000   PIMARIC ACID

```
        16CH2          FORMULA  C20H30O2              MOL WT  302.46
        15//          SOLVENT  CHCL3
       12C CH          ORIG ST  TMS                    TEMP      AMB
       11/ \|
      20 C 13C.CH3      38.60   18.50   37.50   47.60   49.10   25.50
     H3C |   |17         1/3     2/3     3/3     4/1     5/2     6/3
     1C | C9  C14       35.80  138.50   51.90   38.10   19.50   36.00
    / \|/.\ //           7/3     8/1     9/2    10/1    11/3    12/3
   2C 10C H C8          39.00  128.20  147.80  113.20   29.90  185.70
    |   |   |           13/1    14/2    15/2    16/3    17/4    18/1
   3C  5C   C7          17.60   15.40
    \ /.\ /             19/4    20/4
     4C H C6
   19/ .                E.WENKERT,B.L.BUCKWALTER
  H3C 18COOH            J AM CHEM SOC                   94, 4367 (1972)
```

864   U 002000   ISOPIMARADIENE

```
      17   16           FORMULA  C20H32               MOL WT  272.48
    12C CH3 CH2         SOLVENT  CCL4
     11/ \|  //         ORIG ST  TMS                    TEMP      AMB
    20 C 13C.CH
    H3C |   |15          40.10   19.00   42.50   33.10   50.50   23.50
    1C | C9  C14          1/3     2/3     3/3     4/1     5/2     6/3
   / \|/.\ /            121.60  135.20   52.20   35.60   20.30   36.40
  2C 10C H C8            7/2     8/1     9/2    10/1    11/3    12/3
   |   |   ||           37.00   46.30  149.90  109.50   21.80   33.90
  3C  5C   C7           13/1    14/3    15/2    16/3    17/4    18/4
   \ /.\ /              22.60   15.20
    4C H C6             19/4    20/4
   / .
  H3C   CH3             E.WENKERT,B.L.BUCKWALTER
  19   18               J AM CHEM SOC                   94, 4367 (1972)
```

865   U 002000   ISOPIMAROL

```
      17   16           FORMULA  C20H32O              MOL WT  288.48
    12C CH3 CH2         SOLVENT  CCL4
     11/ \|  //         ORIG ST  TMS                    TEMP      AMB
    20 C 13C.CH
    H3C |   |15          39.60   18.50   35.80   37.60   43.70   23.50
    1C | C9  C14          1/3     2/3     3/3     4/1     5/2     6/3
   / \|/.\ /            121.50  135.30   52.00   35.40   20.50   36.50
  2C 10C H C8            7/2     8/1     9/2    10/1    11/3    12/3
   |   |   ||           36.90   46.40  150.00  109.50   21.80   71.90
  3C  5C   C7           13/1    14/3    15/2    16/3    17/4    18/3
   \ /.\ /              18.50   15.90
    4C H C6             19/4    20/4
   / .
  H3C   CH2OH           E.WENKERT,B.L.BUCKWALTER
  19   18               J AM CHEM SOC                   94, 4367 (1972)
```

866   U 002000   ISOPIMARIC ACID

```
      17   16           FORMULA  C20H30O2             MOL WT  302.46
    12C CH3 CH2         SOLVENT  CHCL3
     11/ \|  //         ORIG ST  TMS                    TEMP      AMB
    20 C 13C.CH
    H3C |   |15          39.20   17.90   37.20   46.20   45.40   25.70
    1C | C9  C14          1/3     2/3     3/3     4/1     5/2     6/3
   / \|/.\ /            121.50  136.00   52.40   35.40   20.50   36.00
  2C 10C H C8            7/2     8/1     9/2    10/1    11/3    12/3
   |   |   ||           37.50   46.50  150.70  109.70   21.90  183.90
  3C  5C   C7           13/1    14/3    15/2    16/3    17/4    18/1
   \ /.\ /              17.50   15.70
    4C H C6             19/4    20/4
   / .
  H3C   COOH            E.WENKERT,B.L.BUCKWALTER
  19   18               J AM CHEM SOC                   94, 4367 (1972)
```

867   U 002000   SANDARACOPIMARIC ACID

```
         17  16
     12C CH3 CH2
     11/ \| /
    20 C 13C·CH
   H3C |   | 15
   1C | C9  C14
   / \|/·\ /
  2C 10C H C8
  |    |   |
 3C  5C    C7
  \ /·\ /
  4C H C6
  / ·
 CH3 COOH
 19  18
```

FORMULA	C20H30O2			MOL WT	302.46
SOLVENT	CCL4				
ORIG ST	TMS			TEMP	AMB
38.40	18.30	37.10	47.20	48.70	24.90
1/3	2/3	3/3	4/1	5/2	6/3
35.50	136.20	50.70	37.80	18.80	34.60
7/3	8/1	9/2	10/1	11/3	12/3
37.40	129.30	149.00	110.50	26.20	185.30
13/1	14/2	15/2	16/3	17/4	18/1
16.80	15.30				
19/4	20/4				

E.WENKERT,B.L.BUCKWALTER
J AM CHEM SOC   94, 4367 (1972)

868   U 002000   ALPHA—IONONE

```
12  13
CH3 CH3  O
 \ /  7  ||
  C  CH  C
 /6\ / \ /9\
C5 1C  CH CH3
|   |   8  10
C4 2C
 \3/ \
  C   CH3
  11
```

FORMULA	C13H20O			MOL WT	192.30
SOLVENT	C13H20O				
ORIG ST	CS2			TEMP	AMB
54.30	132.30	122.50	23.20	28.70	32.40
1/2	2/1	3/2	4/3	5/3	6/1
132.70	147.50	196.00	27.50	31.50	26.80
7/2	8/2	9/1	10/4	11/4	12/4
26.80					
13/4					

M.JAUTELAT,J.B.GRUTZNER,J.D.ROBERTS
PROC NAT AKAD SCI US   65, 288 (1970)

869   U 002000   BETA—IONONE

```
12  13
CH3 CH3  O
 \ /  7  ||
  C  CH  C
 /6\ / \ /9\
C5 1C  CH CH3
|  ||   8  10
C4 2C
 \3/ \
  C   CH3
  11
```

FORMULA	C13H20O			MOL WT	192.30
SOLVENT	C13H20O				
ORIG ST	CS2			TEMP	AMB
136.20	134.70	33.30	19.00	39.50	34.00
1/1	2/1	3/3	4/3	5/3	6/1
132.10	141.70	196.20	26.60	21.30	28.60
7/2	8/2	9/1	10/4	11/4	12/4
28.60					
13/4					

M.JAUTELAT,J.B.GRUTZNER,J.D.ROBERTS
PROC NAT AKAD SCI US   65, 288 (1970)

870   U 002000   VITAMIN A ACETATE

```
17  18    19      20
CH3 CH3  CH3     CH3
 \ /  7  |   11  | 15
  C  CH 9C  CH  C13 CH2
 /6\ / \ / \ / \ / \
C5 1C  CH CH CH CH  O
|  ||  8  10 12 14  |
C4 2C              21C
 \3/ \             / \
  C   CH3      22CH3 O
  16
```

FORMULA	C22H32O2			MOL WT	328.50
SOLVENT	CS2				
ORIG ST	CS2			TEMP	AMB
138.30	137.70	33.40	19.70	40.00	34.50
1/1	2/1	3/3	4/3	5/3	6/1
135.90	126.30	135.70	125.10	128.70	125.20
7/2	8/2	9/1	10/2	11/2	12/2
130.20	137.70	61.20	20.50	29.20	29.20
13/1	14/2	15/3	16/4	17/4	18/4
12.60	12.60	169.00	21.80		
19/4	20/4	21/1	22/4		

M.JAUTELAT,J.B.GRUTZNER,J.D.ROBERTS
PROC NAT AKAD SCI US   65, 288 (1970)

871 — U 002000 — BETA—CAROTENE

```
17  18    19      20
CH3 CH3   CH3     CH3
 \ / 7   |  11   |    H
  C   CH 9CH  CH  C13 C15
 /6\ / \ / \ / \ / \ / \ )2
C5 1C   CH  CH  CH  CH
 |  ||   8  10  12  14
C4 2C
 \3/ \
  C    CH3
    16
```

FORMULA	C40H56			MOL WT	536.89
SOLVENT	C S2				
ORIG ST	C S2			TEMP	AMB

138.00	138.00	33.40	19.90	39.90	34.20
1/1	2/1	3/3	4/3	5/3	6/1
135.40	126.40	136.10	125.40	132.80	129.00
7/2	8/2	9/1	10/2	11/2	12/2
131.40	130.20	137.50	21.90	28.90	28.90
13/1	14/2	15/2	16/4	17/4	18/4
12.70	12.70				
19/4	20/4				

M.JAUTELAT,J.B.GRUTZNER,J.D.ROBERTS
PROC NAT AKAD SCI US   65, 288 (1970)

872 — U 002000 — 15,15*—CIS—BETA—CAROTENE

```
17  18    19      20
CH3 CH3   CH3     CH3
 \ / 7   |  11   |    15
  C   CH 9C   CH  C13 CH=)2
 /6\ / \ / \ / \ / \ /
C5 1C   CH  CH  CH  CH
 |  ||   8  10  12  14
C4 2C
 \3/ \
  C    CH3
    16
```

FORMULA	C40H56			MOL WT	536.89
SOLVENT	C S2				
ORIG ST	C S2			TEMP	AMB

138.00	138.00	33.40	19.80	39.90	34.20
1/1	2/1	3/3	4/3	5/3	6/1
135.70	126.50	136.90	125.80	131.60	127.40
7/2	8/2	9/1	10/2	11/2	12/2
129.10	125.50	137.80	21.90	29.00	29.00
13/1	14/2	15/2	16/4	17/4	18/4
12.70	12.50				
19/4	20/4				

M.JAUTELAT,J.B.GRUTZNER,J.D.ROBERTS
PROC NAT AKAD SCI US   65, 288 (1970)

873 — U 002000 — 15,15*—DEHYDRO—BETA—CAROTENE

```
17  18    19      20
CH3 CH3   CH3     CH3
 \ / 7   |  11   |
  C   CH 9C   CH  C13
 /6\ / \ / \ / \ / \
C5 1C   CH  CH  CH  CH-C≡)2
 |  ||   8  10  12  14 15
C4 2C
 \3/ \
  C    CH3
    16
```

FORMULA	C40H54			MOL WT	534.88
SOLVENT	C S2				
ORIG ST	C S2			TEMP	AMB

138.00	138.00	33.40	19.90	40.00	34.40
1/1	2/1	3/3	4/3	5/3	6/1
135.20	127.00	136.90	127.00	130.80	129.30
7/2	8/2	9/1	10/2	11/2	12/2
146.10	111.30	99.00	21.80	29.00	29.00
13/1	14/2	15/1	16/4	17/4	18/4
12.70	15.20				
19/4	20/4				

M.JAUTELAT,J.B.GRUTZNER,J.D.ROBERTS
PROC NAT AKAD SCI US   65, 288 (1970)

874 — U 003000 — 5—ALPHA—ANDROSTANE

```
        18
     12C C C17
     / \|/ \
    11C 13C   C16
   19 |  |  |
  1C C C9 C---C15
   / \|/ \ /14
  2C  C10 C8
  |   |   |
  3C  5C  C7
   \ / \ /
    4C   C6
```

FORMULA	C19H32			MOL WT	260.47
SOLVENT	CDCL3				
ORIG ST	C S2			TEMP	296

37.60	22.00	26.60	28.90	46.90	28.90
1/3	2/3	3/3	4/3	5/2	6/3
32.30	35.70	54.50	36.10	20.70	40.30
7/3	8/2	9/2	10/1	11/3	12/3
40.60	54.90	20.30	38.80	25.30	17.30
13/1	14/2	15/3	16/3	17/3	18/4
12.00					
19/4					

B.BALOGH,D.M.WILSON,A.L.BURLINGAME
NATURE   233, 261 (1971)

875   U 003000   5-ALPHA-CHOLESTANE

```
        21   22  24  26   FORMULA  C27H48                      MOL WT  372.68
        H3C   CH2 CH2 CH3 SOLVENT  C4H8O2/CHCL3
         \  / \ / \ / \ /  ORIG ST CS2                         TEMP     AMB
           20CH  CH2 CH
         18 |   23  25\
        12C C C17        CH3
          / \ | / \      27
        11C 13C   C16
        19 |   |    |
        1C C C9  C---C15
        / \ | / \  /14
      2C   C10 C8
       |    |   |
      3C  5C   C7
        \  / \ /
         4C   C6
```

38.90	22.30	27.00	29.30	47.30	29.30
1/3	2/3	3/3	4/3	5/2	6/3
32.30	35.80	55.20	36.50	21.10	28.30
7/3	8/2	9/2	10/1	11/3	12/3
42.80	56.90	24.30	40.40	56.80	12.20
13/1	14/2	15/3	16/3	17/2	18/4
12.10	36.00	18.80	36.40	24.20	39.70
19/4	20/2	21/4	22/3	23/3	24/3
28.10	22.50	22.70			
25/2	26/4	27/4			

H.J.REICH,M.JAUTELAT,M.T.MESSE,F.J.WEIGERT
J.D.ROBERTS
J AM CHEM SOC   91, 7445 (1969)

876   U 003000   5-BETA-CHOLESTANE

```
        21   22  24  26   FORMULA  C27H48                      MOL WT  372.68
        H3C   CH2 CH2 CH3 SOLVENT  CDCL3
         \  / \ / \ / \ /  ORIG ST CS2                         TEMP      296
           20CH  CH2 CH
         18 |   23  25\
        12C C C17        CH3
          / \ | / \      27
        11C 13C   C16
        19 |   |    |
        1C C C9  C---C15
        / \ | / \  /14
      2C   C10 C8
       |    |   |
      5C  5C   C7
        \  / | \ /
         4C  H C6
```

37.40	21.10	26.40	26.90	40.40	27.10
1/3	2/3	3/3	4/3	5/2	6/3
28.70	35.60	45.60	27.80	20.70	27.80
7/3	8/2	9/2	10/1	11/3	12/3
42.50	56.30	24.10	40.20	56.10	11.90
13/1	14/2	15/3	16/3	17/2	18/4
24.10	35.80	18.50	36.00	23.70	39.40
19/4	20/2	21/4	22/3	23/3	24/3
27.40	22.70	22.30			
25/2	26/4	27/4			

B.BALOGH,D.M.WILSON,A.L.BURLINGAME
NATURE   233, 261 (1971)

877   U 003000   5-ALPHA-ERGOSTANE

```
            25CH3       FORMULA  C28H50                        MOL WT  386.71
        21   22  24|  27 SOLVENT  CDCL3
        H3C   CH2 CH  CH3 ORIG ST CS2                          TEMP      296
         \  / \ / \ / \ /
           20CH  CH2 CH
         18 |   23  26\
        12C C C17        CH3
          / \ | / \      28
        11C 13C   C16
        19 |   |    |
        1C C C9  C---C15
        / \ | / \  /14
      2C   C10 C8
       |    |   |
      3C  5C   C7
        \  / \ /
         4C   C6
```

38.50	20.30	26.40	28.90	46.90	28.90
1/3	2/3	3/3	4/3	5/2	6/3
32.00	35.30	54.60	36.10	18.60	28.00
7/3	8/2	9/2	10/1	11/3	12/3
42.30	56.30	24.10	40.00	56.00	12.30
13/1	14/2	15/3	16/3	17/2	18/4
12.10	36.10	14.20	33.60	30.60	39.00
19/4	20/2	21/4	22/3	23/3	24/2
17.40	31.20	21.90	20.60		
25/4	26/2	27/4	28/4		

B.BALOGH,D.M.WILSON,A.L.BURLINGAME
NATURE   233, 261 (1971)

878   U 003000   CHOLESTAN-3-BETA-OL

```
        21   22  24  26   FORMULA  C27H48O                     MOL WT  388.68
        H3C   CH2 CH2 CH3 SOLVENT  C4H8O2/CHCL3
         \  / \ / \ / \ /  ORIG ST CS2                         TEMP     AMB
           20CH  CH2 CH
         18 |   23  25\
        12C C C17        CH3
          / \ | / \      27
        11C 13C   C16
        19 |   |    |
        1C C C9  C---C15
        / \ | / \  /14
      2C   C10 C8
       |    |   |
      3C  5C   C7
        \  / \ /
      HO 4C   C6
      BETA
```

37.30	31.80	70.40	38.60	45.20	29.00
1/3	2/3	3/2	4/3	5/2	6/3
32.30	35.80	54.80	35.60	21.40	28.30
7/3	8/2	9/2	10/1	11/3	12/3
42.80	56.70	24.30	40.40	56.70	12.10
13/1	14/2	15/3	16/3	17/2	18/4
12.00	35.90	18.60	36.40	24.10	39.70
19/4	20/2	21/4	22/3	23/3	24/3
28.00	22.40	22.60			
25/2	26/4	27/4			

H.J.REICH,M.JAUTELAT,M.T.MESSE,F.J.WEIGERT,
J.D.ROBERTS
J AM CHEM SOC   91, 7445 (1969)

879   U 003000   CHOLESTAN-3-ALPHA-YL-ACETATE

```
        21   22   24   26    FORMULA   C29H50O2              MOL WT   430.72
       H3C   CH2  CH2  CH3 SOLVENT    C4H8O2/CHCL3
        \   /  \  /  \  /    ORIG ST   CS2                   TEMP       AMB
        20CH   CH2   CH
        18 |   23   25\        33.10    26.20    69.50    33.10    40.30    28.40
       12C  C  C17       CH3    1/3      2/3      3/2      4/3      5/2      6/3
        / \|/ \           27   32.10    35.70    54.60    35.80    21.00    28.40
      11C 13C   C16             7/3      8/2      9/2     10/1     11/3     12/3
      19  |    |    |          42.70    56.80    24.40    40.30    56.80    12.00
       1C  C  C9  C---C15      13/1     14/2     15/3     16/3     17/2     18/4
  29  2/ \|/ \ /14             11.20    36.00    18.70    36.40    24.10    39.70
 CH3  C   C10 C8              19/4     20/2     21/4     22/3     23/3     24/3
 |28 |    |    |              28.00    22.50    27.00   169.30    20.70
 C=O  C   5C   C7             25/2     26/4     27/4     28/1     29/4
  \  /3\ /  \ /
   O  4C   C6                 H.J.REICH,M.JAUTELAT,M.T.MESSE,F.J.WEIGERT,
 ALPHA                        J.D.ROBERTS
                             J AM CHEM SOC                   91, 7445 (1969)
```

880   U 003000   CHOLESTAN-3-BETA-YL-ACETATE

```
        21   22   24   26    FORMULA   C29H50O2              MOL WT   430.72
       H3C   CH2  CH2  CH3 SOLVENT    C4H8O2/CHCL3
        \   /  \  /  \  /    ORIG ST   CS2                   TEMP       AMB
        20CH   CH2   CH
        18 |   23   25\        36.90    27.60    73.60    34.20    44.80    28.80
       12C  C  C17       CH3    1/3      2/3      3/2      4/3      5/2      6/3
        / \|/ \           27   32.10    35.70    54.60    35.60    21.40    28.20
      11C 13C   C16             7/3      8/2      9/2     10/1     11/3     12/3
      19  |    |    |          42.70    56.70    24.20    40.20    56.70    12.00
       1C  C  C9  C---C15      13/1     14/2     15/3     16/3     17/2     18/4
  29  2/ \|/ \ /14             12.00    35.90    18.70    36.40    24.10    39.60
 CH3  C   C10 C8              19/4     20/2     21/4     22/3     23/3     24/3
 |28 |    |    |              28.00    22.40    22.60   169.40    20.60
 C=O  C   5C   C7             25/2     26/4     27/4     28/1     29/4
  \  /3\ /  \ /
   O  4C   C6                 H.J.REICH,M.JAUTELAT,M.T.MESSE,F.J.WEIGERT,
 BETA                         J.D.ROBERTS
                             J AM CHEM SOC                   91, 7445 (1969)
```

881   U 003000   CHOLESTA-3,5-DIENE

```
        21   22   24   26    FORMULA   C27H44                MOL WT   368.65
       H3C   CH2  CH2  CH3 SOLVENT    C4H8O2/CHCL3
        \   /  \  /  \  /    ORIG ST   CS2                   TEMP       AMB
        20CH   CH2   CH
        18 |   23   25\        34.00    23.10   129.60   124.30   141.40   122.90
       12C  C  C17       CH3    1/3      2/3      3/2      4/2      5/1      6/2
        / \|/ \           27   31.90    32.00    48.60    35.20    21.20    28.30
      11C 13C   C16             7/3      8/2      9/2     10/1     11/3     12/3
      19  |    |    |          42.60    57.20    24.20    40.20    56.60    12.00
       1C  C  C9  C---C15      13/1     14/3     15/3     16/3     17/2     18/4
        / \|/ \ /14            18.60    36.00    18.80    36.50    24.20    39.80
   2C   C10 C8               19/4     20/2     21/4     22/3     23/3     24/3
   |    |    |               28.10    22.50    22.70
   3C   5C   C7              25/2     26/4     27/4
    \\ / \\ /
     4C    C6                  H.J.REICH,M.JAUTELAT,M.T.MESSE,F.J.WEIGERT,
                             J.D.ROBERTS
                             J AM CHEM SOC                   91, 7445 (1969)
```

882   U 003000   CHOLESTEROL

```
        21   22   24   26    FORMULA   C27H46O               MOL WT   386.67
       H3C   CH2  CH2  CH3 SOLVENT    C4H8O2/CHCL3
        \   /  \  /  \  /    ORIG ST   CS2                   TEMP       AMB
        20CH   CH2   CH
        18 |   23   25\        37.70    31.60    71.30    42.40   141.20   121.30
       12C  C  C17       CH3    1/3      2/3      3/2      4/3      5/1      6/2
        / \|/ \           27   32.00    32.00    50.50    36.50    21.20    28.30
      11C 13C   C16             7/3      8/2      9/2     10/1     11/3     12/3
      19  |    |    |          42.40    56.90    24.30    40.00    56.50    12.00
       1C  C  C9  C---C15      13/1     14/2     15/3     16/3     17/2     18/4
        / \|/ \ /14            19.40    35.80    18.80    36.40    24.10    39.60
   2C   C10 C8               19/4     20/2     21/4     22/3     23/3     24/3
   |    |    |               28.00    22.50    22.80
   3C   5C   C7              25/2     26/4     27/4
    / \ / \\ /
  HO  4C   C6                 H.J.REICH,M.JAUTELAT,M.T.MESSE,F.J.WEIGERT,
                             J.D.ROBERTS
                             J AM CHEM SOC                   91, 7445 (1969)
```

883   U 003000   CHOLESTERYL ACETATE

```
        21   22  24  26    FORMULA   C29H48O2              MOL WT   428.70
        H3C    CH2 CH2 CH3SOLVENT   C4H8O2/CHCL3
          \  / \ / \ / \ /  ORIG ST  CS2                   TEMP        AMB
          20CH  CH2 CH
        18 |  23    25\      37.30   28.20   73.70   38.40  139.90  122.60
         12C C C17        CH3   1/3     2/3     3/2     4/3     5/1     6/2
         /  \|/ \            27  32.20   32.20   50.40   36.70   21.30   32.50
       11C 13C    C16           7/3     8/2     9/2    10/1    11/3    12/3
       19 |   |    |           42.50   57.00   24.60   40.10   56.60   12.00
        1C C  C9  C---C15       13/1    14/2    15/3    16/3    17/2    18/4
    29  2/ \|/ \ /14            19.30   36.10   18.90   36.70   24.30   39.80
   CH3 C   C10 C8              19/4    20/2    21/4    22/3    23/3    24/3
   |28 |    |   |              28.80   22.70   22.90  169.50   20.90
   C=O C   5C   C7             25/2    26/4    27/4    28/1    29/4
    \ /3\ / \ /
     O   4C    C6            H.J.REICH,M.JAUTELAT,M.T.MESSE,F.J.WEIGERT,
                             J.D.ROBERTS
                             J AM CHEM SOC              91, 7445 (1969)
```

884   U 003000   CHOLESTERYL METHYL ETHER

```
        21   22  24  26    FORMULA   C28H48O               MOL WT   400.69
        H3C    CH2 CH2 CH3SOLVENT   C4H8O2/CHCL3
          \  / \ / \ / \ /  ORIG ST  CS2                   TEMP        AMB
          20CH  CH2 CH
        18 |  23    25\      37.40   28.30   80.30   39.00  141.00  121.30
         12C C C17        CH3   1/3     2/3     3/2     4/3     5/1     6/2
         /  \|/ \            27  32.00   32.00   50.50   36.90   21.20   28.20
       11C 13C    C16           7/3     8/2     9/2    10/1    11/3    12/3
       19 |   |    |           42.50   57.00   24.30   40.10   56.60   11.90
        1C C  C9  C---C15       13/1    14/2    15/3    16/3    17/2    18/4
        /  \|/ \ /14            19.30   36.00   18.80   36.40   24.10   39.70
      2C   C10 C8              19/4    20/2    21/4    22/3    23/3    24/3
      |    |   |               28.00   22.50   22.70   55.10
      3C   5C   C7             25/2    26/4    27/4    28/4
      /  \ / \ /
     O   4C    C6            H.J.REICH,M.JAUTELAT,M.T.MESSE,F.J.WEIGERT,
     |                       J.D.ROBERTS
   28CH3                     J AM CHEM SOC              91, 7445 (1969)
```

885   U 003000   7-DEHYDROCHOLESTERYL ACETATE

```
        21   22  24  26    FORMULA   C29H46O2              MOL WT   426.69
        H3C    CH2 CH2 CH3SOLVENT   C4H8O2/CHCL3
          \  / \ / \ / \ /  ORIG ST  CS2                   TEMP        AMB
          20CH  CH2 CH
        18 |  23    25\      38.10   28.10   72.60   36.80  141.00  120.40
         12C C C17        CH3   1/3     2/3     3/2     4/3     5/1     6/2
         /  \|/ \            27  116.70  138.50   46.20   37.20   21.10   28.20
       11C 13C    C16           7/2     8/1     9/2    10/1    11/3    12/3
       19 |   |    |           43.00   54.50   23.00   39.40   56.20   11.80
        1C C  C9  C---C15       13/1    14/2    15/3    16/3    17/2    18/4
    29  2/ \|/ \ /14            16.00   36.30   18.90   36.30   24.00   39.60
   CH3 C   C10 C8              19/4    20/2    21/4    22/3    23/3    24/3
   |28 |    |   ||             28.00   22.50   22.70  169.60   20.90
   C=O C   5C   C7             25/2    26/4    27/4    28/1    29/4
    \ /3\ / \ /
     O   4C    C6            H.J.REICH,M.JAUTELAT,M.T.MESSE,F.J.WEIGERT,
                             J.D.ROBERTS
                             J AM CHEM SOC              91, 7445 (1969)
```

886   U 003000   ERGOSTEROL

```
            25CH3      FORMULA   C28H44O                   MOL WT   396.66
      21   22 24|  27  SOLVENT   C4H8O2/CHCL3
      H3C   CH  CH  CH3ORIG ST  CS2                        TEMP        AMB
        \  / \ \ / \ /
        20CH  CH  CH     38.60   32.60   69.70   41.10  140.70  119.40
       18 |  23    26\      1/3     2/3     3/2     4/3     5/1     6/2
        12C C C17      CH3  116.70  140.60   46.50   37.20   21.20   28.30
        /  \|/ \          28  7/2     8/1     9/2    10/1    11/3    12/3
      11C 13C    C16          43.00   54.60   23.10   39.40   56.00   11.80
      19 |   |    |          13/1    14/2    15/3    16/3    17/2    18/4
       1C C  C9  C---C15     16.00   40.50   19.40  132.20  136.00   43.00
       /  \|/ \ /14          19/4    20/2    21/4    22/2    23/2    24/2
      2C   C10 C8           19.70   33.20   21.00   17.40
      |    |   ||           25/4    26/2    27/4    28/4
      3C   5C   C7
      /  \ / \ /
    HO   4C    C6          H.J.REICH,M.JAUTELAT,M.T.MESSE,F.J.WEIGERT,
                           J.D.ROBERTS
                           J AM CHEM SOC                91, 7445 (1969)
```

---

887   U 003000   LANOSTEROL

```
        21  22  24  26   FORMULA  C30H50O              MOL WT  426.73
       H3C  CH2 CH  CH3 SOLVENT  CDCL3
         \ / \ / \ /    ORIG ST  CDCL3                 TEMP      AMB
        20CH  CH2 C25
          18 |   23   |      35.00   27.40   78.30   38.10   49.80   20.30
        12C C17     CH3       1/3     2/3     3/2     4/1     5/1     6/3
        / \|/ \      27      27.40  133.90  133.90   36.30   17.60   25.80
      11C 13C   C16           7/3     8/1     9/1    10/1    11/3    12/3
      19 |    |14 |          43.70   49.10   30.20   30.20   49.80   15.30
     1C C C9  C---C15        13/1    14/1    15/3    16/3    17/2    18/4
     / \|/ \ /.              18.00   35.10   18.40   35.10   24.20  124.70
   2C   C10 C8C28            19/4    20/2    21/4    22/3    23/3    24/2
    |    |   |              130.20   24.90   16.90   23.50   27.40   14.80
   3C  5C   C7               25/1    26/4    27/4    28/4    29/4    30/4
  / \ / \ /
HO  4C   C6               G.LUKACS,F.KHUONG-HU,C.R.BENNETT,
 30/ .                    B.L.BUCKWALTER,E.WENKERT
H3C 29CH3                 TETRAHEDRON LETTERS           1972, 3515 (1972)
```

---

888   U 003000   DIHYDROLANOSTEROL

```
        21  22  24  26   FORMULA  C30H52O              MOL WT  428.75
       H3C  CH2 CH2 CH3 SOLVENT  CDCL3
         \ / \ / \ /    ORIG ST  TMS                   TEMP      AMB
        20CH  CH2 CH
          18 |   23  25\      35.10   27.40   77.90   38.20   49.80   20.50
        12C C C17     CH3      1/3     2/3     3/2     4/1     5/2     6/3
        / \|/ \        27     27.40  133.00  133.90   36.50   17.60   25.80
      11C 13C   C16            7/3     8/1     9/1    10/1    11/3    12/3
      19 |    |14 |           43.80   49.10   30.30   30.30   49.80   15.20
     1C C C9  C---C15         13/1    14/1    15/3    16/3    17/2    18/4
     / \|/ \ /.               18.00   35.80   18.50   35.80   23.60   38.90
   2C   C10 C8C28             19/4    20/2    21/4    22/3    23/3    24/3
    |    |   |                27.40   22.40   22.00   23.60   27.40   15.00
   3C  5C   C7                25/2    26/4    27/4    28/4    29/4    30/4
  / \ / \ /
HO  4C   C6               G.LUKACS,F.KHUONG-HU,C.R.BENNETT,
 30/ .                    B.L.BUCKWALTER,E.WENKERT
H3C 29CH3                 TETRAHEDRON LETTERS           1972, 3515 (1972)
```

---

889   U 003000   CHOLESTAN-3-ONE

```
        21  22  24  26   FORMULA  C27H46O              MOL WT  386.67
       H3C  CH2 CH2 CH3 SOLVENT  C4H8O2/CHCL3
         \ / \ / \ /    ORIG ST  CS2                   TEMP      AMB
        20CH  CH2 CH
          18 |   23  25\      38.60   37.90  209.10   44.50   46.70   29.10
        12C C C17     CH3      1/3     2/3     3/1     4/3     5/2     6/3
        / \|/ \        27     31.90   35.70   54.10   35.60   21.60   28.30
      11C 13C   C16            7/3     8/1     9/2    10/1    11/3    12/3
      19 |   |   |            42.70   56.50   24.30   40.20   56.60   12.00
     1C C C9  C---C15         13/1    14/2    15/3    16/3    17/2    18/4
     / \|/ \ /14              11.20   35.90   18.70   36.40   24.00   39.60
   2C   C10 C8               19/4    20/2    21/4    22/3    23/3    24/3
    |    |   |                28.00   22.50   22.70
   3C  5C   C7                25/2    26/4    27/4
  // \ / \ /
O   4C   C6               H.J.REICH,M.JAUTELAT,M.T.MESSE,F.J.WEIGERT,
                          J.D.ROBERTS
                          J AM CHEM SOC                 91, 7445 (1969)
```

---

890   U 003000   CHOLESTA-3,5-DIEN-7-ONE

```
        21  22  24  26   FORMULA  C27H42O              MOL WT  382.64
       H3C  CH2 CH2 CH3 SOLVENT  C4H8O2/CHCL3
         \ / \ / \ /    ORIG ST  CS2                   TEMP      AMB
        20CH  CH2 CH
          18 |   23  25\      33.00   23.50  136.10  124.40  160.00  127.90
        12C C C17     CH3      1/3     2/3     3/2     4/2     5/1     6/2
        / \|/ \        27    200.40   46.00   49.80   36.20   21.40   28.70
      11C 13C   C16            7/1     8/2     9/2    10/1    11/3    12/3
      19 |  |   |             43.60   50.90   26.50   39.20   55.30   12.00
     1C C C9  C---C15         13/1    14/2    15/3    16/3    17/2    18/4
     / \|/ \ /14              16.50   35.90   19.00   36.40   24.10   39.60
   2C   C10 C8               19/4    20/2    21/4    22/3    23/3    24/3
    |    |   |                28.00   22.60   22.80
   3C  5C   C7                25/2    26/4    27/4
  \\ / \ / \\
   4C   C6  O             H.J.REICH,M.JAUTELAT,M.T.MESSE,F.J.WEIGERT,
                          J.D.ROBERTS
                          J AM CHEM SOC                 91, 7445 (1969)
```

891   U 003000   CHOLEST-5-EN-7-ON-3-BETA-YL ACETATE

```
        21  22  24  26      FORMULA  C29H46O2            MOL WT   426.69
       H3C   CH2 CH2 CH3SOLVENT  C4H8O2/CHCL3
         \ / \ / \ /         ORIG ST  CS2                TEMP       AMB
        20CH  CH2 CH
       18 |   23  25\
      12C C C17      CH3
       / \|/ \       27
     11C 13C   C16
     19 |   |   |
   1C C C9 C---C15
 29  2/ \|/ \ /14
 CH3 C   C10 C8
|28 |   |   |
C=O C   5C   C7
 \ /3\ / \ / \
  O  4C   C6   O
```

36.10	27.50	72.30	37.70	163.20	126.70
1/3	2/3	3/2	4/3	5/1	6/2
200.10	45.30	49.90	38.30	21.30	28.60
7/1	8/2	9/2	10/1	11/3	12/3
43.20	50.20	26.40	39.00	55.20	11.80
13/1	14/2	15/3	16/3	17/2	18/4
16.90	35.90	18.90	36.40	24.10	39.60
19/4	20/2	21/4	22/3	23/3	24/3
28.00	22.40	22.60	169.30	20.50	
25/2	26/4	27/4	28/1	29/4	

H.J.REICH,M.JAUTELAT,M.T.MESSE,F.J.WEIGERT,
J.D.ROBERTS
J AM CHEM SOC   91, 7445 (1969)

892   U 003000   2-BETA-3-BETA-14-ALPHA-TRIHYDROXY- 5-BETA-CHOLEST-7-EN-6-ONE

```
        21  22  24  26
       H3C   CH2 CH2 CH3FORMULA  C27H44O4        MOL WT   432.65
         \ / \ / \ /         SOLVENT  C5D5N
        20CH  CH2 CH          ORIG ST  CS2        TEMP       AMB
       18 |   23  25\
      12C C C17      CH3
       / \|/ \       27
     11C 13C    C16
     19 |  |14 |
  HO  1C C C9 C---C15
   \ / \|/ \ /.
    2C   C10 C8OH
    |   |   ||
    3C   5C   C7
   / \ / \ /
 HO  4C   C6
      ||
      O
```

37.20	66.80	66.80	31.70	50.30	175.70
1/3	2/2	3/2	4/3	5/2	6/1
119.50	163.00	33.90	37.90	20.70	26.90
7/2	8/1	9/2	10/1	11/3	12/3
46.30	82.80	31.20	30.80	50.20	15.60
13/1	14/1	15/3	16/3	17/2	18/4
24.00	35.40	18.90	36.10	24.00	39.10
19/4	20/2	21/4	22/3	23/3	24/3
27.70	22.60	22.30			
25/2	26/4	27/4			

G.LUKACS,C.R.BENNETT
BULL SOC CHIM FRANCE   1972, 3996 (1972)

893   U 003000   ALPHA-ECDYSONE

```
          OH
        21 22. 24  26    FORMULA  C27H44O6        MOL WT   464.65
       H3C   CH  CH2 CH3SOLVENT  C5D5N
        . / \ / \ /         ORIG ST  CS2           TEMP       AMB
        20CH  CH2 C-OH
       18 |   23  25\
      12C C C17      CH3
       / \|/ \       27
     11C 13C    C16
     19 |  |14 |
  HO  1C C C9 C---C15
   \ / \|/ \ /.
    2C   C10 C8OH
    |   |   ||
    3C   5C   C7
   / \ / \ /
 HO  4C   C6
      ||
      O
```

37.20	66.90	66.90	31.70	50.30	175.70
1/3	2/2	3/2	4/3	5/2	6/1
119.50	162.90	33.90	37.90	20.70	26.10
7/3	8/2	9/2	10/1	11/3	12/3
46.70	82.50	31.30	30.80	47.40	15.50
13/1	14/1	15/3	16/3	17/2	18/4
24.00	41.60	13.30	72.80	25.00	42.20
19/4	20/2	21/4	22/2	23/3	24/3
68.60	29.70	29.40			
25/1	26/4	27/4			

G.LUKACS,C.R.BENNETT
BULL SOC CHIM FRANCE   1972, 3996 (1972)

894   U 003000   CONANINE

```
      22CH3         FORMULA  C22H37N        MOL WT   315.55
       |  21        SOLVENT  CDCL3
       N   CH3      ORIG ST  TMS            TEMP       AMB
      18/ \ /
      12C C   C20
       / \|   |
     11C 13C---C17
     19 |  |   |
   1C C C9 C14 C16
   / \|/ \ / \ /
  2C   C10 C8 C15
  |   |   |   |
  3C   5C   C7
   \ / \ /
    4C   C6
```

39.10	21.80	27.00	29.20	46.80	29.20
1/3	2/3	3/3	4/3	5/2	6/3
32.20	37.80	54.70	36.20	22.30	27.60
7/3	8/2	9/2	10/1	11/3	12/3
50.80	56.00	24.80	39.30	53.90	65.10
13/1	14/2	15/3	16/3	17/2	18/3
12.40	63.00	15.00	40.90		
19/4	20/2	21/4	22/4		

G.LUKACS,A.PICOT,X.LUSINCHI,H.J.KOCH,A.S.PERLIN
COMPT REND C   272, 2171 (1971)

895 — U 003000 CONESSINE

```
        22CH3
          | 21
          N   CH3
         18/ \ /
        12C  C   C20
        / \|   |
      11C  13C----C17
      19 |    |    |
    1C  C  C9  C14 C16
    / \|/ \ / \ /
  2C   C10 C8  C15
23 |    |    |    |
CH3 C  5C   C7
  \ /3\ / \ /
   N   4C   C6
  /
CH3
```

FORMULA	C24H40N2			MOL WT	356.60
SOLVENT	CDCL3				
ORIG ST	TMS			TEMP	AMB

38.50	25.30	64.80	35.60	141.90	120.70
1/3	2/3	3/2	4/3	5/1	6/2
32.20	33.60	50.20	37.00	22.10	27.80
7/3	8/2	9/2	10/1	11/3	12/3
50.20	56.00	24.90	38.90	53.70	64.80
13/1	14/2	15/3	16/3	17/2	18/3
19.60	62.90	15.10	41.00	41.80	
19/4	20/2	21/4	22/4	23/4	

G.LUKACS,A.PICOT,X.LUSINCHI,H.J.KOCH,A.S.PERLIN
COMPT REND C   272, 2171 (1971)

896 — U 003000 DIHYDROCONESSINE

```
        22CH3
          | 21
          N   CH3
         18/ \ /
        12C  C   C20
        / \|   |
      11C  13C----C17
      19 |    |    |
    1C  C  C9  C14 C16
    / \|/ \ / \ /
  2C   C10 C8  C15
23 |    |    |    |
CH3 C  5C   C7
  \ /3\ / \ /
   N   4C   C6
  /
CH3
```

FORMULA	C24H42N2			MOL WT	358.62
SOLVENT	CDCL3				
ORIG ST	TMS			TEMP	AMB

38.10	24.90	64.30	31.50	45.90	29.20
1/3	2/3	3/2	4/3	5/2	6/3
32.40	37.80	54.50	35.10	22.30	27.60
7/3	8/2	9/2	10/1	11/3	12/3
50.90	56.00	24.90	39.30	54.00	65.10
13/1	14/2	15/3	16/3	17/2	18/3
12.40	62.90	15.10	40.90	41.80	
19/4	20/2	21/4	22/4	23/4	

G.LUKACS,A.PICOT,X.LUSINCHI,H.J.KOCH,A.S.PERLIN
COMPT REND C   272, 2171 (1971)

897 — U 003000 DIGITOXIGENIN

```
                O
        22     //
        C----C23
  18    ||    |
  12C CH3 20C   O
  / \|   / \ /
11C  13C----C17 C21
19 |    |    |
1C  C  C9  C14 C16
/ \|/ \8/|\ / \
2C   C10 C O C15
 |    |    | H
3C   5C   C7
/ \ / \ /
HO  4C   C6
```

FORMULA	C23H34O4			MOL WT	374.53
SOLVENT	CDCL3/CD3CD				
ORIG ST	TMS			TEMP	AMB

30.00	28.00	66.80	33.50	35.90	27.10
1/3	2/3	3/2	4/3	5/2	6/3
21.60	41.90	35.00	35.80	21.70	40.40
7/3	8/2	9/2	10/1	11/3	12/3
50.30	85.60	33.00	27.30	51.50	16.10
13/1	14/1	15/3	16/3	17/2	18/4
23.90	177.10	74.50	117.40	176.30	
19/4	20/1	21/3	22/3	23/1	

K.TORI,H.ISHII,Z.W.WOLKOWSKI,C.CHACHATY,
M.SANGARE,F.PIRIOU,G.LUKACS
TETRAHEDRON LETTERS   1973, 1077 (1973)

898 — U 003000 GITOXIGENIN

```
                O
        22     //
        C----C23
  18    ||    |
  12C CH3 20C   O
  / \|   / \ /
11C  13C----C17 C21
19 |    |    |
1C  C  C9  C14 C16
/ \|/ \8/|\ / \
2C   C10 C O C15 OH
 |    |    | H
3C   5C   C7
 \ / \ / \ /
   4C   C6
```

FORMULA	C23H34O5			MOL WT	390.52
SOLVENT	CDCL3/CD3CD				
ORIG ST	TMS			TEMP	AMB

30.00	28.00	66.80	33.50	36.40	27.00
1/3	2/3	3/2	4/3	5/3	6/3
21.40	41.80	35.80	35.80	21.90	41.20
7/3	8/2	9/2	10/1	11/3	12/3
50.40	85.20	42.60	72.80	58.80	16.90
13/1	14/1	15/3	16/2	17/2	18/4
23.90	171.80	76.70	119.60	175.30	
19/4	20/1	21/3	22/2	23/1	

K.TORI,H.ISHII,Z.W.WOLKOWSKI,C.CHACHATY,
M.SANGARE,F.PIRIOU,G.LUKACS
TETRAHEDRON LETTERS   1973, 1077 (1973)

899 — DIGOXIGENIN

```
899          U 003000    DIGOXIGENIN
                  O
            22    //
    OH        C———C23      FORMULA   C23H34O5              MOL WT   390.52
     I18      II   I       SOLVENT   CDCL3/CD3OD
    12C CH3 20C   O         ORIG ST   TMS                   TEMP      AMB
    / \I    / \ /
  11C 13C———C17 C21         30.00    27.90    66.60    33.30    36.40    26.90
  19 I   I   I              1/3      2/3      3/2      4/3      5/2      6/3
  1C C C9  C14 C16          21.90    41.30    32.60    35.50    30.00    74.80
 / \I/ \8/I\ /              7/3      8/2      9/2      10/1     11/3     12/2
2C  C10 C O C15             56.40    85.80    33.00    27.90    46.10     9.40
 I   I   I H               13/1     14/1     15/3     16/3     17/2     18/4
3C  5C  C7                 23.80   177.10    74.60   117.00   176.30
/ \ / \ /                  19/4     20/1     21/3     22/2     23/1
HO  4C  C6
```

K.TORI,H.ISHII,Z.W.WOLKOWSKI,C.CHACHATY,
M.SANGARE,F.PIRIOU,G.LUKACS
TETRAHEDRON LETTERS   1973, 1077 (1973)

900 — STROPHANTHIDIN

```
900          U 003000    STROPHANTHIDIN
                  O
            22    //
            C———C23        FORMULA   C23H32O6              MOL WT   404.51
  O  H  18  II   I         SOLVENT   CDCL3/CD3OD
  \ /12C CH3 20C   O       ORIG ST   TMS                   TEMP      AMB
 19C / \I    / \ /
   I C11 C———C17 C21        24.80    27.40    67.20    38.10    75.30    37.00
   I I   I13 I              1/3      2/3      3/2      4/3      5/1      6/3
 1C I C9  C14 C16           18.10    42.20    40.20    55.80    22.80    40.20
/ \I/ \8/I\ /               7/3      8/2      9/2      10/1     11/3     12/2
2C  C10 C O C15             50.10    85.30    32.20    27.50    51.40    16.20
 I   I   I H               13/1     14/1     15/3     16/3     17/2     18/4
3C  5C  C7                195.70   177.20    74.80   117.80   176.60
/ \ /I\ /                  19/2     20/2     21/3     22/2     23/1
HO  4C O C6
   H
```

K.TORI,H.ISHII,Z.W.WOLKOWSKI,C.CHACHATY,
M.SANGARE,F.PIRIOU,G.LUKACS
TETRAHEDRON LETTERS   1973, 1077 (1973)

901 — 1-ETHYL-5,6-(3-BETA-ACETOXY-5-ALPHA-ANDROST-16-ENO)-1-H-PYRAZOLO(3,4-B)PYRIDINE

```
901          U 003000    1-ETHYL-5,6-(3-BETA-ACETOXY-5-ALPHA-ANDROST-16-
                                   ENO)-1-H-PYRAZOLO(3,4-B)PYRIDINE
  27   26
  CH3-CH2-N———N            FORMULA   C27H37O2N3            MOL WT   435.61
         I   II            SOLVENT   CDCL3
       25C    C22          ORIG ST   TMS                   TEMP      300
        / \ /
       N   C24             36.05    33.25    72.95    26.95    44.25    27.95
   18 II   I               1/3      2/3      3/2      4/3      5/2      6/3
   12C C C17 C23           30.95    34.00    54.15    35.30    20.95    33.45
  / \I/ \ /                7/3      8/2      9/2      10/1     11/3     12/3
 11C 13C  C16              45.10    55.45    29.35   113.50   173.30    17.15
 19 I   I   I             13/1     14/2     15/3     16/1     17/1     18/4
 1C C C9  C———C15          11.75   169.95    20.40   124.40   130.65   129.45
21  2/ \I/ \ /14           19/4     20/1     21/4     22/2     23/2     24/1
CH3 C  C10 C8            149.10    41.30    14.45
I20 I   I   I             25/1     26/3     27/4
C=O C  5C  C7
 \ /3\ / \ /
 O  4C  C6
```

E.BREITMAIER,J.HAEUFEL
UNPUBLISHED   (1973)

902 — ALPHA-D-GLUCOPYRANOSE

```
902          U 005000    ALPHA-D-GLUCOPYRANOSE

 6CH2-OH                  FORMULA   C6H12O6               MOL WT   180.16
   I                      SOLVENT   D2O
   C——O                   ORIG ST   TMS                   TEMP      AMB
  4/5   \
  C OH   C1                91.85    71.25    72.55    69.40    71.25    60.40
 I\I  2/I                  1/2      2/2      3/2      4/2      5/2      6/3
 HO C——C OH
  3 I                     W.VOELTER,V.BILIK,E.BREITMAIER
    OH                    COLLECTION CZECH CHEM COMMUN    38, 2054 (1973)
```

903　　　　U 005000　BETA-D-GLUCOPYRANOSE

```
6CH2-OH
 |
 C--O OH
4/5  \|
C OH  C1
|\|  2/
HO C--C
 3 |
   OH
```

FORMULA	C6H12O6			MOL WT	180.16
SOLVENT	D2O				
ORIG ST	TMS			TEMP	AMB

95.70	73.90	75.55	69.40	75.70	60.60
1/2	2/2	3/2	4/2	5/2	6/3

W.VOELTER,V.BILIK,E.BREITMAIER
COLLECTION CZECH CHEM COMMUN　38, 2054 (1973)

904　　　　U 005000　METHYL-ALPHA-D-GLUCOPYRANOSIDE

```
6CH2-OH
 |
 C--O
4/5  \
C OH  C1
|\|  2/|
HO C--C OCH3
 3 |  7
   OH
```

FORMULA	C7H14O6			MOL WT	194.19
SOLVENT	H2O				AMB
ORIG ST	CS2			TEMP	

99.60	71.90	73.60	70.10	71.60	61.20
1/2	2/2	3/2	4/2	5/2	6/3
55.30					
7/4					

A.S.PERLIN,B.CASU,H.J.KOCH
CAN J CHEM　　　　　　48, 2596 (1970)

905　　　　U 005000　METHYL-BETA-D-GLUCOPYRANOSIDE

```
6CH2-OH
 |   7
 C--O OCH3
4/5  \|
C OH  C1
|\|  2/
HO C--C
 3 |
   OH
```

FORMULA	C7H14O6			MOL WT	194.19
SOLVENT	H2O				
ORIG ST	CS2			TEMP	AMB

103.40	73.40	75.20	70.00	75.20	61.40
1/2	2/2	3/2	4/2	5/2	6/3
57.50					
7/4					

A.S.PERLIN,B.CASU,H.J.KOCH
CAN J CHEM　　　　　　48, 2596 (1970)

906　　　　U 005000　3-0-METHYL-ALPHA-D-GLUCOPYRANOSE

```
6CH2-OH
 |
 C--O
4/5 7 \
C OCH3 C1
|\|  2/|
HO C--C OH
 3 |
   OH
```

FORMULA	C7H14O6			MOL WT	194.19
SOLVENT	H2O				
ORIG ST	CS2			TEMP	AMB

92.10	71.10	82.70	69.10	71.30	60.70
1/2	2/2	3/2	4/2	5/2	6/3
59.90					
7/4					

D.E.DORMAN,J.D.ROBERTS
J AM CHEM SOC　　　　92, 1355 (1970)

907　　　　U 005000　3-0-METHYL-BETA-D-GLUCOPYRANOSE

```
6CH2-OH
 |
 C--O OH
4/5 7 \|
C OCH3 C1
|\|  2/
HO C--C
 3 |
   OH
```

FORMULA	C7H14O6			MOL WT	194.19
SOLVENT	H2O				
ORIG ST	CS2			TEMP	AMB

96.00	73.70	85.20	68.90	75.70	60.70
1/2	2/2	3/2	4/2	5/2	6/3
59.60					
7/4					

D.E.DORMAN,J.D.ROBERTS
J AM CHEM SOC　　　　92, 1355 (1970)

908 — U 005000 ALPHA-D-GLUCOPYRANOSE-PENTAACETATE

```
H3C-C-O-CH2
 16 ||11 |6
    O   C-----O
      /5      \
     /   O   \1  C O
   O C4   || 14   C O
 15 || |\ O-C-CH3/| || 12
H3C-C-O \| 9  2/ O-C-CH3
  10    C-----C    7
    3    | 8 13
        O-C-CH3
         ||
          O
```

FORMULA	C16H22O11			MOL WT	390.35
SOLVENT	CH2CL2				
ORIG ST	CS2			TEMP	AMB
88.60	68.90	69.50	67.70	69.50	61.10
1/2	2/2	3/2	4/2	5/2	6/3
169.80	169.40	169.20	168.80	168.30	20.30
7—11/1	7—11/1	7—11/1	7—11/1	7—11/1	12/4
19.80	19.30				
13/4	14/4				

D.E.DORMAN, J.D.ROBERTS
J AM CHEM SOC   93, 4463 (1971)

909 — U 005000 BETA-D-GLUCOPYRANOSE-PENTAACETATE

```
H3C-C-O-CH2
 16 ||11 |6
    O   C-----O        O
      /5      \ O-C-CH3 || 12
     /   O   \| 7
   O C4   || 14   C1
 15 || |\ O-C-CH3/
H3C-C-O \| 9  2/
  10    C-----C
    3    | 8 13
        O-C-CH3
         ||
          O
```

FORMULA	C16H22O11			MOL WT	390.35
SOLVENT	CH2CL2				
ORIG ST	CS2			TEMP	AMB
91.30	70.00	72.30	67.60	72.30	61.30
1/2	2/2	3/2	4/2	5/2	6/3
169.80	169.30	168.90	168.70	168.40	19.90
7—11/1	7—11/1	7—11/1	7—11/1	7—11/1	12/4
19.80					
13/4					

D.E.DORMAN, J.D.ROBERTS
J AM CHEM SOC   93, 4463 (1971)

910 — U 005000 PARA-NITROPHENYL-ALPHA-D-GLUCOPYRANOSIDE

```
  6CH2-OH
   |
   C--O
 4/5  \    8  9
 C OH   C1  C--C
 |\|  2/|  /    \
HO C--C O-C7   10C-NO2
  3  |     \   /
     OH     C==C
           12  11
```

FORMULA	C12H15O8N			MOL WT	301.26
SOLVENT	C2D6O S				
ORIG ST	TMS			TEMP	AMB
100.45	74.10	76.90	72.50	75.75	63.45
1/2	2/2	3/2	4/2	5/2	6/3
164.85	128.25	119.65	144.35		
7/1	8/2	9/2	10/1		

E.BREITMAIER, W.VOELTER, G.JUNG, C.TAENZER
CHEM BER   104, 1147 (1971)

911 — U 005000 PARA-NITROPHENYL-BETA-D-GLUCOPYRANOSIDE

```
         8  9
  6CH2-OH  C--C
   |      /    \
   C--O O-C7   10C-NO2
 4/5  \|  \    /
 C OH   C1  C==C
 |\|  2/  12 11
HO C--C
  3  |
     OH
```

FORMULA	C12H15O8N			MOL WT	301.26
SOLVENT	C2D6O S				
ORIG ST	TMS			TEMP	AMB
102.70	75.95	80.05	72.40	79.30	63.45
1/2	2/2	3/2	4/2	5/2	6/3
165.15	128.50	119.45	144.55		
7/1	8/2	9/2	10/1		

E.BREITMAIER, W.VOELTER, G.JUNG, C.TAENZER
CHEM BER   104, 1147 (1971)

912 — U 005000 META-NITROPHENYL-BETA-D-GLUCOPYRANOSIDE

```
        12 11
  6CH2-OH  C--C
   |      /    \
   C--O O-C7   C10
 4/5  \|  \    9/
 C OH   C1  C==C
 |\|  2/   8   \
HO C--C        NO2
  3  |
     OH
```

FORMULA	C12H15O8N			MOL WT	301.26
SOLVENT	C2D6 O S				
ORIG ST	TMS			TEMP	AMB
103.55	76.05	79.95	72.60	79.20	63.55
1/2	2/2	3/2	4/2	5/2	6/3
160.55	133.45	151.35	119.55	113.90	126.00
7/1	8/2	9/1	10/2	11/2	12/2

E.BREITMAIER, W.VOELTER, G.JUNG, C.TAENZER
CHEM BER   104, 1147 (1971)

---

913   U 005000   ORTHO—NITROPHENYL—BETA—D—GLUCOPYRANOSIDE

```
              12   11
   6CH2-OH    C—C
      |      ⫽    ⟍
    C—-O  O-C7     C10
   4/5   ⟍|  ⟍8  ⫽
   C OH    C1  C==C
   I⟍|  2/   ⟋   9
   HO C—-C    NO2
    3  |
       OH
```

FORMULA	C12H15O8N			MOL WT	301.26
SOLVENT	C2D6O S				
ORIG ST	TMS			TEMP	AMB
103.25	75.95	80.05	72.40	79.50	63.45
1/2	2/2	3/2	4/2	5/2	6/3
152.40	143.05	127.50	119.85	124.70	136.90
7/1	8/1	9/2	10/2	11/2	12/2

E.BREITMAIER,W.VOELTER,G.JUNG,C.TAENZER
CHEM BER   104, 1147 (1971)

---

914   U 005000   PHENYL—BETA—D—GLUCOPYRANOSIDE

```
               8   9
   6CH2-OH    C—C
      |      ⫽    ⟍
    C—-O  O-C7     C10
   4/5   ⟍|  ⟍  ⟋
   C OH    C1  C==C
   I⟍|  2/
   HO C—-C
    3  |
       OH
```

FORMULA	C12H16O6			MOL WT	256.26
SOLVENT	C2D6O S				
ORIG ST	TMS			TEMP	AMB
103.05	75.80	79.50	72.40	79.30	63.55
1/2	2/2	3/2	4/2	5/2	6/3
153.50	132.15	124.60	119.00		
7/1	8/2	9/2	10/2		

E.BREITMAIER,W.VOELTER,G.JUNG,C.TAENZER
CHEM BER   104, 1147 (1971)

---

915   U 005000   METHYL—4,6—O—BENZYLIDENE—ALPHA—D—GLUCOPYRANOSIDE

```
              6
             O-C
   C—-C     ⟋  |
   ⫽   ⟍  ⟋   C—-O
  12C    9C-C8 4/5  ⟍
   ⟍  ⟋  ⟍ C OH   C1
   C==C    ⟍I⟍|  2/I
   11  10   O C—-C OCH3
            3  |  7
               OH
```

FORMULA	C14H18O6			MOL WT	282.30
SOLVENT	CDCL3/CH3OH(4/1)				
ORIG ST	TMS			TEMP	AMB
99.80	72.20	70.40	80.60	61.90	68.40
1/2	2/2	3/2	4/2	5/2	6/3
54.80	101.40	136.80	127.80	125.80	128.70
7/4	8/2	9/1	10/2	11/2	12/2

E.CONWAY,R.D.GUTHRIE,S.D.GERO,G.LUKACS,
A.M.SEPULCHRE,E.W.HAGAMAN,E.WENKERT
TETRAHEDRON LETTERS   IN PRESS

---

916   U 005000   METHYL—4,6—O—BENZYLIDENE—3—AMINO—3—DEOXY—ALPHA—D—
GLUCOPYRANOSIDE

```
              6
             O-C
   C—-C     ⟋  |
   ⫽   ⟍  ⟋   C—-O
  12C    9C-C8 4/5  ⟍
   ⟍  ⟋  ⟍ C NH2  C1
   C==C    ⟍I⟍|  2/I
   11  10   O C—-C OCH3
            3  |  7
               OH
```

FORMULA	C14H19O5N			MOL WT	281.31
SOLVENT	CDCL3/CH3OH(4/1)				
ORIG ST	TMS			TEMP	AMB
98.40	72.10	52.40	81.00	62.20	68.70
1/2	2/2	3/2	4/2	5/2	6/3
55.00	101.50	136.80	127.80	125.80	128.70
7/4	8/2	9/1	10/2	11/2	12/2

E.CONWAY,R.D.GUTHRIE,S.D.GERO,G.LUKACS,
A.M.SEPULCHRE,E.W.HAGAMAN,E.WENKERT
TETRAHEDRON LETTERS   IN PRESS

---

917   U 005000   METHYL—4,6—O—BENZYLIDENE—BETA—D—GLUCOPYRANOSIDE

```
              6
             O-C
   C—-C     ⟋  |   7
   ⫽   ⟍  ⟋   C—-O OCH3
  12C    9C-C8 4/5  ⟍|
   ⟍  ⟋  ⟍ C OH   C1
   C==C    ⟍I⟍|  2/
   11  10   O C—-C
            3  |
               OH
```

FORMULA	C14H18O6			MOL WT	282.30
SOLVENT	CDCL3/CH3OH(4/1)				
ORIG ST	TMS			TEMP	AMB
103.80	73.90	72.60	80.00	65.70	67.90
1/2	2/2	3/2	4/2	5/2	6/3
56.70	101.30	136.80	127.80	125.80	128.70
7/4	8/2	9/1	10/2	11/2	12/2

E.CONWAY,R.D.GUTHRIE,S.D.GERO,G.LUKACS,
A.M.SEPULCHRE,E.W.HAGAMAN,E.WENKERT
TETRAHEDRON LETTERS   IN PRESS

---

918   U 005000   ETHYL—4,6—O—BENZYLIDENE—1—THIO—BETA—
                      D—GLUCOPYRANOSIDE

```
              6     7 8   FORMULA  C15H20O5S              MOL WT  312.39
            O—C   CH2CH3  SOLVENT  CDCL3/CH3OH
     C——C    / |   |      ORIG ST  TMS                    TEMP      AMB
     ‖   ‖  /  C—O S
 13C   10C—C9 4/5   \|      85.30    74.10    72.90    79.90    69.90    67.90
     \   /   \ C OH  C1      1/2      2/2      3/2      4/2      5/2      6/3
      C==C    \|\| 2/        23.90    14.40   101.70   136.80   127.80   125.80
      12 11    O C—C         7/3      8/4      9/2     10/1     11/2     12/2
               3 |          128.70
               OH            13/2
```

E.CONWAY,R.D.GUTHRIE,S.D.GERO,G.LUKACS,
A.M.SEPULCHRE,E.W.HAGAMAN,E.WENKERT
TETRAHEDRON LETTERS   IN PRESS

---

919   U 005000   METHYL—2—DEOXY—4,6—O—BENZYLIDENE—3—C—(2—METHYL—
                      1,3—DITHIANE—2—YL)—ALPHA—D—GLUCOPYRANOSIDE

```
             6          FORMULA  C19H26O6S2              MOL WT  414.54
 13  14    O—C          SOLVENT  CDCL3
 C——C    / |            ORIG ST  TMS                    TEMP      AMB
 ‖   ‖  /  C—O
12C   9C—C8 4/5  \        98.40    36.35    75.65    79.85    59.15    68.85
 \   /   \ C R   C1       1/2      2/3      3/2      4/2      5/2      6/3
  C==C    \|\|  /|        54.70   100.90   137.00   127.55   125.70   128.30
  11 10    O C——C OCH3    7/4      8/2      9/1     10/2     11/2     12/2
           3  2  7        24.90    58.50    26.00    24.15    26.00
                          15/4     16/1     17/3     18/3     19/3
       S—C17
      /   \
 R = C16   C18
   15/  \   /
   H3C   S—C19
```

G.LUKACS,A.M.SEPULCHRE,A.GATEAU—OLESKER,G.VASS,
S.D.GERO,R.D.GUTHRIE,W.VOELTER,E.BREITMAIER
TETRAHEDRON LETTERS   5163 (1972)

---

920   U 005000   METHYL—2—DEOXY—4,6—O—BENZYLIDENE—3—C—(1,3—
                      DITHIANE—2—YL)—ALPHA—D—GLUCOPYRANOSIDE

```
             6          FORMULA  C18H24O6S2              MOL WT  400.52
 13  14    O—C          SOLVENT  CDCL3
 C——C    / |            ORIG ST  TMS                    TEMP      AMB
 ‖   ‖  /  C—O
12C   9C—C8 4/5  \        98.50    35.80    72.85    78.00    59.25    69.05
 \   /   \ C R   C1       1/2      2/3      3/2      4/2      5/2      6/3
  C==C    \|\| 2/|        55.25   101.65   137.25   127.95   126.15   128.80
  11 10    O C——C OCH3    7/4      8/2      9/1     10/2     11/2     12/2
           3      7       53.10    30.10    25.80    30.65
       S—C16              15/2     16/3     17/3     18/3
      /   \
 R = C15   C17
      \   /
       S—C18
```

G.LUKACS,A.M.SEPULCHRE,A.GATEAU—OLESKER,G.VASS,
S.D.GERO,R.D.GUTHRIE,W.VOELTER,E.BREITMAIER
TETRAHEDRON LETTERS   5163 (1972)

---

921   U 005000   ALPHA—D—GALACTOPYRANOSE

```
   6CH2—OH             FORMULA  C6H12O6                 MOL WT  180.16
     |                 SOLVENT  D2O
  HO C——O              ORIG ST  TMS                     TEMP      AMB
   1/5   \
   C OH   C1            92.35    69.40    68.40    69.20    70.50    61.25
   4\|  2/|             1/2      2/2      3/2      4/2      5/2      6/3
    C——C OH
    3  |               W.VOELTER,E.BREITMAIER,E.B.RATHBONE,E.M.STEPHEN
      OH               TETRAHEDRON                    29, 3845 (1973)
```

---

922 U 005000 BETA–D–GALACTOPYRANOSE

```
6CH2-OH
 |
HO C--O OH
 |/5  \|
 C OH   C1
 4\|  2/
   C--C
   3  |
     OH
```

FORMULA	C6H12O6			MOL WT	180.16
SOLVENT	D2O				
ORIG ST	TMS			TEMP	AMB

96.50	71.90	72.85	68.80	75.20	61.05
1/2	2/2	3/2	4/2	5/2	6/3

W.VOELTER,E.BREITMAIER,E.B.RATHBONE,E.M.STEPHEN
TETRAHEDRON   29, 3845 (1973)

---

923 U 005000 METHYL–ALPHA–D–GALACTOPYRANOSIDE

```
6CH2-OH
 |
HO C--O
 |/5  \
 C OH   C1
 4\|  2/|
   C--C OCH3
   3  |  7
     OH
```

FORMULA	C7H14O6			MOL WT	194.19
SOLVENT	D2O				
ORIG ST	TMS			TEMP	AMB

99.50	69.60	68.30	69.30	70.80	61.30
1/2	2/2	3/2	4/2	5/2	6/3
55.15					
7/4					

W.VOELTER,E.BREITMAIER,E.B.RATHBONE,E.M.STEPHEN
TETRAHEDRON   29, 3845 (1973)

---

924 U 005000 METHYL–BETA–D–GALACTOPYRANOSIDE

```
6CH2-OH
 |    7
HO C--O OCH3
 |/5  \|
 C OH   C1
 4\|  2/
   C--C
   3  |
     OH
```

FORMULA	C7H14O6			MOL WT	194.19
SOLVENT	H2O				
ORIG ST	TMS			TEMP	AMB

103.90	70.80	72.85	68.75	75.20	61.05
1/2	2/2	3/2	4/2	5/2	6/3
57.30					
7/4					

W.VOELTER,E.BREITMAIER,E.B.RATHBONE,E.M.STEPHEN
TETRAHEDRON   29, 3845 (1973)

---

925 U 005000 METHYL–3–O–METHYL–BETA–D–GALACTOPYRANOSIDE

```
6CH2-OH
 |    7
HO C--O OCH3
 |/5 8 \|
 C OCH3 C1
 4\|  2/
   C--C
   3  |
     OH
```

FORMULA	C8H16O6			MOL WT	208.21
SOLVENT	H2O				
ORIG ST	TMS			TEMP	AMB

103.90	69.80	82.00	64.20	75.10	61.20
1/2	2/2	3/2	4/2	5/2	6/3
57.30	56.20				
7/4	8/4				

W.VOELTER,E.BREITMAIER,E.B.RATHBONE,E.M.STEPHEN
TETRAHEDRON   29, 3845 (1973)

---

926 U 005000 METHYL–2,6–O–DIMETHYL–ALPHA–D–GALACTOPYRANOSIDE

```
6CH2-OCH3
 |    9
HO C--O
 |/5  \
 C OH   C1
 4\|  2/|
   C--C OCH3
   3  |  7
     OCH3
      8
```

FORMULA	C9H18O6			MOL WT	222.24
SOLVENT	H2O				
ORIG ST	TMS			TEMP	AMB

96.80	77.45	68.60	69.50	73.15	71.85
1/2	2/2	3/2	4/2	5/2	6/3
55.05	57.70	58.50			
7/4	8,9/4	8,9/4			

W.VOELTER,E.BREITMAIER,E.B.RATHBONE,E.M.STEPHEN
TETRAHEDRON   29, 3845 (1973)

---

927   U 005000   METHYL-2,3,4,6-TETRA-O-METHYL-BETA-
D-GALACTOPYRANOSIDE

```
         11
    6CH2-OCH3
  10  |    7
 H3CO C--O OCH3
    1/5 9 \|
    C OCH3 C1
   4\|    /
     C--C2
     3 |
      OCH3
       8
```

FORMULA	C11H22O6			MOL WT	250.29
SOLVENT	H2O				
ORIG ST	TMS			TEMP	AMB

103.35	79.75	82.20	73.05	74.90	71.00
1/2	2/2	3/2	4/2	5/2	6/3
57.10	58.50	60.20	60.95		
7/4	8-11/4	8-11/4	8-11/4		

W.VOELTER,E.BREITMAIER,E.B.RATHBONE,E.M.STEPHEN
TETRAHEDRON   29, 3845 (1973)

---

928   U 005000   PARA-NITROPHENYL-ALPHA-D-GALACTOPYRANOSIDE

```
    6CH2-OH
     |
   HO C--O
    1/5   \     8  9
   4C OH   C1  C--C
    \|  2/|  //    \
     C--C O-C7  10C-NO2
     3 |      \    /
      OH      C==C
```

FORMULA	C12H15O8N			MOL WT	301.26
SOLVENT	(CD3)2SO				
ORIG ST	TMS			TEMP	AMB

100.75	75.50	71.20	70.45	72.05	63.00
1/2	2/2	3/2	4/2	5/2	6/3
165.05	128.15	119.55	144.15		
7/1	8/2	9/2	10/1		

E.BREITMAIER,W.VOELTER,G.JUNG,C.TAENZER
CHEM BER   104, 1147 (1971)

---

929   U 005000   META-NITROPHENYL-BETA-D-GALACTOPYRANOSIDE

```
        12  11
   6CH2-OH  C--C
     |     //   \
   HO C--O O-C7    C10
    1/5  \|  \    9/
    C OH   C1  C==C
   4\|  2/  8     \
     C--C         NO2
     3 |
      OH
```

FORMULA	C12H15O8N			MOL WT	301.26
SOLVENT	(CD3)2SO				
ORIG ST	TMS			TEMP	AMB

104.20	73.25	76.05	71.10	78.65	63.45
1/2	2/2	3/2	4/2	5/2	6/3
173.05	133.55	160.65	119.55	113.90	126.20
7/1	8/2	9/1	10/2	11/2	12/2

E.BREITMAIER,W.VOELTER,G.JUNG,C.TAENZER
CHEM BER   104, 1147 (1971)

---

930   U 005000   ORTHO-NITROPHENYL-BETA-D-GALACTOPYRANOSIDE

```
        12  11
   6CH2-OH  C--C
     |     //   \
   HO C--O O-C7    C10
    1/5  \|  \8  /
    C OH   C1  C==C
   4\|  2/   |  9
     C--C   NO2
     3 |
      OH
```

FORMULA	C12H15O8N			MOL WT	301.26
SOLVENT	(CD3)2SO				
ORIG ST	TMS			TEMP	AMB

104.10	73.15	76.25	71.10	78.65	63.45
1/2	2/2	3/2	4/2	5/2	6/3
152.55	143.15	127.50	119.95	124.70	137.00
7/1	8/1	9/2	10/2	11/2	12/2

E.BREITMAIER,W.VOELTER,G.JUNG,C.TAENZER
CHEM BER   104, 1147 (1971)

---

931   U 005000   PHENYL-BETA-D-GALACTOPYRANOSIDE

```
        8   9
   6CH2-OH  C--C
     |     //   \
   HO C--O O-C7    C10
    1/5  \|  \    /
    C OH   C1  C==C
   4\|  2/
     C--C
     3 |
      OH
```

FORMULA	C12H16O6			MOL WT	256.26
SOLVENT	(CD3)2SO				
ORIG ST	TMS			TEMP	AMB

104.00	73.55	76.40	71.30	78.30	63.65
1/2	2/2	3/2	4/2	5/2	6/3
160.40	132.50	124.90	119.30		
7/1	8/2	9/2	10/2		

E.BREITMAIER,W.VOELTER,G.JUNG,C.TAENZER
CHEM BER   104, 1147 (1971)

932   U 005000   **ALPHA-L-FUCOPYRANOSE**

```
     5
     C--O
   /1    \
 4/ CH3  \
  C  6    C1
  I\   OH/1
 HO \3 1/ OH
    C--C
    I 2
    OH
```

FORMULA	C6H12O5			MOL WT	164.16
SOLVENT	H2O				
ORIG ST	CS2			TEMP	AMB

92.20	69.40	68.20	71.80	66.00	15.60
1/2	2/2	3/2	4/2	5/2	6/4

D.E.DORMAN,J.D.ROBERTS
J AM CHEM SOC   92, 1355 (1970)

---

933   U 005000   **BETA-L-FUCOPYRANOSE**

```
     5
     C--O
   /1    \ OH
 4/ CH3  \1
  C  6    C1
  I\   OH/
 HO \3 1/
    C--C
    I 2
    OH
```

FORMULA	C6H12O5			MOL WT	164.16
SOLVENT	H2O				
ORIG ST	CS2			TEMP	AMB

96.30	71.80	73.00	71.40	70.50	15.60
1/2	2/2	3/2	4/2	5/2	6/4

D.E.DORMAN,J.D.ROBERTS
J AM CHEM SOC   92, 1355 (1970)

---

934   U 005000   **ALPHA-L-RHAMNOPYRANOSE**

```
     5
 HO C--O
  1/16  \
  C CH3  C1
  4\  2/1
   3C--C OH
    I  I
   OH OH
```

FORMULA	C6H12O5			MOL WT	164.16
SOLVENT	D2O				
ORIG ST	TMS			TEMP	AMB

95.10	71.90	71.05	73.30	69.40	17.90
1/2	2/2	3/2	4/2	5/2	6/4

W.VOELTER,V.BILIK,E.BREITMAIER
COLLECTION CZECH CHEM COMMUN   38, 2054 (1973)

---

935   U 005000   **BETA-L-RHAMNOPYRANOSE**

```
     5
 HO C--O OH
  1/16  \1
  C CH3  C1
  4\  2/
   3C--C
    I  I
   OH OH
```

FORMULA	C6H12O5			MOL WT	164.16
SOLVENT	D2O				
ORIG ST	TMS			TEMP	AMB

94.60	72.45	73.85	72.95	73.15	17.90
1/2	2/2	3/2	4/2	5/2	6/4

W.VOELTER,V.BILIK,E.BREITMAIER
COLLECTION CZECH CHEM COMMUN   38, 2054 (1973)

---

936   U 005000   **ALPHA-D-MANNOPYRANOSE**

```
  6CH2-OH
    I
    C--O
  4/5   \
  C OH OHC1
  I\I 1/I
 HO C--C OH
   3   2
```

FORMULA	C6H12O6			MOL WT	180.16
SOLVENT	D2O				
ORIG ST	TMS			TEMP	AMB

95.20	71.85	71.35	68.05	73.55	62.15
1/2	2/2	3/2	4/2	5/2	6/3

W.VOELTER,V.BILIK,E.BREITMAIER
COLLECTION CZECH CHEM COMMUN   38, 2054 (1973)

937   U 005000   BETA—D—MANNOPYRANOSE

```
  6CH2-OH
   I
   C--O OH
  4/5  \I
  C OH OHC1
  I\I  I/
  HO C--C
    3  2
```

FORMULA C6H12O6   MOL WT 180.16
SOLVENT D2O
ORIG ST TMS   TEMP   AMB

| 94.85 | 72.35 | 74.10 | 67.75 | 77.30 | 62.15 |
| 1/2 | 2/2 | 3/2 | 4/2 | 5/2 | 6/3 |

W.VOELTER,V.BILIK,E.BREITMAIER
COLLECTION CZECH CHEM COMMUN   38, 2054 (1973)

938   U 005000   METHYL—ALPHA—D—MANNOPYRANOSIDE

```
  6CH2-OH
   I
   C--O
  4/5  \
  C OH OHC1
  I\I  I/I
  HO C--C OCH3
    3  2  7
```

FORMULA C7H14O6   MOL WT 194.19
SOLVENT D2O
ORIG ST TMS   TEMP   AMB

101.95	71.70	71.05	67.90	73.70	62.10
1/2	2/2	3/2	4/2	5/2	6/3
55.85					
7/4					

W.VOELTER,V.BILIK,E.BREITMAIER
COLLECTION CZECH CHEM COMMUN   38, 2054 (1973)

939   U 005000   METHYL—BETA—D—MANNOPYRANOSIDE

```
  6CH2-OH
   I    7
   C--O OCH3
  4/5  \I
  C OH OHC1
  I\I  I/
  HO C--C
    3  2
```

FORMULA C7H14O6   MOL WT 194.19
SOLVENT H2O
ORIG ST CS2   TEMP   AMB

101.00	70.30	73.00	66.80	76.30	61.10
1/2	2/2	3/2	4/2	5/2	6/3
56.60					
7/4					

A.S.PERLIN,B.CASU,H.J.KOCH
CAN J CHEM   48, 2596 (1970)

940   U 005000   PARA—NITROPHENYL—ALPHA—D—MANNOPYRANOSIDE

```
  6CH2-OH
   I
   C--O
  4/5   \    8  9
  C OH OHC1  C--C
  I\I  I/I  //    \\
  HO C--C O-C7  10C-NO2
    3  2     \   /
              C==C
             12  11
```

FORMULA C12H15O8N   MOL WT 301.26
SOLVENT (CD3)2SO
ORIG ST TMS   TEMP   AMB

101.50	73.40	72.50	69.45	78.00	63.75
1/2	2/2	3/2	4/2	5/2	6/3
164.10	128.40	119.55	144.45		
7/1	8/2	9/2	10/1		

E.BREITMAIER,W.VOELTER,G.JUNG,C.TAENZER
CHEM BER   104, 1147 (1971)

941   U 005000   METHYL—4,6—O—BENZYLIDENE—ALPHA—D—MANNOPYRANOSIDE

```
          6
        O-C
  C--C   / I
  //  \ /  C--O
 12C   9C-C8 4/5  \
  \   / \ C OH OHC1
  C==C  I\I\ I/I
  11  10  O C--C OCH3
          3  2  7
```

FORMULA C14H18O6   MOL WT 282.30
SOLVENT CDCL3/CH3OH(4/1)
ORIG ST TMS   TEMP   AMB

101.40	70.40	67.60	78.30	62.70	68.00
1/2	2/2	3/2	4/2	5/2	6/3
54.10	101.40	136.80	127.80	125.80	128.70
7/4	8/2	9/1	10/2	11/2	12/2

E.CONWAY,R.D.GUTHRIE,S.D.GERO,G.LUKACS
A.M.SEPULCHRE,E.W.HAGAMAN,E.WENKERT
TETRAHEDRON LETTERS   IN PRESS

942   U 005000   METHYL-4,6-O-BENZYLIDENE-3-AMINO-3-DEOXY-ALPHA-D-MANNOPYRANOSIDE

```
            6
           O-C
    C--C   / |
   //  \\ / C--O
12C    9C-C8 4/5  \
   \    / \ C NH2OHCl
    C==C    \|\| |/|
   11  10   O C--C OCH3
            3  2  7
```

102.00	70.00	50.30	79.40	63.40	68.60
1/2	2/2	3/2	4/2	5/2	6/3
54.50	101.60	136.80	127.80	125.80	128.70
7/4	8/2	9/1	10/2	11/2	12/2

FORMULA C14H19O5N   MOL WT 281.31
SOLVENT CDCL3/CH3OH(4/1)
ORIG ST TMS   TEMP   AMB

E.CONWAY,R.D.GUTHRIE,S.D.GERO,G.LUKACS
A.M.SEPULCHRE,E.W.HAGAMAN,E.WENKERT
TETRAHEDRON LETTERS   IN PRESS

943   U 005000   BETA-D-ALLOPYRANOSE

```
   6CH2-OH
     |
     C--O OH
   4/5   \|
   C      C1
   |\3  2/
  HO C--C
   |   |
  HO   OH
```

93.50	71.30	71.10	66.90	73.50	61.30
1/2	2/2	3/2	4/2	5/2	6/3

FORMULA C6H12O6   MOL WT 180.16
SOLVENT H2O
ORIG ST CS2   TEMP   AMB

D.E.DORMAN,J.D.ROBERTS
J AM CHEM SOC   92, 1355 (1970)

944   U 005000   METHYL-4,6-O-BENZYLIDENE-ALPHA-D-ALLOPYRANOSIDE

```
            6
           O-C
    C--C   / |
   //  \\ / C--O
12C    9C-C8 4/5  \
   \    / \ C     C1
    C==C    \|\3 2/|
   11  10   O C--C OCH3
            |  | 7
           HO  OH
```

100.00	67.70	68.70	77.30	56.80	68.70
1/2	2/2	3/2	4/2	5/2	6/3
55.70	101.40	136.80	127.80	125.80	128.70
7/4	8/2	9/1	10/2	11/2	12/2

FORMULA C14H18O6   MOL WT 282.30
SOLVENT CDCL3/CH3OH(4/1)
ORIG ST TMS   TEMP   AMB

E.CONWAY,R.D.GUTHRIE,S.D.GERO,G.LUKACS
A.M.SEPULCHRE,E.W.HAGAMAN,E.WENKERT
TETRAHEDRON LETTERS   IN PRESS

945   U 005000   METHYL-4,6-O-BENZYLIDENE-2,3-DIDEOXY-ALPHA-D-ERYTHRO-HEXOPYRANOSIDE

```
            6
           O-C
    C--C   / |
   //  \\ / C--O
12C    9C-C8 4/5  \
   \    / \ C     C1
    C==    \|\   /|
   11  10   O C--C OCH3
            3  2  7
```

97.40	28.90	23.40	77.80	64.40	68.90
1/2	2/3	3/3	4/2	5/2	6/3
54.10	101.40	136.80	127.80	125.80	128.70
7/4	8/2	9/1	10/2	11/2	12/2

FORMULA C14H18O4   MOL WT 250.30
SOLVENT CDCL3/CH3OH(4/1)
ORIG ST TMS   TEMP   AMB

E.CONWAY,R.D.GUTHRIE,S.D.GERO,G.LUKACS
A.M.SEPULCHRE,E.W.HAGAMAN,E.WENKERT
TETRAHEDRON LETTERS   IN PRESS

946   U 005000   METHYL-4,6-O-BENZYLIDENE-3-AMINO-3-DEOXY-ALPHA-D-ALLOPYRANOSIDE

```
            6
           O-C
    C--C   / |
   //  \\ / C--O
12C    9C-C8 4/5  \
   \    / \ C     C1
    C==C    \|\3 2/|
   11  10   O C--C OCH3
            |  | 7
           H2N  OH
```

100.80	68.90	52.20	78.30	56.70	67.50
1/2	2/2	3/2	4/2	5/2	6/3
55.60	101.30	136.80	127.80	125.80	128.70
7/4	8/2	9/1	10/2	11/2	12/2

FORMULA C14H19O5N   MOL WT 281.31
SOLVENT CDCL3/CH3OH(4/1)
ORIG ST TMS   TEMP   AMB

E.CONWAY,R.D.GUTHRIE,S.D.GERO,G.LUKACS
A.M.SEPULCHRE,E.W.HAGAMANN,E.WENKERT
TETRAHEDRON LETTERS   IN PRESS

```
947                    U 005000   1,2,5,6-O-DIISOPROPYLIDENE-3-C-
   11     6                       (1,3-DITHIANE-2-YL)-ALLC-FURANOSE
 H3C   O-C
   \  / |                 FORMULA   C16H26O6S2            MOL WT  378.51
    C10 |                 SOLVENT   CDCL3
   /  \ |5                ORIG ST   TMS                   TEMP     AMB
 H3C   O-C    O
   12    |   / \            104.45    83.20    80.50    80.50    73.05    67.95
         | /   \              1/2      2/2      3/1      4/2      5/2      6/3
         |/     \            25.35    26.35    50.50    29.10    26.75
       4C  R     C1          7-12/    7-12/    13/2     14/3     15/3
       \|    2/|
        14  3C---C  O       G.LUKACS,A.M.SEPULCHRE,A.GATEAU-OLESKER,G.VASS,
     S-C   |   17| 8        S.D.GERO,R.D.GUTHRIE,W.VOELTER,E.BREITMAIER
    /   \  OH  O-C-CH3      TETRAHEDRON LETTERS            5163 (1972)
R = C13  C15     |
     \   /      9CH3
      S-C
       16
```

```
948                    U 005000   METHYL-ALPHA-D-ALTROPYRANOSIDE

     6CH2OH                 FORMULA   C7H14O6              MOL WT  194.19
       |                    SOLVENT   H2O
     C--O                   ORIG ST   CS2                  TEMP     AMB
   4/5   \
    C   HO C1                100.80    69.70    69.70    64.50    69.70    61.00
   |\3  |/|                    1/2      2/2      3/2      4/2      5/2      6/3
  HO C--C OCH3               55.10
     | 2  7                   7/4
     HO
                            A.S.PERLIN,B.CASU,H.J.KOCH
                            CAN J CHEM               48, 2596 (1970)
```

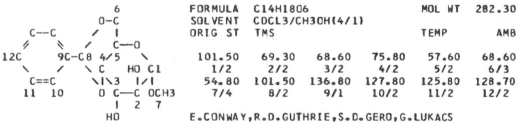

```
949                    U 005000   METHYL-4,6-O-BENZYLIDENE-ALPHA-D-ALTROPYRANOSIDE

         6                  FORMULA   C14H18O6             MOL WT  282.30
        O-C                 SOLVENT   CDCL3/CH3OH(4/1)
   C--C   / |               ORIG ST   TMS                  TEMP     AMB
  //   \ /  C--O
12C    9C-C8 4/5  \           101.50    69.30    68.60    75.80    57.60    68.60
   \   /   \ C   HO C1          1/2      2/2      3/2      4/2      5/2      6/3
   C==C     \|\3  |/|          54.80   101.50   136.80   127.80   125.80   128.70
   11  10    O C--C OCH3        7/4      8/2      9/1     10/2     11/2     12/2
             | 2  7
             HO              E.CONWAY,R.D.GUTHRIE,S.D.GERO,G.LUKACS
                            A.M.SEPULCHRE,E.W.HAGAMAN,E.WENKERT
                            TETRAHEDRON LETTERS   IN PRESS
```

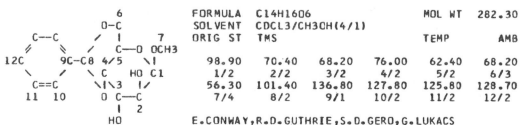

```
950                    U 005000   METHYL-4,6-O-BENZYLIDENE-BETA-D-ALTROPYRANOSIDE

         6                  FORMULA   C14H16O6             MOL WT  282.30
        O-C                 SOLVENT   CDCL3/CH3OH(4/1)
   C--C   / |    7          ORIG ST   TMS                  TEMP     AMB
  //   \ /  C--O OCH3
12C    9C-C8 4/5  \|          98.90    70.40    68.20    76.00    62.40    68.20
   \   /   \ C   HO C1          1/2      2/2      3/2      4/2      5/2      6/3
   C==C     \|\3  |/           56.30   101.40   136.80   127.80   125.80   128.70
   11  10    O C--C             7/4      8/2      9/1     10/2     11/2     12/2
             | 2
             HO              E.CONWAY,R.D.GUTHRIE,S.D.GERO,G.LUKACS
                            A.M.SEPULCHRE,E.W.HAGAMAN,E.WENKERT
                            TETRAHEDRON LETTERS   IN PRESS
```

951

U 005000   METHYL-4,6-O-BENZYLIDENE-3-AMINO-3-DEOXY-ALPHA-D-ALTROPYRANOSIDE

```
            6
          O-C6
   C--C    / |
  //   \  /  C—O
12C    9C-C8 4/5   \
  \    /    \ C   HO C1
   C==C      \I\3 I/I
  11  10      O C—C OCH3
              I  2  7
             H2N
```

FORMULA	C14H1905N			MOL WT	281.31
SOLVENT	CDCL3/CH3OH(4/1)				
ORIG ST	TMS			TEMP	AMB
101.80	69.40	51.30	75.80	57.60	68.70
1/2	2/2	3/2	4/2	5/2	6/3
54.80	101.50	136.80	127.80	125.80	128.70
7/4	8/2	9/1	10/2	11/2	12/2

E.CONWAY,R.D.GUTHRIE,S.D.GERO,G.LUKACS
A.M.SEPULCHRE,E.W.HAGAMAN,E.WENKERT
TETRAHEDRON LETTERS IN PRESS

952

U 005000   METHYL-3-O-ACETYL-4,6-O-BENZYLIDENE-2-DEOXY-2-C-(1,3-DITHIANE-2-YL)-ALPHA-D-ALTROPYRANOSIDE

```
 15  16      O-C6
  C--C    /  |
 //   \  /   C—O
14C   11C-C104/5    \
  \    /     \ C   R C1
   C==C       \I\3 I/I
  13  12       O C—C OCH3
               I  2  7
      S-C18    O
      /   \    I
R = C17  C19  O=C8
      \   /    I
      S-C20   9CH3
```

FORMULA	C20H2606S2			MOL WT	426.55
SOLVENT					
ORIG ST	TMS			TEMP	AMB
102.20	46.10	74.80	69.70	69.50	59.00
1/2	2/2	3/2	4/2	5/2	6/3
55.80	170.50	21.40	99.90	137.60	128.20
7/4	8/1	9/4	10/2	11/1	12/2
126.10	129.20	44.30	27.80	25.30	28.00
13/2	14/2	17/2	18/3	19/3	20/3

A.M.SEPULCHRE,G.LUKACS,G.VASS,S.D.GERO
ANGEW CHEM   84, 111 (1972)
ANGEW CHEM INTERN ED   11, 148 (1972)

953

U 005000   METHYL-2-O-ACETYL-4,6-O-BENZYLIDENE-3-DEOXY-3-C-(1,3-DITHIANE-2-YL)-ALPHA-D-ALTROPYRANOSIDE

```
 15  16      O-C6
  C--C    /  I5
 //   \  /   C—O
14C   11C-C104/    \
  \    /     \ C   IR C1
   C==C       \I\  I/I
  13  12       O C—C OCH3
              3I  2  7
      S-C18    R2
      /   \       8 9
R2 = C17  C19  IR =-O-C-CH3
      \   /          II
      S-C20          O
```

FORMULA	C20H2606S2			MOL WT	426.55
SOLVENT					
ORIG ST	TMS			TEMP	AMB
103.10	77.20	45.00	71.50	69.70	59.60
1/2	2/2	3/2	4/2	5/2	6/3
55.70	169.90	21.10	99.50	138.00	128.60
7/4	8/1	9/4	10/2	11/1	12/2
127.00	129.30	44.20	30.20	25.70	30.60
13/2	14/2	17/2	18/3	19/3	20/3

A.M.SEPULCHRE,G.LUKACS,G.VASS,S.D.GERO
ANGEW CHEM   84, 111 (1972)
ANGEW CHEM INTERN ED   11, 148 (1972)

954

U 005000   METHYL-ALPHA-D-IDOPYRANOSIDE

```
    6CH2OH
      I
   HO C—O
    I/5   \
   4C   HO C1
    \3  I/I
     C—C OCH3
     I  2  7
    HO
```

FORMULA	C7H1406			MOL WT	194.19
SOLVENT	H2O				
ORIG ST	CS2			TEMP	AMB
101.20	70.60	71.50	70.00	70.50	59.90
1/2	2/2	3/2	4/2	5/2	6/3
55.50					
7/4					

A.S.PERLIN,B.CASU,H.J.KCCH
CAN J CHEM   48, 2596 (1970)

---

955   U 005000   ALPHA—D—TALOPYRANOSE

```
    6CH2OH
      |
  HO C——O
    |/5   \
  4C OH OHC1
    \|  |/|
     C——C OH
     3   2
```

FORMULA	C6H12O6			MOL WT	180.16
SOLVENT	H2O				
ORIG ST	TMS			TEMP	AMB

94.70	70.70	69.70	65.10	71.20	61.50
1/2	2/2	3/2	4/2	5/2	6/3

W. VOELTER, E. BREITMAIER
ORG MAGN RESONANCE   5,   311 (1973)

---

956   U 005000   BETA—D—TALOPYRANOSE

```
    6CH2OH
      |
  HO C——O OH
    |/5   \|
  4C OH OHC1
    \|  |/
     C——C
     3   2
```

FORMULA	C6H12O6			MOL WT	180.16
SOLVENT	H2O				
ORIG ST	TMS			TEMP	AMB

94.20	68.65	71.55	68.45	75.70	61.25
1/2	2/I	3/2	4/2	5/2	6/3

W. VOELTER, E. BREITMAIER
ORG MAGN RESONANCE   5,   311 (1973)

---

957   U 005000   BETA—D—TALOFURANOSE

```
  HO—CH2 O
    6|  / \
  HO—CH/   \ OH
    5|/     \|
    C40H  OHC1
      \|   |/
       C———C
       3   2
```

FORMULA	C6H12O6			MOL WT	180.16
SOLVENT	H2O				
ORIG ST	TMS			TEMP	AMB

100.95	75.20	81.90	82.50	71.85	62.80
1/2	2/2	3/2	4/2	5/2	6/3

W. VOELTER, E. BREITMAIER
ORG MAGN RESONANCE   5,   311 (1973)

---

958   U 005000   ALPHA—D—ARABINOPYRANOSE

```
      5
    C——O
   /    \
 4C    HO C1
  |\3  |/|
 HO C——C OH
    |  2
    HO
```

FORMULA	C5H10O5			MOL WT	150.13
SOLVENT	H2O				
ORIG ST	TMS			TEMP	AMB

96.85	71.95	72.55	68.55	66.40
1/2	2/2	3/2	4/2	5/3

E. BREITMAIER, W. VOELTER
TETRAHEDRON   29,   227 (1973)

---

959   U 005000   BETA—D—ARABINOPYRANOSE

```
      5
    C——O OH
   /    \|
 4C    OHC1
  |\3  |/
 HO C——C
    |  2
    HO
```

FORMULA	C5H10O5			MOL WT	150.13
SOLVENT	H2O				
ORIG ST	TMS			TEMP	AMB

92.60	68.70	68.70	68.55	62.55
1/2	2/2	3/2	4/2	5/3

E. BREITMAIER, W. VOELTER
TETRAHEDRON   29,   227 (1973)

960   U 005000   ALPHA-D-ARABINOFURANOSE

```
HO-CH2 O
  5|  / \
   |/   \
  4C    HO C1
   \3   |/|
     C---C OH
     |   2
     HO
```

FORMULA	C5H10O5			MOL WT	150.13
SOLVENT	H2O				
ORIG ST	TMS			TEMP	AMB

101.15	70.25	74.30	81.50	61.30
1/2	2,3/2	2,3/2	4/2	5/3

E.BREITMAIER, W.VOELTER
TETRAHEDRON   29, 227 (1973)

---

961   U 005000   BETA-D-ARABINOFURANOSE

```
HO-CH2 O
  5|  / \
   | /   \ OH
   |/     \|
  4C    HO C1
   \3   |/
     C---C
     |   2
     HO
```

FORMULA	C5H10O5			MOL WT	150.13
SOLVENT	H2O				
ORIG ST	TMS			TEMP	AMB

95.20	75.75	76.85	83.05	62.35
1/2	2,3/2	2,3/2	4/2	5/3

E.BREITMAIER, W.VOELTER
TETRAHEDRON   29, 227 (1973)

---

962   U 005000   METHYL-ALPHA-D-ARABINOPYRANOSIDE

```
    5
    C--0
   /    \
 4C   HO C1
 |\3  |/|
 HO C--C OCH3
   |  2  6
   HO
```

FORMULA	C6H12O5			MOL WT	164.16
SOLVENT	H2O				
ORIG ST	TMS			TEMP	AMB

104.05	72.50	70.85	68.35	66.15	57.10
1/2	2/2	3/2	4/2	5/3	6/4

E.BREITMAIER, W.VOELTER
TETRAHEDRON   29, 227 (1973)

---

963   U 005000   METHYL-BETA-D-ARABINOPYRANOSIDE

```
    5    6
    C--0 OCH3
   /    \|
 4C   HO C1
 |\3  |/
 HO C--C
   |  2
   HO
```

FORMULA	C6H12O5			MOL WT	164.16
SOLVENT	H2O				
ORIG ST	TMS			TEMP	AMB

99.95	69.05	69.05	68.35	62.60	55.30
1/2	2/2	3/2	4/2	5/3	6/4

E.BREITMAIER, W.VOELTER
TETRAHEDRON   29, 227 (1973)

---

964   U 005000   ALPHA-D-RIBOPYRANOSE

```
    5
    C--0
   /    \
 4C      C1
 |\3  2/|
 HO C---C OH
   |   |
   HO  OH
```

FORMULA	C5H10O5			MOL WT	150.13
SOLVENT	D2O				
ORIG ST	TMS			TEMP	AMB

93.80	70.35	69.60	71.30	67.60
1/2	2/2	3/2	4/2	5/3

E.BREITMAIER, G.JUNG, W.VOELTER
CHIMIA   26, 136 (1972)

965   U 005000 BETA-D-RIBOPYRANOSE

```
       5
      C--O
    /      \
  4C        C1
  |\3    2/|
  HO C--C OH
     |  |
     HO OH
```

FORMULA   C5H10O5   MOL WT   150.13
SOLVENT   D2O
ORIG ST   TMS   TEMP   AMB

94.15   69.15   67.60   71.30   63.55
1/2   2/2   3/2   4/2   5/3

E.BREITMAIER,G.JUNG,W.VOELTER
CHIMIA   26, 136 (1972)

---

966   U 005000 ALPHA-D-RIBOFURANOSE

```
  HO-CH2 O
    5|  / \
     | /   \
     |/     \
    4C       C1
     \3   2/|
      C---C OH
      |   |
      HO  OH
```

FORMULA   C5H10O5   MOL WT   150.13
SOLVENT   D2O
ORIG ST   TMS   TEMP   AMB

96.55   75.60   70.35   82.75   61.70
1/2   2/2   3/2   4/2   5/3

E.BREITMAIER,G.JUNG,W.VOELTER
CHIMIA   26, 136 (1972)

---

967   U 005000 BETA-D-RIBOFURANOSE

```
  HO-CH2 O
    |  / \
    | /   \ OH
    |/     \|
   4C       C1
    \3    2/
     C---C
     |   |
     HO  OH
```

FORMULA   C5H10O5   MOL WT   150.13
SOLVENT   D2O
ORIG ST   TMS   TEMP   AMB

101.25   75.60   70.80   83.35   62.90
1/2   2/2   3/2   4/2   5/3

E.BREITMAIER,G.JUNG,W.VOELTER
CHIMIA   26, 136 (1972)

---

968   U 005000 2-DEOXY-ALPHA-D-RIBOPYRANOSE

```
       5
      C--O
    /      \
  4C        C1
  |\3    /|
  HO C--C OH
     |  2
     HO
```

FORMULA   C5H10O4   MOL WT   134.13
SOLVENT   D2O
ORIG ST   TMS   TEMP   AMB

91.65   35.15   64.65   67.50   62.85
1/2   2/3   3/2   4/2   5/3

E.BREITMAIER,G.JUNG,W.VOELTER
CHIMIA   26, 136 (1972)

---

969   U 005000 2-DEOXY-BETA-D-RIBOPYRANOSE

```
       5
      C--O OH
    /      \|
  4C         C1
  |\3    /
  HO C--C
     |  2
     HO
```

FORMULA   C5H10O4   MOL WT   134.13
SOLVENT   D2O
ORIG ST   TMS   TEMP   AMB

93.85   33.80   66.50   67.35   66.00
1/2   2/3   3/2   4/2   5/3

E.BREITMAIER,G.JUNG,W.VOELTER
CHIMIA   26, 136 (1972)

970   U 005000   2-DEOXY-ALPHA-D-RIBOFURANOSE

```
HO-CH2 O
  5|  / \
   |/  \
   |/   \
  4C     C1
   \3  /|
    C---C OH
    |   2
   HO
```

FORMULA	C5H10O4			MOL WT	134.13
SOLVENT	D2O				
ORIG ST	TMS			TEMP	AMB

91.65	41.15	70.95	85.30	61.55
1/2	2/3	3/2	4/2	5/3

E.BREITMAIER,G.JUNG,W.VOELTER
CHIMIA   26, 136 (1972)

---

971   U 005000   2-DEOXY-BETA-D-RIBOFURANOSE

```
HO-CH2 O
  5|  / \
   |/  \ OH
   |/   \|
  4C     C1
   \3   /
    C---C
    |   2
   HO
```

FORMULA	C5H10O4			MOL WT	134.13
SOLVENT	D2O				
ORIG ST	TMS			TEMP	AMB

98.05	41.30	71.25	85.85	62.85
1/2	2/3	3/2	4/2	5/3

E.BREITMAIER,G.JUNG,W.VOELTER
CHIMIA   26, 136 (1972)

---

972   U 005000   METHYL-BETA-D-RIBOPYRANOSIDE

```
   5       6
   C---O OCH3
  /    \|
 4C     C1
 |\3  2/
 HO C---C
    |  |
    HO  OH
```

FORMULA	C6H12O5			MOL WT	164.16
SOLVENT	D2O				
ORIG ST	TMS			TEMP	AMB

103.85	70.40	69.85	72.65	65.55	58.30
1/2	2/2	3/2	4/2	5/3	6/4

E.BREITMAIER,G.JUNG,W.VOELTER
CHIMIA   26, 136 (1972)

---

973   U 005000   METHYL-BETA-D-RIBOFURANOSIDE

```
HO-CH2 O
  5|  / \  6
   |/  \ OCH3
   |/   \|
  4C     C1
   \3  2/
    C---C
    |  |
    HO  OH
```

FORMULA	C6H12O5			MOL WT	164.16
SOLVENT	D2O				
ORIG ST	TMS			TEMP	AMB

108.00	74.35	70.85	82.95	62.90	55.30
1/2	2/2	3/2	4/2	5/3	6/4

E.BREITMAIER,G.JUNG,W.VOELTER
CHIMIA   26, 136 (1972)

---

974   U 005000   METHYL-3,4-O-ISOPROPYLIDENE-3-C-(1,3-DITHIANE-
                                    2-YL)-BETA-D-RIBOPYRANOSIDE

```
      5      6
      C---O OCH3
       \  \|
  4C R    C1
  |\13 2/
  O C---C
 8 |7| |
 H3C-C-O  OH
    |
   9CH3
          S-C11
         /    \
R = C10    C12
         \    /
          S-C13
```

FORMULA	C13H22O5S2			MOL WT	322.45
SOLVENT	CDCL3				
ORIG ST	TMS			TEMP	AMB

99.80	72.05	70.80	72.95	57.30	55.45
1/2	2/2	3/1	4/2	5/3	6/4
108.20	25.45	54.70	29.80	24.80	30.30
7/1	8/4	10/2	11/3	12/3	13/3

G.LUKACS,A.M.SEPULCHRE,A.GATEAU-OLESKER,G.VASS,
S.D.GERO,R.D.GUTHRIE,W.VOELTER,E.BREITMAIER
TETRAHEDRON LETTERS   5163 (1972)

975   U 005000   ALPHA-D-XYLOPYRANOSE

```
      5
     C--O
    /     \
  4C OH    C1
  I\I   2/I
  HO C--C OH
     3  I
        OH
```

FORMULA   C5H10O5   MOL WT   150.13
SOLVENT   H2O
ORIG ST   TMS   TEMP   AMB

92.30   71.60   73.00   69.55   61.05
1/2   2/2   3/2   4/2   5/3

E.BREITMAIER, W.VOELTER
TETRAHEDRON   29, 227 (1973)

---

976   U 005000   BETA-D-XYLOPYRANOSE

```
      5
     C--O OH
    /    \I
  4C OH    C1
  I\I   2/
  HO C--C
     3  I
        OH
```

FORMULA   C5H10O5   MOL WT   150.13
SOLVENT   H2O
ORIG ST   TMS   TEMP   AMB

96.70   74.10   75.90   69.35   65.25
1/2   2/2   3/2   4/2   5/3

E.BREITMAIER, W.VOELTER
TETRAHEDRON   29, 227 (1973)

---

977   U 005000   METHYL-ALPHA-D-XYLOPYRANOSIDE

```
      5
     C--O
    /     \
  4C OH    C1
  I\I   2/I
  HO C--C OCH3
     3  I  6
        OH
```

FORMULA   C6H12O5   MOL WT   164.16
SOLVENT   H2O
ORIG ST   TMS   TEMP   AMB

98.30   71.20   73.20   69.35   60.70   54.60
1/2   2/2   3/2   4/2   5/3   6/4

E.BREITMAIER, W.VOELTER
TETRAHEDRON   29, 227 (1973)

---

978   U 005000   METHYL-BETA-D-XYLOPYRANOSIDE

```
      5       6
     C--O OCH3
    /     \I
  4C OH    C1
  I\I   2/
  HO C--C
     3  I
        OH
```

FORMULA   C6H12O5   MOL WT   164.16
SOLVENT   H2O
ORIG ST   TMS   TEMP   AMB

103.80   72.70   75.70   69.30   64.70   56.60
1/2   2/2   3/2   4/2   5/3   6/4

E.BREITMAIER, W.VOELTER
TETRAHEDRON   29, 227 (1973)

---

979   U 005000   ALPHA-D-LYXOPYRANOSE

```
      5
     C--O
    /     \
  4C OH OHC1
  I\I   I/I
  HO C--C OH
     3  2
```

FORMULA   C5H10O5   MOL WT   150.13
SOLVENT   H2O
ORIG ST   CS2   TEMP   AMB

94.30   70.40   70.90   67.80   63.10
1/2   2/2   3/2   4/2   5/3

A.S.PERLIN, B.CASU, H.J.KOCH
CAN J CHEM   48, 2596 (1970)

980   U 005000   BETA-D-LYXOPYRANOSE

```
        5
      C--O OH
     /     \|
   4CHO  OHC1
    |\|   |/
   HO C---C
      3   2
```

FORMULA	C5H10O5			MOL WT	150.13
SOLVENT	H2O				
ORIG ST	CS2			TEMP	AMB

| 94.30 | 70.40 | 72.90 | 67.00 | 64.20 |
| 1/2 | 2/2 | 3/2 | 4/2 | 5/3 |

A.S.PERLIN,B.CASU,H.J.KOCH
CAN J CHEM   48, 2596 (1970)

---

981   U 005000   SCYLLO-INOSITOL

```
       OH
        |
   HO C---C
    |/|    \
   CHO HO C
     \   |/|
      C---C OH
        |
       HO
```

FORMULA	C6H12O6	MOL WT	180.16
SOLVENT	H2O		
ORIG ST	CS2	TEMP	AMB

73.70
1/2

D.E.DORMAN,S.J.ANGYAL,J.D.ROBERTS
J AM CHEM SOC   92, 1351 (1970)

---

982   U 005000   MYO-INOSITOL

```
       OH
     4  |
   HO C---C OH
    |/|  3\|
   C OH OHC2
   5\6  1/
      C---C
    |   1
   OH
```

FORMULA	C6H12O6			MOL WT	180.16
SOLVENT	H2O				
ORIG ST	CS2			TEMP	AMB

| 72.40 | 72.20 | 72.40 | 71.10 | 74.30 | 71.10 |
| 1/2 | 2/2 | 3/2 | 4/2 | 5/2 | 6/2 |

D.E.DORMAN,S.J.ANGYAL,J.D.ROBERTS
J AM CHEM SOC   92, 1351 (1970)

---

983   U 005000   L-CHIRO-INOSITOL

```
       OH
     4  |
   HO C---C OH
    |/|  5\|
   3C OH  C6
     \2  1/
      C---C
    |    |
   OH OH
```

FORMULA	C6H12O6			MOL WT	180.16
SOLVENT	H2O				
ORIG ST	CS2			TEMP	AMB

| 71.60 | 70.50 | 72.80 | 72.80 | 70.50 | 71.60 |
| 1/2 | 2/2 | 3/2 | 4/2 | 5/2 | 6/2 |

D.E.DORMAN,S.J.ANGYAL,J.D.ROBERTS
J AM CHEM SOC   92, 1351 (1970)

---

984   U 005000   EPI-INOSITOL

```
       OH
     5  |
      C--C
    /|  6\
   4C OH  C1
    |\3  2/|
   HO C---C OH
    |    |
   HO   OH
```

FORMULA	C6H12O6			MOL WT	180.16
SOLVENT	H2O				
ORIG ST	CS2			TEMP	AMB

| 71.70 | 74.50 | 70.10 | 74.50 | 71.70 | 66.80 |
| 1/2 | 2/2 | 3/2 | 4/2 | 5/2 | 6/2 |

D.E.DORMAN,S.J.ANGYAL,J.D.ROBERTS
J AM CHEM SOC   92, 1351 (1970)

985 — U 005000 D-1-O-METHYL-MYO-INOSITOL

```
        OH
     4   |
 HO  C--C  OH
   |/|  3\|
 5CHO   R  C2
    \   |/
     6C--C
     |   |      7
    HO      R = OCH3
```

FORMULA	$C_7H_{14}O_6$			MOL WT	194.19
SOLVENT	H2O				
ORIG ST	CS2			TEMP	AMB

80.50	68.00	72.30	71.10	74.40	71.60
1/2	2/2	3/2	4/2	5/2	6/2
56.90					
7/4					

D.E.DORMAN,S.J.ANGYAL,J.D.ROBERTS
J AM CHEM SOC   92, 1351 (1970)

986 — U 005000 1,2-DI-O-METHYL-MYO-INOSITOL

```
        OH
     4   |  8
 HO  C--C  OCH3
   |/|  3\|
 5CHO   R  C2
    \   |/
     6C--C
     |   |      7
    HO      R = OCH3
```

FORMULA	$C_8H_{16}O_6$			MOL WT	208.21
SOLVENT	H2O				
ORIG ST	CS2			TEMP	AMB

81.00	78.10	72.60	71.40	74.40	71.80
1/2	2/2	3/2	4/2	5/2	6/2
57.40	61.50				
7/4	8/4				

D.E.DORMAN,S.J.ANGYAL,J.D.ROBERTS
J AM CHEM SOC   92, 1351 (1970)

987 — U 005000 1,3-DI-O-METHYL-MYO-INOSITOL

```
     H3CO
     4  8|3
 HO  C--C  OH
   |/|   \|
 5CHO   R  C2
    \   |/
     6C--C
     |   |      7
    HO      R = OCH3
```

FORMULA	$C_8H_{16}O_6$			MOL WT	208.21
SOLVENT	H2O				
ORIG ST	CS2			TEMP	AMB

80.40	63.30	80.40	71.40	74.40	71.40
1/2	2/2	3/2	4/2	5/2	6/2
57.40					
7/4					

D.E.DORMAN,S.J.ANGYAL,J.D.ROBERTS
J AM CHEM SOC   92, 1351 (1970)

988 — U 005000 1,4-DI-O-METHYL-MYO-INOSITOL

```
        OH
     4   |3
 HO  C--C  OH
   |/|   \|
 5C  R2  R1C2
    \   |/      7
     6C--C   R1 = OCH3
     |   |      8
    HO      R2 = OCH3
```

FORMULA	$C_8H_{16}O_6$			MOL WT	208.21
SOLVENT	H2O				AMB
ORIG ST	CS2			TEMP	

80.30	67.80	71.70	82.20	73.70	70.50
1/2	2/2	3/2	4/2	5/2	6/2
56.70	59.70				
7/4	8/4				

D.E.DORMAN,S.J.ANGYAL,J.D.ROBERTS
J AM CHEM SOC   92, 1351 (1970)

989 — U 005000 2-O-METHYL-CHIRO-INOSITOL

```
        OH
     4   |
 HO  C--C  OH
   |/|  5\|
 3C  OH   C6
    \2  1/
     C--C
     |   |
 H3CO   OH
     7
```

FORMULA	$C_7H_{14}O_6$			MOL WT	194.19
SOLVENT	H2O				
ORIG ST	CS2			TEMP	AMB

67.20	80.10	71.90	72.80	70.44	71.30
1/2	2/2	3/2	4/2	5/2	6/2
56.80					
7/4					

D.E.DORMAN,S.J.ANGYAL,J.D.ROBERTS
J AM CHEM SOC   92, 1351 (1970)

990   U 005000   3-O-METHYL-CHIRO-INOSITOL

```
        OH
    7  4  |
 H3CO C--C OH
   |/|  5\|
   C3 OH   C6
     \2  1/
      C--C
      |  |
     HO  OH
```

FORMULA   C7H14O6   MOL WT   194.19
SOLVENT   H2O
ORIG ST   CS2   TEMP   AMB

71.70	69.80	82.50	72.10	70.60	71.40
1/2	2/2	3/2	4/2	5/2	6/2

59.40
7/4

D.E.DORMAN,S.J.ANGYAL,J.D.ROBERTS
J AM CHEM SOC   92, 1351 (1970)

991   U 005000   ERYTHRITOL

```
1CH2-OH
  |
2CH-OH
  |
3CH-OH
  |
4CH2-OH
```

FORMULA   C4H10O4   MOL WT   122.12
SOLVENT   H2O
ORIG ST   CS2   TEMP   AMB

66.20	75.30
1/3	2/2

W.VOELTER,E.BREITMAIER,G.JUNG,T.KELLER,D.HISS
ANGEW CHEM   82, 812 (1970)
ANGEW CHEM INTERN ED   9, 803 (1970)

992   U 005000   PENTAERYTHRITOL

```
    1CH2-OH
    2|
HO-H2C-C-CH2-OH
      |
    CH2-OH
```

FORMULA   C5H12O4   MOL WT   136.15
SOLVENT   H2O
ORIG ST   CS2   TEMP   AMB

64.30	48.30
1/3	2/1

W.VOELTER,E.BREITMAIER,G.JUNG,T.KELLER,D.HISS
ANGEW CHEM   82, 812 (1970)
ANGEW CHEM INTERN ED   9, 803 (1970)

993   U 005000   RIBITOL

```
1CH2-OH
  |
2CH-OH
  |
3CH-OH
  |
4CH-OH
  |
5CH2-OH
```

FORMULA   C5H12O5   MOL WT   152.15
SOLVENT   H2O
ORIG ST   CS2   TEMP   AMB

65.50	75.40	75.60
1/3	2/2	3/2

W.VOELTER,E.BREITMAIER,G.JUNG,T.KELLER,D.HISS
ANGEW CHEM   82, 812 (1970)
ANGEW CHEM INTERN ED   9, 803 (1970)

994   U 005000   XYLITOL

```
1CH2-OH
  |
2CH-OH
  |
HO-HC3
  |
4CH-OH
  |
5CH2-OH
```

FORMULA   C5H12O5   MOL WT   152.15
SOLVENT   H2O
ORIG ST   CS2   TEMP   AMB

65.90	75.20	73.90
1/3	2/2	3/2

W.VOELTER,E.BREITMAIER,G.JUNG,T.KELLER,D.HISS
ANGEW CHEM   82, 812 (1970)
ANGEW CHEM INTERN ED   9, 803 (1970)

995   U 005000   D—ARABITOL

```
1CH2-OH
  |
HO-HC2
  |
3CH-OH
  |
4CH-OH
  |
5CH2-OH
```

FORMULA   C5H12O5   MOL WT   152.15
SOLVENT   H2O
ORIG ST   CS2   TEMP   AMB

66.50	73.60	74.00	74.50	66.20
1/3	2/2	3/2	4/2	5/3

W.VOELTER,E.BREITMAIER,G.JUNG,T.KELLER,D.HISS
ANGEW CHEM   82, 812 (1970)
ANGEW CHEM INTERN ED   9, 803 (1970)

---

996   U 005000   D—MANNITOL

```
1CH2-OH
  |
HO-HC2
  |
HO-HC3
  |
4CH-OH
  |
5CH-OH
  |
6CH2-OH
```

FORMULA   C6H14O6   MOL WT   182.17
SOLVENT   H2O
ORIG ST   CS2   TEMP   AMB

76.30	75.30	73.60
1/3	2/2	3/2

W.VOELTER,E.BREITMAIER,G.JUNG,T.KELLER,D.HISS
ANGEW CHEM   82, 812 (1970)
ANGEW CHEM INTERN ED   9, 803 (1970)

---

997   U 005000   D—SORBITOL

```
1CH2-OH
  |
2CH-OH
  |
HO-HC3
  |
4CH-OH
  |
5CH-OH
  |
6CH2-OH
```

FORMULA   C6H14O6   MOL WT   182.17
SOLVENT   H2O
ORIG ST   CS2   TEMP   AMB

65.80	74.50	72.90	74.30	76.10	66.10
1/3	2/2	3/2	4/2	5/2	6/3

W.VOELTER,E.BREITMAIER,G.JUNG,T.KELLER,D.HISS
ANGEW CHEM   82, 812 (1970)
ANGEW CHEM INTERN ED   9, 803 (1970)

---

998   U 005000   GALACTITOL

```
1CH2-OH
  |
2CH-OH
  |
OH-HC3
  |
HO-HC4
  |
5CH-OH
  |
6CH2-OH
```

FORMULA   C6H14O6   MOL WT   182.17
SOLVENT   D2O
ORIG ST   TMS   TEMP   AMB

63.25	69.25	70.15
1/3	2/2	3/2

W.VOELTER,E.BREITMAIER,E.B.RATHBONE,E.M.STEPHEN
TETRAHEDRON   29, 3845 (1973)

---

999   U 005000   3—O—METHYL—D—GALACTITOL

```
    1CH2-OH
      |
    2CH-OH
   7  |
H3CO-HC3
      |
  HO-HC4
      |
    5CH-OH
      |
    6CH2-OH
```

FORMULA   C7H16O6   MOL WT   196.20
SOLVENT   D2O
ORIG ST   TMS   TEMP   AMB

62.90	70.15	79.40	70.80	68.75	63.35
1/3	2/2	3/2	4/2	5/2	6/3
60.20
7/4

W.VOELTER,E.BREITMAIER,E.B.RATHBONE,E.M.STEPHEN
TETRAHEDRON   29, 3845 (1973)